THUS LIFE BEGAN

THUS LIFE BEGAN

Allan Broms

Illustrated by Howard S. Friedman

1968

DOUBLEDAY & COMPANY, INC., GARDEN CITY, NEW YORK

Permission to adapt drawings from the following sources is gratefully acknowledged:

The Science of Life by H. G. Wells, Julian S. Huxley, and G. P. Wells, published by Garden City Publishing Company and Cassell & Co., Ltd., by permission of Professor G. P. Wells and Sir Julian Huxley: *Fig. 1.*

Charles Darwin by Sir Gavin de Beer, published by Doubleday & Company, Inc., and Thomas Nelson & Sons, Ltd. Copyright © 1963 by Sir Gavin De Beer: *Fig. 2.*

General Zoology by T. I. Storer and R. L. Usinger. Copyright © 1957 by McGraw-Hill, Inc. Used by permission of McGraw-Hill Book Company: *Fig. 9; Fig. 12.*

Life: An Introduction To Biology, 1st ed., by George Gaylord Simpson, Colin S. Pittendrigh, and Lewis H. Tiffany. Copyright © 1957 by Harcourt, Brace & World, Inc.: *Fig. 6*, which was originally redrawn from "The Structure of Hereditary Material" by F. Crick. Copyright © 1954 by Scientific American, Inc., all rights reserved; *Fig. 7*, also originally redrawn from Crick; *Fig. 16*, which was originally redrawn in part from *Vertebrate Paleontology* by A. S. Romer, University of Chicago Press, 2nd ed., 1945, and in part from *The Life of Vertebrates* by J. Z. Young.

Life: An Introduction to Biology, 2nd ed., by George Gaylord Simpson and William S. Beck. Copyright © 1957, 1965 by Harcourt, Brace & World, Inc.: *Fig. 4; Fig. 5; Fig. 8*, which was originally redrawn from *A Textbook of General Botany*, 5th ed., by G. M. Smith, E. M. Gilbert, G. S. Bryan, R. J. Evans, and J. T. Stauffer, Macmillan, 1953; *Fig. 11*, which was originally redrawn from *A Textbook of Zoology* by T. J. Parker and W. A. Haswell, Macmillan, 1940; *Fig. 13*, which was originally redrawn in part from Parker and Haswell, and in part from Storer and Usinger; *Fig. 18*, which was originally redrawn in part from *The World of Life* by W. F. Pauli, Houghton-Mifflin, 1949, and in part from *Life Science* by T. S. Hall and F. Moog, Wiley, 1955; *Fig. 20*, which was originally redrawn in part from *Man and the Biological World*, 2nd ed., by J. S. Rogers, T. H. Hubbell, and C. F. Byers, McGraw-Hill, 1952, in part from *College Physiology* by Pace and McCashland, Crowell, 1955, in part from *The Dancing Bees* by K. Von Frisch, Harcourt, Brace & World, 1955, and in part from Storer and Usinger; *Fig. 21.*

Evolution Emerging, Vol. II, by William K. Gregory, published by Macmillan Company for The American Museum of Natural History. Copyright © 1951 by The American Museum of Natural History: *Fig. 14; Fig. 15; Fig. 17; Fig. 19.*

CONTENTS

Together. The Bees and the Flowers. The Busy Bee's
Business. From Under the Shadows. Direct Sex Contact. The Evolution of Motherhood. The Urges of Sex.

The Broad Incidental Advance. On Seizing Opportunities.
The Warm Bloods Take Over. The Emergence of Man.
What We Owe the Babies. Thus Life Began.

Chapter 1

UNCOVERING A MYSTERY

In a previous book I began to tell the over-all story of evolution, an obviously ambitious project. That book, *Our Emerging Universe*,* began with the grandeur and immensities of the universe at large, its billion galaxies, the myriad superhot stars, our own star Sun, cool planets, great and small, Earth core and heaving crust, oceans of water and air—all culminating for man in this Earth as his habitable home.

The story thus begun was clearly prologue, with no living actors yet present. The stage was nevertheless being set, a landscape of barrenness with as yet no sign whatever of any life. Then, too, it was no fixed scene but a creeping panorama of time and change. There were alternations of sunshine and rain, of calm and storm, of secure stability and heaving turmoil, but without life the waste and emptiness were always there. The air, too, was oddly and forbiddingly compounded, being indeed so mephitic that the life we now know would have found it unbreathable. Probably a billion years dragged by, perhaps several billions, before the action of life's play actually began.

Then at last entered the first living being of us all. It made no "entrance," however, certainly not as stage folk understand that word. For it was not at all dramatic. No one could have even noticed that life came upon the scene, and not just because there was as yet no audience present. Even had there been, it would not have been noticed, for it was really so minute and

* Doubleday & Co., Inc., 1961.

inconspicuous, so formless and unidentifiable, that no one could have realized that something new and important was there at all. In fact, that whole entrance (with its very small *e*) was most mysterious, the great puzzle being of course how life ever began at all.

Oddly enough, however, even this mystery of the origin of life really seemed to be no mystery at all until modern scientific times. Indeed, as a mystery it was itself a scientific discovery.

However, conceived as a mere paltry problem, readily to be solved, the question of how life began apparently goes back to the very beginnings of human thinking. Every primitive people seems to have had its own legends to explain the creation of Man and of the world of life about him. It could be accomplished readily by some god with powers in some degree superhuman, and done rather simply, say by forming Man from the dust of the ground and then merely breathing into his nostrils the breath of life. Naturally, these legends state, the god shaped man in his own image; it was not suspected that matters might be quite the other way around, with Man instead shaping the god in *his* human image.

After that initial event there was certainly no mystery, nothing but the commonplace reproduction of offspring, with parents begetting children generation after generation, something so matter-of-fact that it could be taken for granted and was surely nothing to be wondered about. Even when there seemed to be no parents to give birth or lay eggs, there was still no mystery. For obviously life was merely arising spontaneously in a quite ordinary manner from ordinary materials which often took on life.

Spontaneous Generation

A very few generations ago, for instance, it was familiar and accepted boyhood lore that a horsehair soaked in water would turn into a water snake. We knew but little of this threadworm, whose name is Gordius, and how it hatches and grows in the body of some insect host. In the tub or pool of water we readily noticed the flashing reflection of light on the shifting and twisting snaky worm, and paid no attention whatever to the grasshopper or beetle which had died to bring it there. In other words, we took for granted the spontaneous generation of life.

The learned name for that is abiogenesis, which simply means the genesis of life from the nonliving. The belief is very old and was once universally accepted—reasonably enough, in the light of the facts then known. For of course everyone could see that plants grow out of the inert soil, maggots swarm out of rotting meat, and flies out of dung heaps; frogs creep forth from mud and slime, and mice from grain heaps. Obviously life everywhere generates spontaneously and constantly out of lifeless matter.

Even the most learned scholars were not so all-wise that they could not but see this. We find spontaneous generation believed and taught by a long line of great Greek philosophers—culminating in Aristotle, who expounded the idea fully. This became most important, for what Aristotle thought and said was considered gospel for many centuries of the Middle Ages, at least to the venerable Church Fathers, and to alchemists, physicians, and all others who claimed wisdom in those days. They one and all considered spontaneous generation quite obvious and certain; wherever conditions were right, life always appeared in profusion. Even such modern-minded scientific luminaries as René Descartes and Sir Isaac Newton shared this view.

On the other hand, it was also recognized that plants grow from plant-borne seeds, and that animals are hatched from eggs or born alive from parent bodies. Increasingly, as knowledge widened and became more detailed, all manner of ifs, buts, and other doubts inevitably crept in to modify and limit the old faith in spontaneous generation.

Yet that faith was not really shaken until 1668 when the Italian physician Francesco Redi reported a series of experiments with the maggots which appear on decaying meat, following a suggestion made by William Harvey of England that such small life hatches from invisible seeds or eggs, in this case perhaps laid by flies. Redi simply screened the mouths of meat jars to keep flies from laying their eggs on the meat, whereupon the maggots failed to appear. The faith was shaken, but it was not destroyed; even Redi himself accepted spontaneous generation for such creatures as intestinal and wood worms.

About this time, too, the Dutch microscopist Antony van Leeuwenhoek, using simple but very powerful magnifying lenses, products of his own patiently acquired grinding skill, discovered a whole new world of minute microorganisms invisible to the naked eye. Over several decades he observed with sharp eyesight, common sense, and scientific integrity, and sent his rambling and gossipy Dutch letters to the Royal Society of London, reporting in detail drawings and full descriptions on the "wretched beasties" he found in liquid infusions, souring milk, rotting meat, fermentations, excreta, yeasts, and what not. All were teeming with busy life which seemed to spring into being almost before one's eyes. Furthermore, these facts were fully confirmed by other eager investigators, several of them respected members of the Royal Society itself. Honors, such as life membership in that august society, were heaped upon him, and he was visited by the great scholars and even by royalty itself, all eager to peer through his magic magnifiers, but not permitted to handle them. The facts about this new world of minute and simple life forms became well known to everyone, and tended to renew any failing faith in spontaneous generation.

Life Only from Life

But hardheaded Leeuwenhoek himself disagreed. He had personally conducted a simple and to him conclusive experiment.

He had carefully examined fresh rain water and found it wholly devoid of life. But then, after a lapse of days, life did appear in profusion. From this he concluded, and thereafter insisted, that the microorganisms developed from something which must have entered from the air. Soon this was demonstrated by his follower Louis Joblot, who boiled a hay infusion and then covered one portion, which thereupon did not develop infusoria, while another portion, left open to the air, was soon swarming with minute life.

This was in 1718, but the world remained unconvinced. Indeed, other experimenters, such as the priest John T. Needham, failed to get such conclusive results until, in 1765, the Abbé Lazzaro Spallanzani, making hundreds of experiments, carefully heated and sealed his containers to keep out the air, and found no living organisms. He simply did what any modern housewife does in her cold-pack canning to prevent her food delicacies from spoiling.

The belief in spontaneous generation was dying hard, however, and it was not until a century later (1862) that Louis Pasteur, by inventing a swan-neck flask to keep out contamination and by an astounding "knack for cleanliness" applied in a series of brilliantly executed experiments, finally proved beyond doubt that even microorganisms are not generated spontaneously. Within a decade that fact was considered firmly established, and today no informed scientist believes in the spontaneous generation of life forms as we know them. In fact, that conclusion was soon formulated into a virtual scientific law, expressed in the words "Life comes only from life."

Yet the question inevitably arose: Is that actually going too far? It seems to deny that life ever did begin. If it is strictly true, then how did life ever come to appear upon the Earth?

After all, the experiments of Redi, Joblot, Spallanzani, and Pasteur really proved only that complex forms of life—such as we now know maggots, infusoria, and bacteria to be—can develop only from previous life. That is very different from saying that life in its simplest original forms must have somehow arisen from nonliving matter. No experiment so far devised has actually proved that impossible—nor, shall we say, unlikely.

Note, however, that even spontaneous generation does not include, or even imply, any real theory, clear or unclear, as to the way in which nonliving matter becomes living. That belief was merely accepted on the basis of common and superficial observation, not too carefully examined or put to test. Living beings *seemed* to arise from the nonliving. Beyond that, one merely assumed that there was involved some inherent magic which was not to be understood anyway.

Yet for those few who did raise thoughtful questions, two theories were extant. One was old and widely accepted; we call it the Vitalist Theory. The other was newer, was first called the Mechanist Theory, and as now developed, quite dominates modern scientific thinking on the subject. We shall consider each in turn.

The Vitalist Theory

The Vitalist Theory has appeared often and in many forms. It always assumes, however, that some special stuff or force, a breath of life, a living spirit, a spark of life, a something supramaterial, has somehow been injected into lifeless matter, bringing it to life. Plato called this vital something "psyche"; Aristotle included it in his "entelechy"; Paracelsus named it "spiritus vitae"; van Helmont spoke of "archai," and Leibnitz of "monads." In 1707 the German physician Georg Ernst Stahl formulated the idea that life was governed by special nonphysical laws. Later Buffon explained that "organic molecules" by suitable combination formed living matter, and while this sounds much like modern scientific talk, it was still vitalistic in meaning. John T. Needham, arguing in 1749 against the early experiments of Spallanzani, contended that the thorough boiling of a decoction destroyed the creative "vital force." Felix Pouchet, as late as 1859, arguing against Pasteur and repeating the ideas of Buffon and Needham, held that wandering particles containing the vital force were the cause of spontaneous generation. But soon thereafter Pasteur convinced the world that spontaneous generation does not in fact occur, and so forced modification of that much of Vitalist thinking, at least in scientific circles.

Some (including Pasteur) did realize that the problem of the original origin of life still remained, and of course the Vitalist Theory was one ostensible explanation. Yet by this time thinking on the problem was becoming more realistic, with scientists generally giving up the idea of a distinct vital force. They were coming to realize that it amounted to explaining life as due to its "vitality," which was as meaningless as explaining the wetness of water by its "aquacity." Eventually it was realized that Vitalism solved the problem of the origin of life by offering empty words, even though those words sounded satisfyingly profound. The minds that are content with impressive words are less likely to ask further questions and the Vitalist Theory proved generally barren, rather effectively closing the door on further and deeper scientific investigation.

The Mechanist Theory

On the other hand, the so-called Mechanist Theory does invite such investigation and so results in an ever-widening accumulation of pertinent facts and a progressive updating of our ideas on the problem of life's origin.

The name Mechanist, however, proved rather unfortunate. It was right enough at the outset, when the new viewpoint was still as narrow as the name implies. But today that viewpoint has been so much broadened that the old name hardly applies and may even be misleading.

Actually the Mechanists of today do not believe that life is only mechanism, but rather, that it consists of natural physical and chemical processes and must have originated by right combinations of physical and chemical conditions. We may not yet know all about those processes and conditions, but they can be systematically studied with valid hope that we may someday learn the real secret of the nature and origin of life. A more accurate term would be the Naturalistic or the Physicochemical Theory of life and its origin.

Unfortunately, Pasteur's disproof of spontaneous generation did not at first tend to clarify, but rather confused the issue. His conclusion that only something already living can now bring forth life seemed to justify the older Vitalist contention that life must be explained by and must have originated from some special and supernatural "vital spark" injected into nonliving material. At least it was so interpreted widely at the time.

One result is that even today Pasteur is often regarded as a Vitalist, though he repeatedly defined his real position. He stated explicitly that his disproof of spontaneous generation was applicable only to the existing forms of life, such as the microorganisms with which he had experimented. Throughout his career he retained an intense interest in the problem of the initial chemical origin of life by natural process, being regretfully kept from pursuing this problem by urgent practical studies in other fields. He had learned from his very earliest experiments that the chemistry of life was specialized, though still basically natural. He did not depart from this naturalistic position at any time, but summed it up concisely in these words: "Vital phenomena are only physical and chemical phenomena." This was certainly not Vitalist language.

Of course, if the Vitalist was right and there is a something extra needed, that vital spark not of tangible physics and chemistry, then the quest of the physicochemist is all in vain. For the assumed vital spark is then manifestly something divine and beyond understanding, and therefore not subject to fruitful investigation. In any case, while Vitalism held full sway, the quest got little encouragement, and practically no progress was made in advancing knowledge of even the gross structures and workings of life forms.

The Rise of Anatomy

For about a millennium and a half no one had seriously questioned the zoological writings of Aristotle (fourth century B.C.), nor those on human anatomy by the Greek physician Galen (second century A.D.). Both had been sensible and careful investigators but were nevertheless pioneers who inevitably made beginners' mistakes. Aristotle gathered his data from wherever and whomever he could, and depended largely upon mere outward appearances. And Galen, according to his own account, drew largely on dissections of apes and other animals, on wounds of gladiators in his care, and occasional examinations of human skeletons. Neither, of course, ever claimed the infallibility later vested in them by the medieval Schoolmen. During the Middle Ages, however, when actual facts discrepant with their writings came to light, they were neatly explained as due to interim changes in the animal forms and human structures. Some clear discrepancies were indeed discovered, notably by the artist-scientist Leonardo da Vinci, but as he merely jotted them down in his private notebooks and sketches, nothing came of that.

The year 1543 is memorable for the publication of two pioneer scientific works destined to revolutionize human thinking. One, on the *Revolutions of the Heavenly Bodies*, was written by the Polish astronomer Nicholas Copernicus, who argued that the Sun, rather than the Earth, was the center of the visible Universe. This, though it helped greatly to straighten out our general scientific thinking, had scarcely any direct effect in the field of anatomy and other life studies.

The other work, however, laid the very foundations of modern anatomy. Its title was *De Humani Corporis Fabrica* ("The Anatomy of the Human Body"), and was written by the twenty-eight-year-old Flemish physician Andreas Vesalius. Despite his youth, it represented years of his own careful dissection of the human body, all fully described and accurately illustrated by engravings in seven formidable volumes. He corrected innumerable mistakes of Galen but praised him as the foremost among the teachers of anatomy. But he despised and excoriated the blind followers of Galen who never investigated the human body themselves. By this he undoubtedly added to his own troubles, and troubles he certainly had. Dissection of the human body was forbidden by the Church, and he was constantly dissecting before his student classes, not secretly but openly and defiantly. Ecclesiastical pressures had already driven him from Paris to Padua, and then to the temporary asylum of the Spanish Court which was then squabbling with the Papacy over quite other matters. Finally, accused by the Inquisition, he was forced to make a pilgrimage of atonement to the Holy Land, and returning, was shipwrecked on the Greek island of Zante, there to die of starvation and exposure.

Because his great work was fortunately published, Vesalius advanced the science of anatomy more than anyone of his time. Yet he was not alone as a great investigator. He had himself studied under able teachers and taught several brilliant followers. Among his contemporaries was Bartolomeo Eustachi, held by some as an even greater anatomist, perhaps because he used magnifiers to see more detail. His remarkable drawings and revealing text were ready in 1552 but were not published for 162 years. Another pioneer was Michael Servetus, who in 1545 trustingly reported to John Calvin his discovery of the circulation of the blood through the lungs, only to have this included in the evidence of heresy for which Calvin burned him at the stake in 1553. Also among the martyrs was Charles Étienne, who described the valves in human veins and died in the dungeons of the Inquisition.

Circulation of the Blood

Those valves in the veins were to lead to a great anatomic discovery which profoundly changed our whole concept of life. They had become very much a puzzle. First, there were no such valves in the arteries, and it was obvious to the anatomists that those in the veins were so arranged as to prevent the flow of blood away from the heart. As it was then believed (and had been since the time of Galen) that the blood surged back and forth through the heart between the veins and arteries, this presented difficulties. Furthermore, to permit such surging, the wall or septum between the two halves of the heart was supposed to be perforated with openings. But in 1555 Vesalius had demonstrated that there were no such openings, whereupon it was assumed that the septum must at least be porous to let the blood through. All of this assumed surging, we now know, was a mistake.

The correction of that mistake by the English physician William Harvey was to prove a major advance both in the science of anatomy and in our view of the nature of life. Harvey had studied in Padua under a student of a student of Vesalius and had returned to England to become an influential Royal Physician. After many observations and experiments, he published a small book in 1628, entitled in part *De Motu Cordis et Sanguinis* ("The Motion of the Heart and Blood"). But he had started to lecture on the idea of that book a dozen years before.

The idea was simply that the blood did not surge back and forth as currently believed, but circulated in one direction, out from the heart through the arteries and back to the heart through the veins. The heart itself was a force pump, essentially equivalent to the mechanical pumps already in use. There was no plunger, but the heart did contract to force the blood out into the arteries, and then relax and open up to let the blood from the veins flow in. And as in a pump, there were valves in the heart (as well as the veins) which let the blood flow only the one way. The pumping also accounted for the audible heartbeats, and for the pulse one could feel in certain blood vessels.

This idea of the one-way circulation of the blood was not entirely new. We know that Servetus had already described such a circulation through the lungs as early as 1545. Also, the Italian Andrea Cesalpino, as Harvey acknowledged, had taught a general circulation through the whole body some time between 1570 and 1590. But now Harvey's little book finally proved this most thoroughly and convincingly.

He showed, first, that the blood flows through the arteries away from the heart. He stopped that flow by pressing on arteries, whereupon they emptied on the side away from the heart. Then he stopped the flow by pressing the veins, and they emptied on the side toward the heart. That meant that the blood flowed in just one direction—it circulated instead of surged.

This also meant that the blood going out through the arteries to the body organs, and returning via the veins to the heart, must somehow pass through the body organs from the arteries to the veins. In other words, the full circuit had to be completed (Figure 1). We now know that the arteries branch into smaller and smaller tubes which finally become microscopically fine capillaries, and that these then join into larger and larger veins leading back to the heart. Harvey, however, never did discover and prove the existence of these capillaries, and this remained the one weak gap in his demonstration of the circulation of the blood. Oddly, he even denied the existence of the capillaries, although he was familiar with Galen's work which told of such fine blood vessels. And Servetus, too, had discovered such a passage of blood through the lungs. But the capillaries cannot be seen by the naked eye, and Marcello Malpighi was perhaps the first to see them with a lens, reporting in 1661 that he

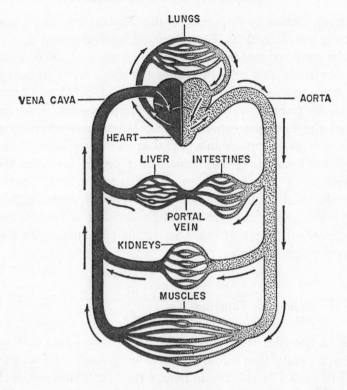

Fig. 1. Circulation of the blood.

had seen blood circulating through these fine tubes in a frog's lung. Finally, in 1688, Leeuwenhoek gave a most detailed description of the blood circulation through the gills of a tadpole.

Until those capillaries were thus actually proved, Harvey had to face one other possibility: that the blood was being freshly and continuously formed in the vein system, presumably from digested food, and then somehow dissipated to nothing in the artery system. To us this seems preposterous and impossible to believe; but then we are prone to underestimate the capacity of human beings for believing the impossible, indeed for even preferring preposterous explanations.

Harvey, however, disposed of this explanation most conclusively, simply by determining how much blood would have to
be thus produced and then dissipated in a given period of time,
and comparing this with the amount of food taken in during
that same time. He measured the amount of blood in a given
animal by draining it from the slaughtered carcass. Next, he
figured the pumping capacity of the heart by measuring the
volume of the heart chambers and counting the rate of the
heartbeat. Then, using most conservative figures, he found the
amount of blood pumped through the heart to be still many
times the weight of the food from which it would have to be produced. His proof was overwhelmingly decisive. A limited and
quite constant supply of blood was being circulated again and
again through the entire body.

The Revolution in Thinking

To us this idea seems so simple and commonplace that we
may well wonder how it could possibly bring about what we may
justifiably call a "revolution in human thinking." However, such
a revolution need not be measured merely by the bigness of the
new idea so much as by the overwhelming mass and ramifica-
tions of the errors which it clears away. A right idea, however
simple, may become truly revolutionary if it displaces enough
wrong, misleading, and futile thinking. Thus Newton's simple
laws of gravitation and motion, which can all be stated fully and
clearly in one modest paragraph, substituted manifest and de-
pendable order throughout the astronomical Universe for a
previous tangle of incoherent complications which never did
make sense.

However, the revolution in anatomic thinking was not quite
like that. For one thing, there was revealed no simple and universal law which could be stated so briefly and which could ex-

plain so much so clearly and coherently. Rather, there was a substitution of investigated facts for traditional fictions, in which the new habit of careful investigation was far more important than the particular facts uncovered. Not that the facts were unimportant in themselves, for together and eventually they truly defined the actual forms and structures which required proper explaining. Thus, those valves of the veins and heart, the closed septum between the heart halves, and the further related facts which Harvey gathered by careful observation and directed experiments, what were they but the precise factual description of the problem he had to explain? Here, as is so often the case, the exact description of the problem led automatically to the right solution—the circulation of the blood. It was one solution which fitted the facts, all the facts without discrepancies. And probably, here again, the scientific approach was more important than the particular explanation. For as we look back over three centuries, what seems most important to us was the emphatic example Harvey set in the use of the experimental method in biology, which was in fact followed more and more consistently from that day to this in all scientific studies of life.

Yet we may be mistaken in thus defining this revolution as it was recognized by the pioneer anatomists of the sixteenth and seventeenth centuries. For something else probably impressed the contemporary world far more. What struck the thoughtful of that day were undoubtedly the tangible facts disclosed rather than the method of disclosure. Harvey's thin book was to them just what it purported to be, factual proof of the circulation of the blood, and no more.

But they nevertheless drew new conclusions from the new facts accumulated, broad conclusions as to the fundamental nature of life. There were the bones pivoted at the joints and moved by the pull of muscles shortened because they swelled. Here were obvious mechanical levers. There was the heart pump, and the automatic valves of heart and veins, and the bloodstream driven by that pump—these, too, essentially mechanical. And for good measure, mechanism was often introduced where none existed. The nerves, for example, were thought to be tubular to carry pulses of fluid or "vital spirits," a mistake discovered by Jan Swammerdam about 1667 though not published until 1737. Also, there was then a general background of pioneering in mechanics and mechanism, largely by clockmakers, dominated by Galileo, who had experimentally discovered the laws of falling bodies and swinging pendulums. So the whole trend of scientific thinking was strongly mechanistic, and by 1644 the Mechanist Theory of life was definitely formulated by the French philosopher-scientist René Descartes. Animals, he said, are machines. He gave way somewhat in the case of Man: the lower animals are automatic machines, but the human animal is a machine guided by a soul.

Furthermore, while he did believe in spontaneous generation, he considered it a natural process, physical and something else— hinting at the broader physicochemical viewpoint of today.

But the physics of that day was almost entirely mechanics. And chemistry, after much preliminary experimenting and rather confused thinking, was not to become really meaningful for another century and a quarter. Then, in the 1770s, through the work of Scheele of Sweden, Priestley of England, and Lavoisier of France, oxygen was isolated and identified, a proper understanding of combustion was gained, and it was realized that the energy of living matter was derived from a respiration-oxidation process closely equivalent to combustion. Thereby the narrow Mechanist Theory began to be broadened to the Physicochemical Theory we now hold.

Asking Better Questions

Nearly two centuries have passed since then and in every field of science our knowledge has multiplied far beyond the

most farseeing dreams of these pioneer searchers. As we ourselves do, they asked questions as to the nature and origin of
life, but for sheer lack of pertinent information, their answers
were merely crude guesses. In the light of our present detailed
knowledge, our own answers of today, if not final, certainly
come much closer to the truth.

And perhaps more important, we have now developed the
scientific method of research to high effectiveness. To get the
right answers we ask the right questions the right way.

It will not do, however, merely to ask broad questions such as
"What is the nature of life?" and "How did that life originate?"
and then accept imposing and sweeping words as sufficient answers. That is the lazy man's way, and it gets him nowhere. We
must break down those general problems into detail problems,
and to do that we must begin by digging out all the pertinent
facts, which are indeed many. Also, as we gather them, we
must put those facts step by step into meaningful order, and
then we shall find that the right questions shape themselves
and usually force upon us the right answers. That is essentially
what is happening to us today. We have gathered pertinent
facts (though there are still many lacking) put them in compatible order, and they are now finally telling us the answers we
have so long sought.

In a large sense it has so far been the uncovering of a
mystery which early Man did not even know was there. For
until recent centuries the origin of life was hardly thought of
as a mystery. It was simple enough to mix water with dust to
make a plastic clay, and then to mold it to human or animal
shape. There then remained only the small matter of adding a
puff of breath to make it live. There seemed no mystery in
that. Indeed, it took Mankind centuries of scientific research
to uncover the intricacies of structure, the subtleties of chemical
and physical functioning, which go into that combination of
matter and energies we call life. And now finally, with the
realization of the mystery and the defining of its elements and

nature, we are strangely discovering that the mystery at the same time is resolving itself, dissipated into the ever-clearer answers which it also provides.

Now obviously, the details of both questions and answers have become more and more technical. Fortunately it is still possible, by selecting the pertinent and sticking to essentials, to make the subject nevertheless broadly understandable to the layman in science. Yet evidently this cannot be done by any thumbnail answer; we must first provide enough of the facts involved, and of the background of natural laws which give them meaning. This we can undoubtedly do most easily by continuing to tell the absorbing story of how both the facts and the laws were progressively discovered and then followed up and applied to give more and clearer understanding.

Chapter 2

CREATION AND CATASTROPHE

An essential feature of life, indeed a requirement for success and survival among all living things seems to be the adaptation of the structures and functions of those living things to the conditions under which they live. Often such adaptations are so obvious and remarkable that they can be overlooked only by the most thoughtless and unobserving. On the other hand, some essential adaptations are so hidden and illusive that they quite escape our closest study.

Today we explain such adaptations scientifically as the natural results of evolution, and in some instances we can actually trace the progress of shifting relations between a changing environment and the adaptive modifications as shown by fossils over some period of the geologic past. Furthermore, since Darwin, we now understand why such adaptation is indeed inevitable, a subject we shall take up a bit later.

Creative Design

But before Darwin and his Evolution Theory, adaptations were theologically explained as purposely designed by the Creator to help His creatures to survive. Jan Swammerdam, who pioneered in studying insects with the magnifying lens, praised the anatomy of the bee "because God's wisdom is so mathematically proven therein." This, too, was the theme of naturalist John

Ray's book, *The Wisdom of God manifested in the Works of Creation*, published in 1691 and a best-seller for over a century. It was followed a decade later by Nehemiah Grew's *Cosmologia Sacra* and by Archdeacon William Paley's *Natural Theology, or Evidences of the Existence and Attributes of the Deity Collected from the Appearances of Nature*, both strongly arguing for purposive creative design. The movement finally culminated during the 1830s with the *Bridgewater Treatises*, eight book-length essays written by eminent scholars selected by the Archbishop of Canterbury, the Bishop of London, and the President of the Royal Society of London, all intended to prove the "power, wisdom and goodness of God, as manifested in the creation."

This theological argument for creative design was most convincing in its day. But its whole force in the scientific world was soon quite overcome when Charles Darwin's *Origin of Species* appeared in 1859. This revolutionary volume not only summarized the overwhelming evidence for evolution as against special creation, but also provided a simple and convincingly obvious explanation of evolutionary adaptation by natural selection.

The idea of evolution itself did not originate with Charles Darwin; he merely explained its simple cause and effectively marshaled the evidence in its favor. Already the scientific evidence, accumulating on every hand, was making some theory of evolution quite inevitable.

The Idea of Evolution

In fact, the idea of evolution was already old. As pointed out by Henry Fairfield Osborn in *From the Greeks to Darwin* (1894), even some of the ancient Greek philosophers, starting with Thales of Miletus in the seventh century B.C., had held crude evolutionary ideas. However, their teachings come to us largely secondhand and usually so ambiguously expressed that often we hardly know what they meant. It should also be remembered that their ideas were mostly speculative, based on very little soundly verified scientific knowledge. As the geneticist C. H. Waddington of the University of Edinburgh put it:

> The Greek philosophers, who thought of almost every notion which mankind has been able to conceive, certainly thought of this one too; but in their usual way they tasted it, and sniffed at it, but never really tested it by experiment or detailed observation.

At least the evolutionary ideas which they did hold apparently did not influence significantly the development of the pre-Darwinian evolution theories. Those theories arose instead out of a growing accumulation of discoveries in several fields, which could be consistently explained only on the assumption that over the ages past, life forms had evolved by descent one from another. But while there was this increasing ferment of evolutionary opinion among scientists, nothing conclusive came of it until 1859, when Darwin clearly summarized all the evidence and added a broad and plausible explanation of why life evolved.

Creation and the Flood

Prevailing opinion up until that time, even among scientific men, centered about the idea of special creation of all life forms. Originally this meant outright acceptance of the Biblical account in which Deity spoke, "Let there be" and it thereupon was. But even more important to the development of evolutionary theory is the story of how Noah and his Ark saved the created kinds of animals from world-wide flood. It was simply taken for granted that each existing species of animal had descended without change from an original pair carried in the Ark.

This was possible to believe if one knew only the few familiar animals of a limited neighborhood. But the century of voyages of discovery following Columbus was to change all that. From distant lands scattered over the world were to come descriptions of a multitude of new and strange creatures and many actual specimens of such creatures, often brought together into private and royal zoos, where at least the informed could see and compare them. Soon questions were inevitably asked: How could they all have found room in the Ark, together with sufficient food for forty days, the limited dimensions of the Ark being clearly given? And when the Ark landed, how could those now found overseas have traveled to reach the distant continents and islands they now inhabit?

As early as 1614, Sir Walter Raleigh, realizing that the Ark had not been big enough to carry all known animal species, concluded that new species had since been added by crossbreeding, citing as example the mule crossbred from horse and ass. By 1660 Sir Matthew Hale explained that only broad archetypes were preserved by the Ark, from which all present species had then evolved, as lions and tigers from cats. Even as late as 1828 the pioneer embryologist Karl Ernst von Baer accepted variation from archetypes but considered it planned and directed. As more and more species were discovered, the episode of the Ark became increasingly difficult to accept.

Sorting and Classifying

With the increase in known animal forms, and of plant forms as well, another problem also became important, the practical one of sorting them out by some manageable system of classifying and naming. In the sixteenth century Konrad von Gesner tried to do this, but his work lacked any basic order. In the next century John Ray, seeking a "natural" classification, was also not really successful. Finally, in the eighteenth century, the Swedish naturalist Karl von Linné—Carolus Linnaeus in Latin—hit on a binominal system of classification which proved so effective that it remains in use to this day. First, because Latin was the international scholarly language, he gave all species names (whatever their derivations) in Latin form. Second, he used two names, one for the broad group or genus (e.g. *Canis* for dogs), the other for the particular species (e.g. *lupus* for wolf), the full name being *Canis lupus*. And third, throughout his system he classified by pairs of opposite characteristics, often the presence or absence of some distinguishing feature, as the vertebrates, with backbones, as against the invertebrates, without backbones.

Like John Ray, Linnaeus favored a *natural* classification, and realized that his own often fell short by being artificial. But "natural" to us now implies groupings based on kinship and common descent. This, however, conflicted with the accepted ideas of special creation and of fixity of species, derived of course from the prevailing Biblical viewpoint. Kinship by common descent was therefore not considered and no meaning for "natural" became clear.

The Great Chain of Being

Yet the systematic classification of life forms did result in an over-all view of the whole world of life and with it a realization that there was much orderly arrangement, with lower and higher forms joined by a continuity of intermediate gradations between them. Before the theory of evolution finally explained this, another broad idea prevailed—that the organic world was originally created as a single Great Chain of Being, a series starting with the humblest and crudest, and then extending by continuous gradations to the highest and most perfect.

This idea can be traced back to Plato, but did not take real root until the eighteenth century. In 1705 the German philosopher Gottfried Wilhelm Leibnitz presented the idea of a single

linear series but thought there might be small variations from
it. The continuity of the series was held important, and in
1715 William Derham, in a work entitled *Astro-Theology*, as-
serted that any links missing from the Great Chain here on
Earth would certainly be found on other planets. By 1764
Charles Bonnet described the series as starting with the stones
(possessing sensations) on up through vegetables to animals, to
man himself, and even up to the "blessed angels."

Such a continuity of life forms was bound to suggest a progression in time, and in the 1760s Jean Baptiste Robinet, while
accepting the single Great Chain of Being, held that it represented stages by which Nature tried out all the constituent
parts in the development of the human form. Earth history
was "the apprenticeship of Nature in learning to make a Man."
This, though obviously a departure from a single original creative act, was still not the idea of evolution by descent with variation from generation to generation. However, that idea was already in the air.

Benoît de Maillet

A popular volume in the mid-eighteenth century was *Tel-
liamed*, professedly the name of a Hindu sage but actually the
name of its French missionary author, Benoît de Maillet, spelled
backward. Probably written shortly before his death in 1738, it
first appeared in Amsterdam a decade later, and in English in
1750. It was a rather fumbling mixture of fantasy with sound
anticipations of later evolutionary ideas in geology and biology.
It regarded otters and seals as transitions of life forms moving
from the sea to the land and air, saw in flying fishes a like stage
between fishes and birds, held that human beings derived from
mermen and mermaids, or perhaps from apes which had learned
to speak. On the sounder side, however, it recognized the great
age of the world, described the process of successive depositions

of geologic strata, and the true nature of fossils as the remains of life. But it carefully disowned all these unorthodox ideas as unchristian, blaming them discretely on the Hindu sage interviewed long before in faraway Egypt.

Buffon and Evolution

Between 1749 and 1787, Count Georges Louis Leclerc de Buffon wrote brilliantly and voluminously for a wide popular audience on the subject of natural history. It is often difficult to pin him down as to what he actually believed, partly because he avoided declaring his ideas firmly, but also because he often changed his mind or contradicted himself. Apparently he began as a radical thinker (for his time) and later retreated into more conservative views. In 1750 he rejected the authority of the Bible, but in 1751, under pressure from the Church, recanted as follows:

> I declare that I consider my Hypothesis on the Creation of planets only as an assumption that I do not intend to contradict the text of the Holy Scripture, and that I firmly believe in everything which is stated there about the Creation.

Under such pressure he learned caution in his writing. Again and again he used the discreet device of presenting some theory merely as a fancy, but supporting it by most convincing evidence and argument, and then pretending to retract it by a weak rebuttal. He accepted the then-current idea of the Great Chain of Being but made it an evolutionary series, declaring that "all animals have developed from one single animal." But then he followed with, "but no, it is certain—certain by revelation —that all animals have shared equally the grace of Creation, each has emerged from the hands of the Creator as it appears to us today."

It will not do merely to charge Buffon with insincerity, for in later writings we do find him raising truly scientific objections to the theory of descent, yet from time to time and in special cases apparently changing his mind even in this. But if Buffon did vacillate, he was shortly succeeded by others who did not but declared themselves firmly for evolution by descent.

The Pioneers of Evolution

The Englishman Erasmus Darwin, grandfather of Charles Darwin, came first. His works, dating from 1789 to 1803, argued strongly for evolution by descent from a few archetypes (which he called filaments). Yet even in his most important work, *Zoonomia* (1794–96), only twenty pages out of 2537 were devoted to this subject. He apparently had little influence on subsequent evolutionist thinking; even his grandson Charles declared that his ideas "did not produce any effect on me."

The Frenchman Jean Baptiste de Monet, whom we know as Lamarck, started as a botanist but in 1793 obtained the Chair of Invertebrate Zoology at the Museum of Natural Sciences in Paris and began an important basic revision of the classification of the lower animals, based in part on a pioneer study of their fossil remains in the strata of the Paris Basin. Originally a believer in the fixity of species and the single linear series of life forms, he became convinced of evolution by descent and eventually by a branching type of evolution. He first published his views on descent in 1802 and expanded them in 1809 in his *Zoological Philosophy*. Unfortunately he presented his ideas rather arbitrarily, without supporting evidence, and perhaps for that reason had little influence among his contemporaries, though similar ideas were being broached about the same time by Gottfried Reinhold Treviranus in Germany and Lorenz Oken in Switzerland. However, an incidental idea which Lamarck may have borrowed from Erasmus Darwin, as to the manner of evolution, was later to become the subject of much controversy, making his name familiar to our own time.

One colleague, Étienne Geoffroy Saint-Hilaire, a long-time believer in evolution, came to Lamarck's support, though he differed with him on various details. He was, however, rather superficial and held self-contradictory ideas, among them a dualistic Vitalist-Mechanist view of evolutionary factors. Particularly, he tried to force all animal forms into one basic pattern, and in 1830, at several meetings of the French Academy, he got into a running debate with his associate Cuvier over this "Unity of Plan." Only very incidentally was the theory of descent taken up, Cuvier rejected it. But Saint-Hilaire, like Lamarck, did not trouble to refute objections with facts, while the thoroughgoing Cuvier was full of the facts of comparative anatomy to prove overwhelmingly a branching classification of animal forms into several basic patterns. According to his scientific contemporaries, Cuvier won the debates conclusively, including of course the rejection of the incidental item, evolution by descent.

Cuvier and Catastrophism

Baron Georges Léopold Chrétien Frédéric Dagobert Cuvier held the Chair of Vertebrate Zoology at the Museum of Natural Sciences while Lamarck held that of Invertebrate Zoology. But in contrast, his career was one of constant high recognition for brilliant achievements, doubtless fairly based on thoroughness and accuracy in his studies of both existing and fossil animals. He is generally credited with the virtual founding of the sciences of both comparative anatomy and paleontology, the study of fossils. Both taught him a common lesson, that all the several structures of any animal are consistently correlated to its way of life. The meat eaters, for example, are built for speed, have sharp claws, tearing teeth, a simple stomach, etc. Knowing such correlations in detail, he was able to perform marvels of identification and reconstruction, often from single bones, if we are to believe the legends that grew up about him.

His detailed knowledge also led him to a new classification of the animal kingdom into the four fundamental branches: vertebrates, articulates, molluscs, and radiates. These have since been broken down further, especially the radiates, mostly through knowledge later gained with the compound microscope. At any rate, Cuvier proved that the old idea of a single linear series was quite untenable, either as the Great Chain of Being or as the Unity of Plan of Evolutionist Saint-Hilaire.

Fortunately the rock strata of the Paris Basin were relatively simple and undisturbed, and together with nearby areas provided a vast cemetery rich in fossil remains of corals, shells, and mammals, an abundant and revealing field both for Lamarck's study of invertebrates and for Cuvier and his associate Alexandre Brongniart in their study of extinct vertebrates. This, plus his own numerous dissections of animals, made Cuvier, according to the historian H. T. Pledge, "the first man to enjoy the full luxury of a bird's eye view of life spread out backwards in time as well as around in space."

With such a background of knowledge, one might well think that Cuvier would have become an Evolutionist, or would at least have listened open-mindedly to his Evolutionist associates. But he did not, perhaps because they argued their case so speculatively rather than scientifically. They did speak arbitrarily, neglected to answer objections, and altogether played loosely with facts. Also Cuvier was perhaps personally biased, as suggested by his obituary on Lamarck, which was so embittered and unfair that his scientific colleagues refused to have it published. Besides, those words of Pledge about the "view of life spread out backwards" were hardly true, for the fossil record, even as enriched by Cuvier, was still most scanty, being full of gaps needing filling by "missing links." Particularly in the Paris

Basin, there were obvious gaps in the geologic series suggesting disastrous interruptions. At any rate, Cuvier became a convinced Catastrophist.

Lest the meaning of this geologic word be misunderstood, we had better review briefly the conflicts of opinion then current in the field of geology.

Neptunism versus Vulcanism

As might be expected, again it all began with the story of Noah and the Flood. When fossils were found in the deeply buried rock layers, or even on mountaintops, and it came to be recognized that they were actually remains of life forms (a revived idea dating back more than two thousand years to the Greek Xenophanes of Colophon) it was simply assumed that they had been left there by the Flood. Then came Abraham Gottlob Werner, who in 1775 announced that there was order, both of relative position and time, in the rocks of his native Saxony, and then naïvely assumed that all the rocks of the world must be in the same order and that they had been formed successively by precipitation by cooling of the heated waters of a sea assumed to have originally covered the whole Earth. This central idea led his many enthusiastic followers to call themselves Neptunists.

This dubious belief was first seriously challenged in 1785, and more fully in 1795, by the Scotsman James Hutton, whose rather dull and inept writings were finally popularized by John Playfair in 1802. Hutton had traveled widely and done much basic field work, and concluded from his detailed observations that natural processes such as we see at work today are sufficient to explain all the formations of the geologic past. In this he ignored the Biblical Flood and all other abnormal catastrophes, and in so doing of course clashed directly with the Neptunists.

On the other hand, he did include volcanic action and lava flows as normal and natural events, and from this his idea became known as Vulcanism, or sometimes Plutonism. There then followed a period of intemperate dispute, at first over the narrow issue of Neptunism versus Vulcanism. But in due time the controversy settled down to the broader and more significant issue between Catastrophism and Uniformitarianism, as the Huttonian Theory came to be called when further developed.

Originally the Huttonian viewpoint rather overemphasized the constancy and continuity of the geologic processes, such as erosion and deposition responsible for the rock strata. It rather ignored the fact that those strata were discontinuous. Werner had indeed noted this important fact and attempted to explain the few discontinuities he knew as due to changes in the methods of precipitation from the primitive turgid sea. But neither Werner nor Hutton paid attention to the fossils in the strata, and thus both missed the real clue to a deciphering of geologic history.

Order in the Fossil Record

That clue was instead to be discovered by a simple English surveyor who had no theories whatever. He was William Smith, perhaps the only one of his numerous namesakes to attain high scientific eminence by inadvertence. He was self-educated and possessed a keen eye for detail and a tenacious memory. He did his surveying during the period of canal building, both for drainage and for transport of an increasing volume of fuel, materials, and manufacture in a growing industrial England using much coal for power. As he tramped about surveying, planning, and supervising coal mining and the cutting of canals and roads all over the land, he had unusual opportunities to note the strata thus exposed, and particularly the fossil shells they contained.

But being a wholly practical man, he gave little thought to the historical meaning of those fossils as remains of ancient life forms, and used them solely for identifying and recognizing the strata for his own utilitarian purposes as engineer and in due time as geologic consultant.

He did, however, quite incidentally formulate certain scientific regularities of basic importance to historical geology, and it is for these alone that he is remembered today. First, each stratum contains its own distinctive group of fossils by which it can be positively identified. Second, the vertical order of the strata is always the same, though the full series may not be everywhere present. Third, there may be an overlapping of some fossils from one stratum to another, but once a given fossil had disappeared it never reappears higher and later in the series of strata.

These were the facts as he found them, but not being particularly scientific-minded, he drew no further inferences nor conclusions. In fact, for a long time he did not follow the scientific practice of publishing an account announcing his discoveries. He merely went about for a score of years, talking casually of his facts to anyone who would listen, thus earning for himself the sobriquet of "Strata Smith."

This was, of course, talking in vain to the wrong people, those with no interest in nor appreciation of what it all meant. For it did have most vital meaning, but because he waited until 1815 to publish his own great Geologic Map of England and a few papers on strata identification, he was twice anticipated by others and missed becoming the founder of paleontology. For in 1801 H. Steffens announced that as we move upward through the geologic strata, fossils of increasingly higher forms of life appear. And more important, in 1811 Cuvier and Brongniart wrote fully on the geology of the Paris Basin, on the meaning of its fossils, and on the revolutions of the surface of the globe indicated by those strata and fossils.

The Geologic Revolutions

Those geologic revolutions became extremely important, both in fact and in the conflicts of theory. They were marked by drastic changes in the fossils, those distinctive of one stratum ending abruptly, those of the next appearing as abruptly. Obviously, since the fossils had often changed so greatly, deposition must have been interrupted, probably with long lapses of intervening time. Such an interruption could be caused by an uplift of sea bottom to dry land, and a subsequent submergence and renewal of deposition. But meanwhile the strata may have been tilted or folded or considerably eroded, the new layers being then laid horizontally and unconformably upon the old. Of course, the interruptions and changes in fossils could be either great or small, extensive or merely local.

Today in historical geology we reserve the word "revolution" for only those major interruptions involving uplift of great mountain chains; lesser uplifts are known as disturbances. And with our modern methods of dating ancient rocks by radioactivity, applied to geologic strata all over the world, we have discovered that during the past half billion years the great periods of mountain building have occurred in cycles roughly averaging forty million years in length. By and large, they turn out to have been slow alternating cycles of crustal uplift and sinking, erosion and deposition, with even some shiftings of continental areas.

But when Cuvier first faced those manifest gaps in the fossil record of the Paris Basin, he could think of nothing but disastrous catastrophes, sudden and overwhelming, which wiped out existing life. He found that in this series of strata the fossils of land and aquatic animals had alternated three times, and concluded that there had been three floods, the Biblical one being the last. He then gathered testimony from the legends and writings of the Jews, Egyptians, Armenians, Chinese, Hindus, and American Indians that such world-wide and sudden floods had occurred, the latest some five or six thousand years ago according to his calculations. This was his theory of Catastrophism, which continued to be accepted, even in some scientific circles, until Darwinian evolution finally superseded it.

If all life over the whole world had been thus repeatedly destroyed by catastrophic floods, where did the new and higher life come from to repopulate the world? Cuvier's own answer was that there were some few areas not actually flooded, on which were preserved a few life forms which would then multiply and spread to fill the world again with life. But this did not explain why the new life forms were often new and on a higher level. Others who accepted Catastrophism resorted to new acts of divine creation after each extermination, each time on a higher level of life forms, culminating of course in man himself. As for the orthodox and uncritical multitude who just ignored the discovered facts, there was still Noah, his Ark, and the pairs of animal kinds preserved by it.

In England during the 1820s the leading geologist and teacher of geologists was the clergyman William Buckland, who taught a more religious version of the Catastrophic doctrine and in 1823 published his *Reliquiae Diluvianae; or Observations of the Organic Remains Contained in Caves, Fissures, and Diluvial Gravel, and Other Geological Phenomena, Attesting the Action of a Universal Deluge.* He held that the Noachian Flood and prior geologic cataclysms were miraculous, and thereby "returned natural history to the explicit service of religious truth." However, by 1836, in his contribution to the *Bridgewater Treatises,* he had abandoned the Flood, even though he remained a Catastrophist. Yet he was still considered sufficiently orthodox to be appointed Dean of Westminster in 1845, from which we may assume that a significant liberalizing of opinion was going on.

Geology Becomes a Science

This was undoubtedly largely due to the influence of one of Buckland's own students who had meanwhile brought geologic thinking to a new and realistic maturity. Charles Lyell, during the years 1830 to 1833, published three volumes on the *Principles of Geology*, supporting the Uniformitarian viewpoint by abundant new evidence, convincing argument, and a delightful literary style. By showing that the generally slow actions of everyday forces are sufficient for producing all geologic phenomena of the past, he dispelled any need for the miraculous explanations of Catastrophism. In his discussions of the distributions of animals and plants, of their kinships and origins, of the formation and arrangement of strata, and of the imperfections of the fossil record, he laid a firm foundation on which Darwin was later to build his Evolution Theory. In the words of Huxley, Lyell's work "was the chief agent in smoothing the road for Darwin." Yet at that time, odd though it must now seem, Lyell was not himself a believer in evolution.

Through all this there ran the incidental but important problem of the time element. Cuvier, we have seen, accepted a date for the last flood fairly consistent with the Biblical account. But he also included two previous floods not referred to in any Bible story, and these presupposed inconsistently early datings. But on the whole, the Catastrophists were not much troubled by the time problem, for they could date their catastrophes to suit their preconceptions and orthodoxies.

Not so the Uniformitarians and Evolutionists; they needed much time for the slow natural forces to effect the great visible geologic changes, and for life forms to evolve by slight steps. For those who still accepted the authority of the Bible, this raised the difficult problem of reconciling the few days of creation with the known long lapses of time required by geology.

Some did adopt the idea that the "days" of creation were meant to represent long geologic periods, separated usually by catastrophes. But the Biblical references to "the morning and the evening" of each day made this difficult. Those who ignored the Mosaic account were naturally not bound by such words or other limitations. We find that Buffon, for example, had allowed nearly 200,000 years for the slow cooling of the Earth from its birth out of the Sun until it should finally become too cold for any life. But that figure became millions of years even for the early geologists, and kept growing. Today, without more exact methods of radioactive dating, the figures have become more reliable and now total several billion years.

"The Vestiges of Creation"

When a scientific idea becomes the subject of wide discussion and public interest, a popular science book on it is pretty sure to appear. So it was with the theory of evolution; in 1844 an anonymous book came out, *The Vestiges of the Natural History of Creation*, which ran through ten English editions in the next fifteen years, plus two German editions. The author was finally identified as the publisher Robert Chambers. Its many editions attested to its popular style and appeal, and it certainly promoted interest in and discussion of evolution. Nevertheless it was a very mixed-up book, careless of its facts and full of contradictions and loose arguments. Scientific men, who knew the facts and reasoned more rigorously, rejected it out of hand and branded it as deplorable. Yet it spread the idea of evolution, kept even the scientists aware of it, and so, by stimulation at least, doubtless prepared the way for Darwin.

Also by the early 1850s several scientists did declare themselves for evolution. The botanist Matthias J. Schleiden (formulator of the cell theory), in his 1850 book, *The Plant and Its Life*, devoted four pages to evolution, stating that "The geological progression is a fact which can only be explained by descent." Another botanist, Franz X. von Unger, in an 1852 "Essay on the History of the Vegetable Kingdom," argued that descent was obvious from the geological progressions of fossils, and wondered that others before him had missed this. Meanwhile the philosopher Herbert Spencer, who was to play a large part in the support of Darwin, had by 1850 become an Evolutionist when he realized that human societies had developed from primitive beginnings. He expanded the idea, wrote an essay on it in 1852, and during the next half century wrote his voluminous *Synthetic Philosophy* based on the universality of evolution. All this meant that in the 1850s, the idea of evolution was in the air, and time was ripening for Darwin.

Chapter 3

WHY LIFE MUST EVOLVE

In June 1858 Charles Darwin received a letter which brought him keen disappointment. It was from an admiring fellow naturalist, Alfred Russell Wallace, announcing a new theory explained in an accompanying paper. In effect, it explained why life must inevitably adapt and evolve. It in fact presented the same great theory on which Darwin had himself been working for twenty years. But delaying publication until he had gathered all possible facts on it, he had announced it only to the geologist Sir Charles Lyell, the botanist Sir Joseph Hooker, and by letter to Asa Gray, the American botanist. Lyell, after reading a short abstract written some fourteen years before, had warned Darwin to announce it at once, lest he be forestalled. So it was to Lyell that Darwin now wrote, enclosing Wallace's paper and stating:

> Your words have come true with a vengeance—that I should be forestalled. . . . I never saw a more striking coincidence; if Wallace had my MS. sketch written in 1842, he could not have made a better short abstract! Even his terms now stand as heads of my chapters. Please return me the MS., which he does not say he wishes to publish, but I shall, of course, at once write and offer to send to any journal. So all my originality, whatever it may amount to, will be smashed, though my book, if it will ever have any value, will not have deteriorated.

But both Lyell and Hooker ruled against this generous surrender of his priority. They arranged to read both Wallace's and his own statements of the theory before the Linnean Society, which was done on July 1, 1858. Strangely enough, there was hardly any discussion, which Hooker explained, saying:

> The interest excited was intense, but the subject was too novel and too ominous for the old school to enter the lists, before armouring. After the meeting it was talked over with bated breath: Lyell's approval and perhaps in a small way mine, as his lieutenant in the affair, rather overawed the Fellows, who would otherwise have flown out against the doctrine.

Then for a year and a half nothing seemed to happen, except that Darwin set about writing a kind of abbreviated abstract of his work on the origin of species, although he had intended a more complete book including all his data. But Wallace's letter and the public announcement, and the fact that he found he could not successfully condense his vast amount of material, forced him to write an early and rather extensive book, which was published in November 1859. Called *On the Origin of Species by Means of Natural Selection*, every copy of the first edition of 1250 was sold the very first day. Obviously, though little was being said, there was great interest in the new theory.

The Battle on the Origin

Then the storm broke: such a controversy as the scientific world has not seen before or since. Little attention was paid to Darwin's real contribution, the causal factor of natural selection; it was the doctrine of evolution which was being attacked. Animated by deep-seated prejudices, scientists and bishops alike protested against the doctrine that life forms had evolved one from another—and presumably Man, too, from some lowly brutish ancestors, obviously ape and monkey.

Now and then some truly scientific objections appeared calling in the evidence of fact, but here Darwin was well prepared. He had so carefully considered all sides in preparing and presenting his theory that many of these reasonable arguments had been foreseen and already disposed of. And when, in the years to follow, other legitimate objections were raised, Darwin was ever-ready to consider them on their merits, even though at that time they could not yet be met. In matters of scientific fact and thought Darwin was truly his own severest critic.

But before the arguments of prejudice, distortion, ridicule, and abuse the gentle and guileless Darwin was defenseless. He was not to remain undefended, however, for there arose his "knights in shining armor," men to whom battle was as bread: Huxley, Haeckel, and Gray. The formidable Thomas Henry Huxley rose to champion the new cause, fighting a brilliant battle that will never be forgotten, facing fable with fact, stigmatizing unfairness and stupidity, doing more than any other ten men to win for the theory its first respectable standing. He called himself "Darwin's bulldog," while others described him as the "profound and terrible Huxley." Meanwhile, in Germany, the vigorous and learned Ernest Haeckel was writing (and proving) the detailed story of our evolution, establishing himself as Darwin's Huxley on the Continent. And in America, Asa Gray, though less fiery and aggressive, was nonetheless effective in his able promotion and defense of the new theory.

Darwin had not discussed Man's ancestry in his book of 1859, which emphasized instead the cause of the origin of species, but of course both his opponents and proponents realized very well that Man, too, must be included as also evolved. Twelve years later Darwin was himself to offer *Descent of Man*, his own careful discussion of that subject. But already in 1863, Huxley had written *Evidences of Man's Place in Nature*, in which he frankly insisted on the kinship of apes and Man. Even then this was already a seasoned controversy with him, on which he had again and again taken his bold public stand. And this has ever since remained the heart of a bitter controversy which has raged for and against Darwin.

Such bitterness of opposition to the animal origin of Mankind arose not only from a resentment against a descent from a brutish ape, but also from an increasing realization of what this implied as to Man's nature and ideas. They, too, must have evolved. There were those who accepted the physical evolution of Man's body but contended that his superior mind, and particularly his distinctive soul, had at some point been added by divine power. At this the consistent evolutionists of course demurred, insisting that both body and mind (with which latter they included soul) gradually emerged together by the slow natural processes of evolution.

But this also rather pointedly implied an evolution of Man's scientific and religious ideas. The wholehearted Evolutionist held that at the outset, emerging Man had no such ideas whatever, and that they must have originated as awakening Man began interpreting his experiences and observations. The more orthodox-minded dissented from this naturalistic view and claimed that at least religious ideas must have been given, even to primitive Man, by divine revelation in one way or another. Some, however, did admit that such revelation may have been gradual and progressive, perhaps even derived from contemplation of Nature's powers and mysteries. Yet this was simply admission of the Evolutionist viewpoint, even though it was somewhat more palatably worded to sound like a form of revelation. Its effect, futhermore, was still to question the sacred origin and verity of the currently cherished religious beliefs.

Anthropology and Religion

These threatening ideas did not long remain mere implications; they soon took tangible form as the actual origin of man, his works, and his ideas began to be revealed. Within four years after the *Origin*, Charles Lyell, now an avowed Evolutionist, published his *Antiquity of Man*, tracing early man's mental and cultural progress as revealed by his primitive tools and other archeological objects already being dug up and realistically interpreted. Then in 1871 the pioneer anthropologist Edward B. Tylor, in his *Primitive Culture*, gave a detailed account of religious ideas actually held by primitive peoples, and offered a reasonable explanation of how they developed such views. And in 1876 Herbert Spencer devoted the first volume of his *Principles of Sociology* to an equivalent account and explanation. Tylor described this simple primitive religion as "animism," giving an old word new meaning. Spencer, more vividly, called his explanation the "ghost theory," but without sensational intent. Both pointed out that early Man, very naturally but mistakenly, ascribed certain familiar phenomena such as echoes, reflections, dreams, and the breath lost at death as manifestations of spirit doubles of human and other living beings, and then extended this explanation to all other effects invisibly caused. This same belief in spirit beings was also central to current religions, and because these presumably evolved from the mistaken beliefs of early Man, the very foundations of current beliefs were brought into serious question.

In fact, the manifest conflict between evolution and current religion was even more direct, as the explicit basis for the central doctrine of Christian salvation was the fall of Man. By the sin of Adam and Eve came evil, toil, sorrow, and death into the world of previous perfection and bliss. Now came the theory of evolution declaring that Man had risen, not fallen. The clash was clear. Intentionally or not, the Evolution Theory did conflict with prevailing religious opinions. So for the orthodox-minded who could not surrender, there was nothing to do but resist evolution. Among these were the geologist Adam Sedgwick, the anatomist Richard Owen, and the biologist-glacialist Louis Agassiz, all high authorities in their sciences but also strong in their religious beliefs.

Others were for compromise, by some yielding and reconciling in the face of the facts evidencing evolution. However, the currently accepted religious traditions were based on texts too detailed and explicitly worded to permit any adequate yielding without rejection of manifest meanings expressed in clear language. Or reconciling meant the twisting of facts or the obvious implications of those facts. So it was that the Evolutionists found themselves, willy-nilly, locked in battle with the believers in traditional religion, and remain so to this day, although now largely with those who hold the fundamentalist attitude of direct denial of any fact, however well authenticated, which conflicts with their religious preconceptions.

In all this religious controversy Darwin himself took no active part. With Huxley doing battle for him, meeting eagerly and effectively all theological challengers, he really had no need to take part. But also, from all we know of his character, he had neither aptitude nor desire to debate such issues, which must have appeared to him as scientifically quite beside the point.

Certainly it was not from any antireligious conviction that he proposed his theories of evolution. In fact, during his period of formal schooling he had completed studies for the ministry, but this was on his father's insistence and not on his own initiative. He did not become a country parson from any religious doubts at that time, but because his overwhelming interest in natural history drew him away. In later years he confessed to eventual loss of faith in religion, but seemed almost to regret that loss.

Charles Darwin, Naturalist

Unquestionably it was this eager interest in natural history which animated the whole course of his education, activities, and accomplishments. His father, a successful physician, bewailed his youthful idling and wasting of life with mere "rat-catching" and aimless collecting. Finally he had been packed off to the University of Edinburgh to study medicine, but apparently neglected all studies not related to natural history. However, he found there a most able and inspiring group of teachers in this field, among them the geologist Adam Sedgwick, the botanist John S. Henslow, and the zoologist Robert Grant. He did more than just attend their lectures, for he walked with them afield as both student and friend, all being drawn to this adolescent with his eager passion for knowledge of Nature. Dr. Grant was an enthusiastic follower of Lamarckian evolution and on at least one walk expounded this doctrine to young Darwin. But neither that nor a reading of the evolutionary writings of his own grandfather Erasmus proved convincing, and all Charles Darwin got out of it was a familiarity with the ideas of evolution then current.

After two years, tiring of the boredom of medical studies, he began study for the ministry at Cambridge. He did graduate, but there, too, he continued to attach himself to the naturalists and to dabble with his pet interest, geology. Finally, in 1831, came his great opportunity, an offer on the warm and confident recommendation of his teacher-friend Professor Henslow to accompany the Admiralty ship *Beagle*, Captain Robert Fitz Roy commanding, as naturalist on a surveying trip around the world. But by this time his father was thoroughly exasperated with his aimlessness and lack of application to any professional purpose and would not at first give his consent, and was only persuaded on the urging of Josiah Wedgwood, the uncle of Charles, that "the pursuit of Natural History, though certainly not professional, is very suitable for a clergyman." The fact that all the expenses of the trip, including the natural-history work, would have to be paid for by the Darwins, apparently did not influence the decision. At any rate, consent was finally given, and in December 1831 the *Beagle* set sail, with Charles Darwin aboard, on a planned two-year trip which actually took nearly five years to complete (Figure 2).

Darwin took with him for shipboard reading the first volume (just published) of Charles Lyell's *Principles of Geology*,

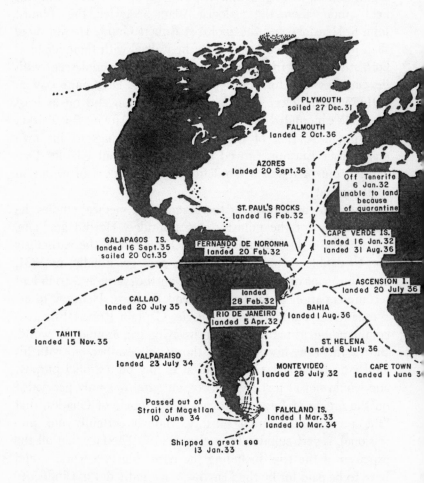

PLYMOUTH
sailed 27 Dec. 31

FALMOUTH
landed 2 Oct. 36

AZORES
landed 20 Sept. 36

Off Tenerife
6 Jan. 32
unable to land
because
of quarantine

ST. PAUL'S ROCKS
landed 16 Feb. 32

CAPE VERDE IS.
landed 16 Jan. 32
landed 31 Aug. 36

GALAPAGOS IS.
landed 16 Sept. 35
sailed 20 Oct. 35

FERNANDO DE NORONHA
landed 20 Feb. 32

ASCENSION I.
landed 20 July 36

CALLAO
landed 20 July 35

landed
28 Feb. 32

RIO DE JANEIRO
landed 5 Apr. 32

BAHIA
landed 1 Aug. 36

TAHITI
landed 15 Nov. 35

ST. HELENA
landed 8 July 36

VALPARAISO
landed 23 July 34

MONTEVIDEO
landed 28 July 32

CAPE TOWN
landed 1 June 3[ ]

Passed out of
Strait of Magellan
10 June 34

FALKLAND IS.
landed 1 Mar. 33
landed 10 Mar. 34

Shipped a great sea
13 Jan. 33

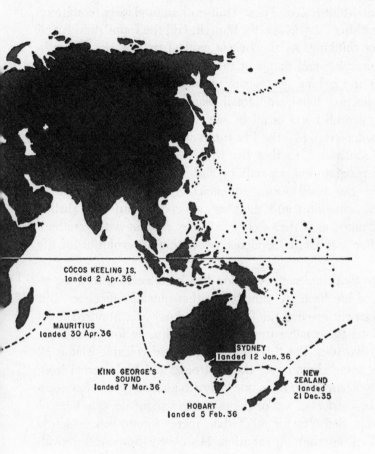

COCOS KEELING IS.
landed 2 Apr. 36

MAURITIUS
landed 30 Apr. 36

KING GEORGE'S
SOUND
landed 7 Mar. 36

SYDNEY
landed 12 Jan. 36

HOBART
landed 5 Feb. 36

NEW
ZEALAND
landed
21 Dec. 35

THE VOYAGE OF THE BEAGLE
1831—1836

Fig. 2.

and received the second volume (dealing with biological problems) at Montevideo. These Uniformitarian classics, confirmed by everything Darwin saw for himself, laid the foundation for all his later thinking. As the *Beagle* worked its way slowly southward surveying and mapping the east coast of South America, Darwin made long geologizing excursions on land, observing and collecting living and fossil plant and animal forms, and making careful notes of all he saw. Two broad facts impressed him particularly: (1) the life forms varied by gradations as he moved southward, so that the wider differences occurred with greater geographical separation; and (2) the living forms resembled the fossil forms of each region (such as modern armored armadillos and their extinct counterparts the shelled glyptodonts), as if they were related by descent with variation. Here then was factual evidence suggesting an evolution of life forms.

Up to that time such evolution had been ascribed to some response of life forms to climate or other outside influences. But when Darwin reached the Galápagos Islands, six hundred miles west along the equator from South America, he found facts upsetting that idea. For this compact group of volcanic islands all had the same climate, yet their tortoises and birds varied from island to island, even from one valley to another, as if mere separation by barriers of sea or ridges led to variant development of life forms. Some factor other than mere climate was evidently at work in determining variation. His observations were providing materials for thought, raising even basic questions which would need new basic answers, some of which he was himself destined to give the world.

On his return to England in 1836 he became busy arranging and studying his collections and notes, and most important getting acquainted with Charles Lyell, his intimate friend and scientific confidant from then on. Also, by 1839 he published his first book, the *Journal of Researches* on the *Beagle* voyage, and married his cousin Emma Wedgwood. His next three books were all geological: *Structure and Distribution of Coral Reefs* (1842), *Geological Observations on Volcanic Islands* (1844), and *Geological Observations on South America* (1846). Then he turned at last to biology with a series of technical monographs on the barnacles and their relatives (1851–54). Even before his *Origin of Species* of 1859, he had served as Secretary of the Geological Society, and was already making a name for himself as a scholar and as a respected member of the scientific community.

Following publication of the *Origin of Species*, Darwin continued his researches, and between the old facts from his voyage and the new facts gathered patiently over the years, he published ten more significant works: *On the Various Contrivances by which British and Foreign Orchids Are Fertilized by Insects* (1862); *Variation of Animals and Plants under Domestication* (1868); *Descent of Man* (1871); *The Expression of the Emotions in Man and Animals* (1872); *Insectivorous Plants* (1875); *Climbing Plants* (1875); *Effects of Cross and Self Fertilization in the Vegetable Kingdom* (1876); *Different Forms of Flowers on Plants of the Same Species* (1877); *Power of Movement in Plants* (1880); and *Formation of Vegetable Mold through the Action of Worms* (1881). He died in 1882, and his greatness was recognized by burial in Westminster Abbey.

The Origin of the Origin

The full title of Darwin's great book of 1859 was *An Abstract of an Essay on the Origin of Species through Natural Selection*. His explanation has ever since been known as the theory of natural selection. The term obviously parallels "artificial selection" as practiced by plant and animal breeders, Darwin having done much experimental research in this practical field. By "natural selection" he meant merely that in the struggle for existence the fittest animals and plants tend to survive, while the unfit tend to be eliminated, there being thus a natural selection of those living forms which change toward fitness to their environments. How they change and why they vary at all, he did not pretend to know, merely accepting it as observed fact that they did. He also assumed that each organism thus selected would transmit by heredity to its offspring its change toward fitness, so perpetuating the change and slowly adding to it through succeeding generations, causing a gradual evolution of new forms, new varieties and species. He did speculate on the cause and method of heredity, but his ideas on that have been supplanted by our more recent discoveries, and for his purposes it was enough to assume the unquestionable fact of heredity.

The problem of the origin of species had become important to him ever since his *Beagle* voyage had raised the questions of gradations of life forms with geographical distribution, of variations arising with isolation, and the resemblances he found between the fossil and living forms of an area. Soon after his return he definitely attacked the problem, starting a notebook on it in 1837. The next year he read—"just for amusement," he says—an "Essay on Population" by the Reverend Thomas Malthus. This popular essay had borrowed an idea from Benjamin Franklin that population tends to increase faster than the food supply, so that overcrowding and poverty inevitably result, causing war and disease, the natural checks to overpopulation. It at once struck him that in the resulting struggle for existence "favourable variations would tend to be preserved and unfavourable ones to be destroyed. The result of this would be the formation of new species."

Here then was a working theory, but he decided not even to write it out for some time. His first brief sketch was dated 1842, and was expanded two years later into one of 230 pages, but neither account was published. Altogether, for more than twenty years, he gathered and arranged the facts which bore on the problem, to make completely sure that he was right, and carefully prepared to convince the world.

Darwin and Wallace

Strangely, this theory of natural selection came to both Darwin and Wallace from reading the same essay by Malthus. Both had seen much of the struggle for existence among the wild who were always crowding for space and food, always battling as hunter and hunted. Both men had explored the teeming tropical jungles where the battle of life was incessant. In fact, when Wallace wrote his epoch-making letter to Darwin, he had been at work in the jungles of the Malay Archipelago studying its wildlife. He had read Malthus some time before and one day, when laid up with a tropical fever, started thinking about the essay on overpopulation and its natural checks. Like a flash the idea came: in that struggle for existence the fittest would survive and evolution would result. By the very next day he had written it out and two days later sent his article to Darwin. Its title was "On the Tendency of Varieties to depart indefinitely from the Original Type." Long afterward he stated:

> I had the idea of working it out, so far as I was able, when I returned home, not at all expecting that Darwin had so long anticipated me. I can truly say now, as I said many years ago, that I am glad it was so; for I have not that love of work, experiment and detail that was so pre-eminent in Darwin, and without which anything I could have written would never have convinced the world.

From these words, and the attitude of Darwin already quoted, it is apparent that we have here a pair of scientific rivals seldom recorded in the history of discovery. Darwin will always remain the example of what a scientist should be, careful of his facts, slow in assertion, holding firmly only to what the facts establish. Born on February 12, 1809, on the same day as Abraham Lincoln, he shared with that other great man the spirit of gentle kindness and that unselfish generosity which would have credited Wallace with the theory he had himself labored so long and carefully to develop, had not his friends (and the equally generous Wallace) ruled against that sacrifice of the credit rightly his due. And Wallace, the younger man, born in 1823 and surviving to 1913, remained Darwin's ever-friendly critic and correspondent, and over the ensuing decades actively contributed fresh and significant ideas as the scientific world developed the basic understanding of life's evolution which these two pioneers had thus well begun.

As each was extending the credits for originality to the other, it turned out that both had been anticipated by still others. In 1786 Joseph Townsend, in a "Dissertation on the Poor Laws," foresaw the Malthusian problem and clearly recognized the struggle for existence and the selection of the fittest. In 1813 Dr. Charles William Wells read a paper before the Royal Society of London on the case of a piebald woman, in which he put forth the theory of natural selection. In neither case, however, did the author point out the evolutionary consequences, the formation of new species.

Not so, however, with the ideas set forth in 1831 by the Scottish botanist Patrick Matthew in his book *On Naval Timber and Arboriculture*. For his was, in the words of Darwin, "a most complete case of anticipation." This might well have been a reluctant admission on Darwin's part, for Matthew was making himself quite obnoxious, having cards printed announcing himself as the original discoverer of natural selection and being generally up in arms over the failure of the world to recognize him. The reasons for that failure seem to have been: first, his account was published in the appendix to a technical book of narrow scientific interest and had been missed; second, it came before evolutionary ideas had won any serious standing; and third, Matthew had drawn Catastrophist, rather than evolutionary, conclusions from his theory.

Convincing the World

Furthermore, none of these early natural selectionists offered any sufficient body of evidence supporting the idea of evolution. The first to do this popularly was Robert Chambers in his *Vestiges of . . . Creation* of 1844, and then doing it carelessly and badly, and of course without the idea of natural selection. Much of the effectiveness of Darwin's *Origin of Species* arose from his careful marshaling of detail, a convincing body of supporting evidence patiently accumulated over those two decades of delay and hesitation in publishing.

Since the publication of the *Origin* an overwhelming mass of further evidence has accumulated, from the geological record, from resemblances between obviously related forms, from their individual developments which tend to sum up their ancestral histories. More recently there have been studies of like susceptibilities to diseases of our animal kin and ourselves, and most convincing blood tests indicating that our nearest living relatives are indeed the apes, with the monkeys next. The fact of evolution is today not doubted in the scientific world. For all the evidence converges consistently to prove it.

However, the particular Darwinian theory of natural selection has been occasionally doubted, although no better theory has ever been offered. William Bateson voiced such doubts rather vigorously at a scientific congress in 1914, whereupon the Fundamentalist opponents of evolution began quoting him as against the whole theory of evolution. Although he repeatedly explained that he only questioned certain aspects of the theory of natural selection, not the fact of evolution itself, they still misquote him to this day. Eventually the American Association for the Advancement of Science found it necessary to break all precedent and declare officially the unaltered acceptance by the scientific world of the fact of evolution.

However, it should be realized that the theory of natural selection, as presented by Darwin, had a peculiar persuasiveness all its own. It at last provided a clear cause and method for evolution, the very lack of which had until then made the general theory of evolution seem doubtful. Enough evidence was already at hand to justify belief in evolution, if some reasonable cause for its occurrence could be found. Here was just such a cause, in Nature itself, so simple and obvious that one saw it at once.

Its parallel in Man's own world was of course the familiar and well-demonstrated development of new forms of domesticated plants and animals by conscious "artificial selection." Darwin had studied this practical art most thoroughly, and in fact began the *Origin* by discussing it fully. Man directs his conscious selecting to produce the forms of life he desires. Nature, without conscious purpose, also selects by mere survival of the fittest, and the result is that forms of life keep changing toward fitness to survive. Here then was the explanation of all forms of adaptation, by natural process rather than creative design. Here, too, were a reason and a method for evolutionary change in life forms.

Life Must Evolve

What made this method of evolution all the more convincing was its apparent inevitability. Given life forms vigorously and prolifically propagating their kinds, itself an obvious advantage for race survival, a struggle for existence must ensue from overcrowding, both within each kind and between the kinds. Given also the two facts of even occasional variation of offspring from their parents in any advantageous way, and the preservation of such variation by heredity in later generations, then adaptive evolution became quite inevitable. The facts of prolific propagation and the resulting struggle for existence were obvious enough.

But the facts of variation and of inheritance of such variations had to be proved. They were undoubted facts in the state of domestication; otherwise, artificial selection would not have worked, and the many improved breeds all testified that it did work. But the question was: Did adequate variations occur in the state of wild Nature, and were they then inherited?

Here Darwin's own observations obviously became most important. The gradations of life forms down along the east coast of South America, the variant forms produced by mere isolation in the several Galápagos Islands, the many diverse and often complex adaptations of flowers to fertilizing insects, etc., all were evidences that variations in the wild state actually occurred, and had also been preserved by heredity. They were admittedly results, rather than directly observed instances of individual change and inheritance, but they were nevertheless convincing. And it may be said that Darwin used well the facts he did have to make them effectively convincing.

Darwin was never able, however, to offer any adequate explanations for either the causes of variations or the process and mechanism of heredity. These were to come later as the result of much detail study into the nature of life, especially its intimate cellular structures and processes, and with the gradual and controversial development of the new sciences of genetics dealing with just how life inherits and changes. Beginnings had been made in Darwin's own time, but they were made by others, and we shall devote coming chapters to the stories of how discovery progressed in these two vital fields.

The modern upshot of those studies firmly supports Darwin's two basic assumptions: adequate and significant variations do occur; and they are then inherited. Given these, natural selection of favorable and inheritable variations by survival of the fittest in the struggle for existence must follow. As a necessary result, life must, on the whole, inevitably evolve. Furthermore, such evolution is adaptive, fitting the life forms to survive under the conditions of environment and struggle they must face.

For either they thus adapt or they lose out in the struggle, the big name for which is extinction. There appear a few seeming exceptions, forms which persist unchanged, according to the geological record, even up to hundreds of millions of years. But this probably only means that conditions have not changed essentially and that the old adaptations therefore still hold good. In any case, there must have been an earlier evolution by adaptation to originate the persistent forms.

In short, adaptive evolution by natural selection seems to be an inexorable and universal law dominating all living things. In fact, as we shall see later, it came with the very emergence of life from the nonliving, and indeed conditioned that first elemental life to accelerate and accentuate its definite emergence.

Chapter 4

THE NATURE OF LIFE

The great Evolutionist-philosopher Herbert Spencer had a remarkable capacity for meaningful generalizing, nowhere more manifest than in his famous definition: "Life is the continuous adjustment of internal relations to external relations."

Although written about a century ago, there is still nothing essentially wrong with that definition, except that for popular understanding it is too general and needs filling in with some tangible features to make it meaningful and vivid. We all do have, however, an approximate idea of what distinguishes living matter from the nonliving, and if we stop to think, can probably fill in essentials from our own common knowledge, somewhat like this:

Life consists of units of matter which, first, somehow react continuously to contacts and conditions outside themselves. Second, each unit takes in food to grow and to derive needed energies, and then gives off unused wastes. Third, each has a self-contained organization, with physical and chemical processes, for carrying on such processes. Fourth, it perpetuates that organization and its activities by some method of reproducing its kind. And at least among animals there seems to be some awareness of itself and the world about it.

Now the scientist may accept this as a fairly good, though perhaps a bit inexact description of what life does and nonliving matter does not do. But when he talks of the nature of life, he is probably thinking of something else. For his concern is likely to be less with what life does and rather more with what enables life to do what it does. To start with, of what does the stuff of life consist? Also, how is it organized, and how does this organized stuff then operate, physically and chemically, to do the things which mark it as living? In short, he wants to know what natural forces, relations, and processes cause matter to live. And inevitably he will start asking just how did all this first get started.

Furthermore, being a modern scientist, habitually explaining everything else in the Universe as due to natural causes, he will look for natural causes here, too. A couple of centuries ago he might have still believed in Vitalism, or held the new Naturalistic Theory perhaps with some misgivings. But now, in the face of all the accumulated evidence, such uncertainties will have vanished, and he is undoubtedly a convinced and declared believer in Naturalism.

The Chemicals of Life

As the science of chemistry developed, the Naturalistic Theory of life received strong support and was greatly broadened by the gradual discovery that all living substances consist largely of just four chemical elements—carbon, hydrogen, oxygen, and nitrogen—with only minute amounts of a few other essential elements.

Furthermore, certain simple combinations of these four elements were found to be really basic to life substances and to the products of life. These were ordinary water (H_2O), carbon dioxide (CO_2), ammonia (NH_3), and a large group of hydrocarbons, the simplest of which is methane (CH_4).

This of course emphasized the importance of chemistry to life and thus made the new viewpoint physicochemical rather than only mechanistic. Significantly, too, we have strong reasons for thinking that all these simple compounds were present in the atmosphere, surface waters, and accessible crustal rocks of the early Earth a few billion years ago when the first primitive life was presumably emerging from nonliving matter. But we shall get back to all that later.

The formulas above given for these fundamental compounds reveal something very important, namely the combining ratios of their constituent atoms. To see this better, we will add to their chemical formulas these graphic diagrams of the molecular structures:

Water	Ammonia	Methane	Carbon dioxide
H_2O	NH_3	CH_4	CO_2

$$H - O - H \qquad H - N - H \qquad \begin{array}{c} H \\ | \\ H - C - H \\ | \\ H \end{array} \qquad O = C = O$$
$$ | $$
$$ H $$

In the water molecule, one oxygen atom holds two hydrogen atoms. In the ammonia molecule, one nitrogen atom holds three hydrogen atoms. In the methane molecule, one carbon atom holds four hydrogen atoms. It is as if each hydrogen atom had but one hand, each oxygen atom two hands, each nitrogen atom three hands, and each carbon atom four hands. The carbon-dioxide molecule is then pictured as two oxygen atoms, each with two hands, holding the four hands of one carbon atom.

Of course there are no actual "hands," so the chemist very properly talks instead of valence bonds, and describes hydrogen as monovalent, oxygen as divalent, nitrogen as trivalent (usually), and carbon as tetravalent. And he considers the tetravalency of carbon extremely important, making it possible for that element to combine in the vast multitude of complex substances involved in the chemistry of living things. In fact, organic chemistry, which began by dealing with only life substances and products but has since broadened, is often defined simply as the chemistry of the carbon compounds.

Incidentally, there is no present mystery about those valences or combining ratios of the several chemical elements. They arise quite understandably from the physical structures of the atoms, particularly the numbers of their electrons.

An atom can be pictured as consisting of a central mass or nucleus composed of relatively heavy protons and neutrons, around which orbit very lightweight electrons. Each proton carries a unit positive electric charge, each electron a unit negative electric charge. As positive and negative electric charges balance and attract each other, and because each neutron consists of a proton and an electron, each neutron is electrically neutral. The number of positive protons in the nucleus are not thus balanced, and so normally serve to keep the same number of negative electrons circling about the nucleus. Thus, our everyday hydrogen atom has a nucleus of just one proton, capable of holding one electron in orbit. The other elements, with atom nuclei of more protons, have more electrons in orbit.

The electrons, however, tend to orbit in a definite series of what we have visualized and call shells—the first of which can hold only one or two electrons, the second only up to eight. Each further shell can then hold up to eight circling electrons as an outer shell, but up to eighteen as an inner shell. The shells which are fully filled prove to be stable, so stable that their atoms have no tendency to join with other atoms by exchanging electrons. Those are the atoms of the chemically inert elements; helium (with a full shell of two electrons), neon (with two full shells, $2 + 8 = 10$ electrons), argon (with three full shells, $2 + 8 + 8 = 18$ electrons), krypton (with four full shells, $2 + 8 + 18 + 8 = 36$ electrons), etc. None of these stable atoms has ever combined with other atoms—until recently when the stable xenon was successfully united with that fiercely combining element fluorine.

Most elements, however, have atoms with too few or too

many electrons for such inherent shell stabilities. These tend to pick up, lose, or exchange electrons to gain stability, which they do by combining with other atoms, borrowing, lending, or trading as many electrons as are required for stabilizing. Thus, hydrogen, with its single electron, lacks one of the stable two for the innermost shell and therefore has a valence of one. Oxygen, with eight electrons, is short two of the stable ten, and has a valence of two. Nitrogen, with seven electrons, lacks three of ten, explaining its valence of three. Carbon, with six electrons, is rather special, for it has four too many for the stable two, and four too few for the stable ten, and so has valences of four both ways. Therefore it is capable of borrowing, giving up, or sharing electrons in many ways as it combines. This versatility, including its resulting proneness to combine with other carbon atoms to form chains, makes it basic to organic and living chemistry.

Organic Molecules

Important in the chemistry of life and life products are several simple chemical combinations called radicals which act much like single atoms with definite valences. First is the hydroxyl radical (OH), which we diagram as –O–H to show that it has one free hand, a valency of one. It is obviously a water molecule with one hydrogen atom missing.

Second is the carboxyl radical (COH), pictured as $-C\diagup^{H}_{\diagdown O}$ to show that it also has one free hand. It combines with larger molecule groups to confer acidity on them.

Third is the amino radical (NH$_2$), pictured as $-N\diagup^{H}_{\diagdown H}$ to show that it also has a valency of one, in this case conferring alkalinity to larger molecule groups.

The methyl radical (CH_3), pictured as $-C\diagup^H_H \diagdown H$, is less common and, on occasion, apparently important. It is clearly a methane molecule minus one hydrogen atom.

As an example of a larger molecule group, here is a simple sugar with the formula $C_6H_{12}O_6$, and the structure:

$$
\begin{array}{ccccccc}
H & H & H & H & H & & \\
| & | & | & | & | & & H \\
H-C-C-C-C-C- & C\diagup \\
| & | & | & | & | & \diagdown O \\
\text{O-H} & \text{O-H} & \text{O-H} & \text{O-H} & \text{O-H} & &
\end{array}
$$

or more simply

$$
\begin{array}{cccccc}
H & H & H & H & H \\
| & | & | & | & | \\
H-C-C-C-C-C-COH. \\
| & | & | & | & | \\
OH & OH & OH & OH & OH
\end{array}
$$

This sugar, known as glucose, is evidently built about a chain of six carbon atoms, with each carbon atom holding by four hands, each oxygen atom by two hands (include those in the OH radicals), and each hydrogen atom and hydroxyl radical by one hand. There is also a carboxyl radical holding by its one free hand.

If now we take away a hydrogen atom from such a sugar molecule and an OH from another, each will have a free hand. Joining the two molecules with these free hands, we get a larger compound molecule, and in this way can build up very complex carbohydrate molecules. Some plant starches having giant molecules are compounded in this way out of thirty or forty basic molecules. Characteristically, however complex the carbohydrate, the hydrogen and oxygen atoms occur on the same two-to-one ratio as in water, and only the proportion of carbon and the structural arrangement vary.

Another broad group of organic compounds are the fats. They are built up about glycerine molecules, again carbon chains with H atoms attached, but with the OH units replaced by fatty-acid groups. Each such group is a carbon chain with H atoms and an acid carboxyl unit attached.

A still more vital group of life substances are the proteins, characterized by the presence of nitrogen, and compounded by the joining together of a variety of fundamental units which we describe as amino acids. To build an amino acid we once more start with some fatty-acid molecule with a carboxyl radical at one end. We also replace one H with an amino radical $-N\begin{smallmatrix}\nearrow H\\ \searrow H\end{smallmatrix}$. The result is an amino-acid molecule, acid at the carboxyl end and alkaline at the amino end. About twenty such amino acids are known, each distinct, and often quite complex, in chemical structure. As acids and alkalies readily join chemically, such amino acids tend to string together into chains and other forms of molecules in vast variety as the huge composite molecules of proteins so important to the processes of life. In their building, other elements besides the basic four are often added, giving the proteins even more capacities for doing vital jobs in the life economy. For example, chlorophyll (the green of plants) has a bit of magnesium in its makeup, and hemoglobin (the red blood pigment) has a bit of iron.

When the pioneers in chemistry first realized that the basic elements consist of minute unit atoms, and that these join into molecules of definite compositions, they soon worked out a method of rough description by listing the kinds of atoms included, and giving the numbers of such atoms per molecule. They designated the elements by letters, such as C for carbon, Ca for calcium, O for oxygen, H for hydrogen, N for nitrogen, etc. And they drew up formulas, such as $C_6H_{12}O_6$ for glucose.

But in due time they discovered that compounds which were manifestly different had exactly the same formulas—for example, the sugars fructose and glucose. The differences, they learned, were due to variations in internal arrangements, and some of these they can suggest by breaking up and arranging the formula into unit groups. Thus, fructose was described as CH_2OH-$(CHOH)_3COCH_2OH$, and this formula could obviously be interpreted only by an organic chemist.

To make matters clearer, a graphic picture of the molecular structure could sometimes be drawn, such as that already given for glucose. But this, too, had its limitations. Such a picture, drawn on a flat surface, is strictly two-dimensional, while an actual molecule has three dimensions in which to arrange itself. So when we want to picture a complex molecule truly, we may have to resort to a three-dimensional model, often hard to make.

The fact of the matter is that molecules come in all sizes and shapes, from a simple pair of two atoms up to proteins of tens of thousands of atoms, arranged in chains, rings, and helixes, with unit groups, side chains, and foldings with secondary contacts and bonds. To analyze all these variant complexities, which often prove theoretically significant and even useful practically, has taxed to the utmost the ingenuity, skill, and patience of the biochemists. For example, consider a molecule of myoglobin. It is a constituent of muscle fiber, much like the hemoglobin of blood corpuscles but only about one fourth the molecular size. Only recently its structure has been deciphered by X-ray diffraction studies, a method that is a refinement of something quite familiar in the old days of crystal chandeliers with pendant glass prisms. A ray of sunlight striking a prism was broken up into a multitude of rays which spotted the walls of the room with a scattered pattern of colors. Had one taken a picture and then had the skill for computing the optics of it all, one could have worked out the shapes and positions of the pendants. Today, by passing an X-ray beam through a myoglobin crystal and photographing the pattern of spots, and then analyzing their distribution and intensities using modern computers, we can infer the minute structure of the myoglobin molecule. It turns out to be an intricately folded structure. In a later chapter we shall come across another instance of X-ray diffraction photography revealing a helical structure which gave a basic clue to our modern understanding of the material by which life forms reproduce and inherit.

Probably because organic molecules are large and loosely held together, they are likely to be unstable, subject to disturbing conditions and contacts. We could say they react, for better or worse, to stimuli. Yet this means not that they are consciously sensitive, but merely that they are chemically reactive. Furthermore, because each molecule has a distinctive chemical makeup, it is prone to react in its own distinctive way to a given stimulus. All of this, of course, approaches one of the characteristics of living matter—selective reactivity.

Chemical Speeding Up

Ordinary chemical reactions, however, are often slow, and not at all fast enough for the needs of life. Speeding up these reactions may be quite necessary, either to get enough done or to get it done fast enough. To a hunter animal seeking food, or a hunted animal trying to avoid becoming food, fast reactivity may decide between capture and escape. Fast reactivity, in any and all ways, is largely a matter of speedy chemical reactions.

In our industrial laboratories we speed up chemical reactions largely by means of catalysts. These are substances, particularly metals, which somehow accelerate chemical reactions without being themselves used up to become part of the new end products. For instance, hydrogen and oxygen mixed at room temperatures react and unite slowly, but the presence of powdered platinum causes instantaneous union. The powdering of the platinum increases its exposed surface and its effectiveness, and only a small amount of catalyst is needed to promote a large and continuing reaction. Such catalysis is so effective that it has become a mainstay of our practical chemical industry.

The usefulness of catalysis to life processes is greatly enhanced by a large group of protein compounds called enzymes which act as catalysts themselves or as catalyst helpers. Used with ordinary catalysts, they often multiply effectiveness by incredible ratios. Thus the hydrogen ion (the H atom minus its electron) acts as a catalyst to break up the cane-sugar molecule, but the organic enzyme invertase does it about ten million times as energetically. Often the inorganic catalyst must also be present for the enzyme to work. The salivary enzyme amylase, which converts starches to sugars, requires a small mixture of inorganic salts such as sodium chloride (ordinary table salt) in order to work at all. The salt alone will act as a catalyst to do the converting, but very feebly and slowly, the presence of the amylase multiplying its effectiveness greatly. Often more than one enzyme, or even a succession of enzymes, must be present to promote a given chemical reaction. What all of this means in speeding up life processes can be emphasized by pointing out that enzyme action is behind even our most instant and swift muscular movements.

Enzymes differ from ordinary catalysts in three vital ways: first, they are complex chemical compounds, namely proteins; second, they are always of organic origin; and third, they do more specific jobs of chemical incitement than inorganic catalysts. At times, instead of speeding up chemical processes, they may slow them down, or keep them at a controlled speed, all of which may be important for managing the chemical processes of life to the best advantage.

But how do catalysts and enzymes work? Is this such a mysterious magic as the Vitalists have predicated as the essence of life? Apparently nothing of the sort. Basically, the action of a catalyst depends upon its capacity to attract and hold atoms or molecules of the chemicals it helps join. Thus, in our case of the hydrogen and oxygen gases mixed at room temperatures, their component molecules are in constant high-speed and random motions, making only transitory approaches and contacts. But attracted and held on the surfaces of powdered platinum, they are momentarily brought to rest close enough together for chemical reactions to occur. Thereupon the new molecules escape from the platinum surface, making room for further holdings and reactions, all without using up the platinum catalyst. Powdering the platinum greatly multiplies the usable surfaces exposed, and therefore multiplies the effective rate of catalytic action.

In the case of the organic enzymes, the basic process is the same, a holding action bringing together molecules for chemical recombination. However, the enzymes are themselves complex protein structures with specific surface patterns to which are attracted specific molecules, which are then held in specific arrangements permitting only the specific chemical combinations into specific products. In short, the enzyme provides the working pattern for the resulting product, and its catalytic action is therefore always specific. For this reason the enzymes provide the very definite controls which assure effective chemical performance in the living laboratory.

The Chemistry of Life

So we have started with four basic elements, plus occasional help from minute amounts of other elements, and by successive natural and understandable combinations have reached giant molecules and aggregations of molecules in a great variety of structures and properties, among these properties a beginning of selective reactivity.

Those substances are of course normally produced in the natural laboratories of plant and animal organs, and for some time the Vitalists could argue plausibly that the chemistry of life was somehow different, and no one could ever produce in man-made laboratories any of the distinctive products of living organisms, to say nothing of the very stuff of life. But in 1828 Friedrich Wöhler artificially produced urea, hitherto done only by living organisms. This was a hard blow to the Vitalist view, and more was to come as the distinction between living and nonliving chemistry gradually broke down. By 1887, Emil Fischer was even compounding in the laboratory such complex organic substances as sugars. With further progress in this field, the science of organic chemistry branched off as a complicated specialty, full of headaches, but still dealing with ordinary chemical elements combining in understandable ways according to fundamental laws soundly based on ordinary chemistry. With all of this, the conviction was enforced that life is complicated but not essentially different physics and chemistry. Thereby, of course, the Vitalist Theory finally lost all scientific standing, and from now on we can spell "vitalist" without the capital V.

If life is thus characterized by an entirely natural chemistry, the implication is clear that it must also have originated by some natural chemical process or processes. To reach the present variety and complexity of living substances and products, there must have been a long and probably devious, though always natural evolution in the chemistries of living things.

Tracing any such chemical evolution must now be exceedingly difficult, and perhaps in its entirety quite beyond us. First, it was probably too involved to be reconstructed by mere chemical logic. Of course we do search the ancient rock formations for fossils giving possible hints, although the crucial first steps were not likely to have left records at all helpful, because the earliest life forms were probably too soft-bodied to leave any traces. But we do have "living fossils," those still surviving forms with primitive characteristics, which may give us real clues. These we will of course follow up. And today scientists are also carrying on most promising experiments at re-creating the conditions and chemical steps by which life may have originated.

However, we must not again make such a mistake as that of the first Mechanists. They thought life was merely mechanism; we must not think of it as merely chemistry. We have discovered that physical organization is also importantly involved, and that the evolution of that organization also needs to be traced, and experimented with, to account fully for the nature and origin of life.

The Microscope and the Cell

Naturally our knowledge of the structures of living things began with those exterior features obvious to the naked eye.

Much was also learned of the gross anatomies of both plants and animals because they were being constantly cut up for food and other uses. Something was also revealed even of human anatomy by the wounds of war and accident, and in due time by such inquisitive students as Leonardo da Vinci and by daring scientists such as Andreas Vesalius, who defied the Church ban on human dissection.

But until comparatively recent times little was known of the more minute structures of any living things. But we have noted how Leeuwenhoek studied the lively realm of microorganisms disclosed by his improved magnifying lenses. And Eustachi used magnifiers to make a beginning in the study of the really minute details of human organs. But more refined knowledge of the very minute structures of all forms of life waited on the development of a good compound microscope giving clear images at higher magnifications. The compound microscope has a small front or objective lens which forms a well-enlarged image of a minute object, which image is then further multiplied in size by a second or eyepiece lens. Its invention is often ascribed to Zacharias Janssen as early as 1590, but as he was then probably only two years old, this seems highly unlikely. Johann Kepler designed (but apparently did not make) one in 1611, and Galileo is reported to have possessed one about that time. It was certainly in use by 1620, but because of optical imperfections remained inferior to the well-made high-power magnifiers used by Leeuwenhoek, Swammerdam, and others, until major improvements were worked out by several optical innovators from William H. Wollaston and Joseph J. Lister prior to 1830 and on to Ernest Abbe in 1886. Such earlier improvement, however, had as its immediate effect an important general advance in our knowledge of the detailed structures of living tissues.

As early as 1665, with a compound microscope which he himself had slightly improved, Robert Hooke had seen "cells" in the dead bark of trees. By 1824 R. J. H. Dutrochet had found cellular structures in the living tissues, and by 1833 Robert Brown had discovered the nucleus of the cell, calling it the cytoblast. Soon (1838) Matthias J. Schleiden published his theory that plant tissues all consist of walled cells, each cell with a nucleus. The next year Theodor Schwann extended this theory to include animal tissues (though cell walls were not always apparent), making plants and animals structurally akin and laying the foundation for later detailed studies of the workings of all things living. For the lowest forms of life apparently consisted of single cells, the higher forms of many cells. Always the cell was the basis of living structures, an idea which caused a veritable revolution in all biologic thinking (Figure 3).

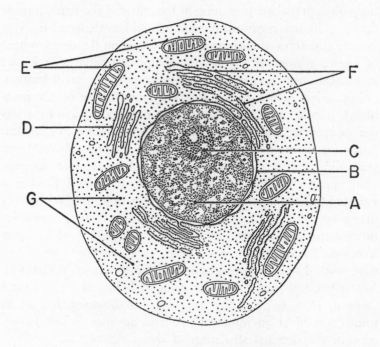

Fig. 3. Typical Cell Structure.

Thereupon and thereafter the cell itself was studied intensively. Even free single cells were found diverse in shape, and those of multicellular organisms were naturally shaped by mutual crowding and the differing jobs they had to do. Cell walls varied from mere surface tensions to tough membranes or shells, or were apparently lacking for many animal cells which were distinguishable only by their contained nuclei. Cell walls were found to have the capacity for selective passage through them of certain foods, wastes, and other substances. The fluid contents contained both living granules and mere undigested or stored nonliving foods, wastes, etc.

Most important seemed to be that more opaque and probably denser central nucleus, which evidently dominated the cell life, though there seemed to be no nuclei in red blood corpuscles (considered to be cells) or in the cells of bacteria and blue-green algae, presumably forms close to the very beginnings of life. Near the nucleus there might be a centrosome, later described by E. B. Wilson as the "dynamic center" as it leads in the dividing of the cell. Certain plant cells also have chloroplasts, granules containing the green stuff chlorophyll by which sunlight energy is captured by chemical action for storage in foodstuffs. And today we are very busy studying unit structures called mitochondria and ribosomes, of which more later.

Protoplasm, the Life Stuff

The living content of the cell was first called sarcode by Felix Dujardin in 1833, and then protoplasm by Hugo von Mohl in 1846, and was found common to both plants and animals by Max Schultze in 1861. Thomas Henry Huxley emphasized its importance by calling it the "Physical Basis of Life." Chemically it is a complex mixture of proteins, themselves compounded in vast variety from some twenty-odd amino acids. But then it seemed to be a semifluid jelly, and there was long debate as to its physical structure and what that structure might mean to its being alive; was it network, foam, granules, or plain viscous fluid?

Meanwhile, too, the Darwinian Theory had started everyone thinking about the origin of life, and we find Ernest Haeckel speculating on that origin in a very simple pre-cell or moneron, and Huxley searching for that origin in a simple protoplasmic submarine slime, which he prematurely named "bathybius." The finding of that origin did not then seem far away.

But further research disclosed many complexities within the cell, definite working structures which often go through significant physical and chemical changes. Our optical microscopes, attaining thousandfold magnifications, gave us a good start. Now with modern electron microscopes and their supermagnifications we can lift finer cell details to visibility and see even the ultraminute viruses. And recently, using the new phase microscope which converts hidden differences of density to visible contrasts, we have begun to watch (without any killing by staining) even the contents of the cell in living motion and change. Furthermore, we have developed and applied a whole new battery of ingenious research techniques to reveal the secrets of cell and virus, chemical as well as physical.

Of course the accumulation of new information from this continuous research is constantly adding new understanding, plus a lot of new problems. Without entering into too many details at this point, we can sum up several broad and significant conclusions which must apparently be drawn.

First, there is a growing realization that each cell is a well-ordered laboratory in which cycles of physicochemical processes are carried on step by step under rather definite controls. These controls are largely specific enzymes, that numerous group of proteins which quicken, retard, direct, and otherwise modify chemical reactions. And whatever the job of the individual cell may be in the over-all economy of the living body, it has evolved just the right set of enzymes, in proper positions, and triggered in proper sequences, to do that job effectively. And even when the entire living body is but a single cell, this must also be true, the cell being essentially a complex laboratory, well-ordered and controlled, to carry on all its life functions.

A view of almost any working chemical laboratory built by man is usually dominated by an array of glassware, evidently containers of various shapes connected by tubing, etc. Transparent glass is normally used because the chemist must see and check on what is going on, but also because generally glass is unaffected by the chemicals involved and so makes a good container. It may have to be some special glass if breakage by heating and cooling is to be prevented. And other materials are necessarily used when no kind of glass is resistant to the chemicals. There is usually a separate unit for each process step, such as mixing, heating, chemical reaction, the sizes being large enough for amounts involved, time required, etc. Shapes are fitted to the process steps, such as broad bottoms of flasks for absorbing heat, goosenecks for catching and passing on condensing vapors, etc. And there are accessory units, heating devices, valves for controlling flow, settling basins, centrifugal separators, mechanical mixers, colloidal mills, etc. And somewhere in the materials employed are likely to be catalysts to accelerate, direct, or otherwise control the several reaction steps.

In the natural laboratory of a living cell much of this intricate array of materials and equipment is obviously not present, and in any case could hardly be produced, set up, and utilized by that minute unit of life. Transparency is ordinarily not needed, as there is no outside supervisor watching to exercise control, the cell unit being rather self-contained and in large measure automatically reactive to outside influences. Compactness is a prime requirement, and any devices used must fit into and work within the confines of the cell. Structural materials must of course be those available to or producible by the organism. Foodstuffs as energy sources must be convertible to substances which can be absorbed, stored, transported to, and utilized by the cell, and waste products must be at least transportable out of the organism. Proper chemical reactants, largely enzymes, metal catalysts, and other co-enzymes, must be available at the right points and moments, for facilitating and determining the sequences of reactions. And, as we shall learn later, there must be present special units evolved for controlling accurate self-reproduction of the cell, and these must be provided with proper materials and accessory aids for doing their jobs.

Yet all this formidable complexity of functions is carried on by a remarkably economical array of basic devices. Looking into the contents of a cell with an electron microscope magnifying tens or hundreds of thousands in diameter reveals an apparently incoherent mess, and untangling its working order has proved a long and difficult research job, largely because it is all so minute and hard to take apart, test, and otherwise work with. Much of the contents are obviously viscous or fluid (largely water), probably sometimes intermixed, sometimes separated. The separators are membranes, usually visible, an exterior covering for the cell as a whole, plus interior membranes dividing into unit containers. These membranes, however, are not tight walls, but are permeable by fluids passing in or out by osmosis regulated by variations in pressures, electrical charges, and other physicochemical factors on the two sides. They are apparently largely composed, at a minimum, of two monomolecular films of lipids (fatty stuffs), capable of being either water-resistant (hydrophobic) or water-accepting (hydrophilic) as need and conditions mysteriously determine. The outside cell membrane serves for the selective exchange of materials between the environment and the cell interior, while the internal membranes serve for similar exchanges between compartments. Some compartments appear as separate enclosed granules, often dense or solid, but others seem connected, even to the cell wall, by a general labyrinth of membranes. And not only do the membranes thus serve as separators and selective sieves for passage of fluids, but they also seem to provide surfaces to which attach working units, such as enzymes or RNA chains (see Chapter 7), for carrying on particular activities. So with a surprising economy of basically simple structures, the cell carries on its multiplicity of laboratory functions.

But if the cells we know are thus complex and well organized, it is not at all likely that they represent the original form taken by the first life as it evolved from nonliving matter. And so again, like the old believers in spontaneous generation, we may find ourselves looking for origins too high in the scale of life. And again, perforce, we have to turn our eyes to even lower forms which may not seem to live in any complete sense, perhaps so low that we could not readily identify them as being among the living at all.

Do we have such borderline forms? The answer seems to be yes. At least we have some which we may well suspect. There are the sulfur and iron bacteria which live by very primitive chemistries quite at odds with the ordinary chemistry of living things. Perhaps these are near the transition forms between the nonliving and the living. Or perhaps they can only furnish clues. And we have the viruses, even more minute and chemically simple as life forms, but unable to grow and reproduce except in some living host cell, which obviously could not have been yet present at the origin of life. At any rate, whether or not the viruses do help solve the problem of the very origin of life, they have otherwise much to tell us. So we shall return to all these suspected forms later.

Again, obviously, we are to find no quick and easy answer to our problem of life's origin and must become reconciled to tackling it the hard way, by diligent accumulation and thorough study of pertinent facts. It is very unlikely now that we shall ever find any convenient and laborsaving aggregation of matter, physically and chemically so utterly simple that we can consider it as prototype of either the preliving or the barely living. Instead, we had better go right on reviewing all that seems most pertinent of what we have learned of life and its processes, chemical and physical, and then try again by any and all approaches which seem in any way promising.

Chapter 5

HOW WE INHERIT

When first presented, the Darwin-Wallace theory of natural selection had a strong appeal because it seemed so simple and obvious. If variations did occur and were then inherited, the fittest would necessarily survive in the struggle for existence, and adaptive evolution must result.

But the theory quickly ran into serious difficulties. Some of these Darwin had in a measure foreseen, though they proved more formidable than he had expected. Others were quite new. Nearly all involved problems of the very heredity and variation necessary for effective natural selection.

Thus variations among domesticated plants and animals were of course known to occur, being then deliberately chosen to breed improved stocks. Here Darwin made very sure of his facts, and in the *Origin* opened his argument with a convincing account of this very useful "artificial selection." But variation of species in the wild state was quite another matter, not so easily observed and proved, and was actually in most serious dispute among naturalists. But Darwin's observations of the gradations of plants and animals in South America and the Galápagos Islands had convinced him that such variations must have in fact occurred, and he therefore felt justified in making that assumption.

But were such variations large or small, and if small, did they aid survival enough to have selective value? How, for example, could the complex eye of the vertebrate have evolved gradually, for what use would there be for a partially developed eye, nonfunctioning because incapable of image forming, to bring about its step-by-step selection and evolution? We shall find in a later chapter that there is today a realistic and sufficient answer, but to Darwin and his contemporaries this appeared as a formidable difficulty.

On the basis of his observations, Darwin thought that variations were small, which implied that much time was needed for evolution to bring about the wide over-all diversification of the known life forms. In this he was supported by the Uniformitarian geologists led by Charles Lyell, for they, too, demanded long eons of time for the slow processes of erosion and deposition to accomplish the great changes observed in the Earth's surface features and in the deep accumulations of strata recording the past. But in 1862 Lord Kelvin, highest authority among the physicists, applied mathematics to the then-prevailing theory of the formation of the Sun and planets from a primitive nebula of gas and dust by condensing, heating, and final cooling, and cut the time allowable to a few ten millions of years, not nearly enough for the needs of the geologists and evolutionists. We know today that Lord Kelvin was mistaken, for the scientists later found a method of radioactive dating which gave billions of years for the ages of Sun and Earth. And still later it was learned that atomic fusion provides the Sun with an ample energy supply to last for those billions of years (see *Our Emerging Universe* for the full account). But in Darwin's day this objection of insufficient time was really formidable.

Lamarckism

Then in 1867 an even more devastating objection was raised by the Scottish engineer Fleeming Jenkin. Hardheaded and mathematical, he contended that a new variation of a single individual plant or animal would have no chance to survive in Nature; it would be very quickly overwhelmed and lost during crossbreeding by blending with the much more numerous non-variants of its kind. Oddly, the essence of the modern answer to that difficulty was already published in the proceedings of an obscure scientific society in Austria, but it was not noticed then, and was not to be resurrected for a third of a century.

At the time there seemed to be but one possible answer: that many like variants must appear simultaneously, enough to avoid being swamped out by crossbreeding. But this implied either of two assumptions rather inconsistent with natural selection. Either the evolution was being directed (presumably supernaturally) to produce the many needed similar variants, or some influence in the environment was stimulating the simultaneous or continuous appearance of these many like variants. Darwin in effect chose the latter explanation.

This Darwin did repeatedly, in letters to scientific friends, by revisions in subsequent editions of the *Origin*, and in later books amplifying the evolution theory. In effect, he gave up the primacy of natural selection in favor of an older theory of evolution which his own was originally designed to supplant.

That older theory was indeed old, for we find it widely assumed since the time of Hippocrates about 400 B.C., whenever adaptation by variation was recognized. It was generally no more than the vague idea that environment, need, effort, or exercise produced bodily changes, and when thus acquired, these changes were then inherited by later generations.

For the last century and a half such ideas have been associated with the name of Lamarck and so described as Lamarckism. In our own times we are prone to think of this as limited to the body changes resulting from use or disuse, and the inheritance of such acquired characteristics. But Lamarck's actual ideas, while including these, were much broader and looser, on occasion even fantastic. For example, he explained the horns of cattle thus: Bulls are short-tempered; when they lose their tempers, blood rushes to their heads and deposits horny matter; result—horns. It must have been such mad thinking which in 1844 led Darwin to write, "Heaven forfend me from Lamarck's nonsense."

Yet Darwin himself, in soberer vein, turned to much the same basic ideas to answer Fleeming Jenkin. His theories remained vague, however, except in one respect. For Darwin felt the need for some tangible mechanism for securing the inheritance of the characters acquired by bodily change, and in 1868, in his *Variation of Animals and Plants under Domestication,* offered his "provisional hypothesis of Pangenesis." In his own words:

> I assume that cells . . . throw off minute granules or atoms, which circulate freely throughout the system . . . subsequently becoming developed into cells like those from which they were derived. These . . . may be called . . . simply gemmules. They are supposed to be transmitted from the parents to the offspring and are generally developed in the generation which immediately succeeds, but often transmitted in a dormant state during many generations, and then developed. . . . Hence, strictly, it is not the reproductive elements . . . which generate new organisms, but the cells themselves throughout the body.

Weismann's Challenge

But within a score of years all this was to be vigorously challenged by the German Darwinist August Weismann. Moreover, he was originally led to this dissent, as he himself remarked, by the impossible complications involved in the gemmule hypothesis. In general, he denied the existence of any factual evidence in support of the inheritance of acquired characters. Specifically, he denied the existence of the assumed gemmules or any equivalent organic mechanism for such inheritance. Instead, he insisted that heredity was carried solely by the reproductive germ cells and that the body or soma cells, once they were differentiated during body growth, could have practically no effect on these germ cells. The heredity-carrying germ plasm had therefore a continuity all its own, while the soma cells died with each generation. All this meant, of course, that variations must first occur in the germ plasm and then be transmitted to offspring by the germ plasm only.

But this was not mere theory on Weismann's part, for much of the factual background of cell structure and reproductive process had been learned during the half century following the perfecting of the compound microscope. The cell basis of living tissues had soon been discovered by Schleiden and Schwann. Then in 1841, R. A. von Kölliker had shown that the male spermatozoon came from a cell, and by 1865 it was realized that it was in fact itself a cell. Darwin, in accord with his theory of pangenesis, had assumed that the entire mass of the fluid semen carrying the spermatozoa took part in the fertilizing of the female egg cell. But Oscar Hertwig in 1875 had demonstrated that such fertilizing was done by a single spermatozoon penetrating the egg.

Meanwhile the ensuing multiplication and differentiation of the cells to become the growing body had been studied, starting in 1855 with Rudolph Virchow's discovery of general cell division. With the development of improved techniques (largely German) for differential staining of the cell contents to bring out structural contrasts, the details of the process of cell division were revealed. Haeckel, as early as 1866, had guessed that the cell nucleus was the bearer of heredity. By 1880 Alexander Fleming had learned that the chromosomes of the cell nucleus apparently split longitudinally, with the halves passing to the two resulting daughter cells, and from this, in 1883, Wilhelm Roux drew the conclusion, later to be fully confirmed, that the transmitting of hereditary characters was done by unit divisions arranged linearly within the chromosomes. These units were later to be called genes, a name suggested by Wilhelm L. Johannsen in 1909.

Weismann, in 1885, brought this growing knowledge together in his theory of the germ plasm, adding to it his own ideas on the distinction between soma and germ cells, the continuity of the germ plasm, and the noninheritance of acquired characteristics. Yet even in these he found that he had been somewhat anticipated. Thus, Richard Owen in 1849 and Gustav Jäger in 1878 had distinguished between body and germ cells, while M. Nussbaum in 1880 had presented the idea of the continuity of the germ plasm.

As to Weismann's denial of the inheritance of acquired characteristics, that at least was new in its vigor and thoroughness. He reviewed the so-called evidence for such inheritance and found none of it authentic. He himself conducted a series of test experiments, cutting off the tails of several generations of mice, with no resulting shortening of the tails in succeeding generations. But this was hardly convincing, and the real proof came instead from the thousands of tests subsequently made by his opponents in their eager efforts to prove that acquired characteristics were inherited. He had challenged them to produce such proofs, and they certainly did try, but to this date not one authentic instance of such inheritance has been forthcoming. For in every instance where positive results have been claimed, rigorous scientific checkups have proved the tests defective, careless, even fraudulent, and, above all, that they could not be confirmed when repeated—an essential of scientific proof.

The most notorious case of fraud was that connected, rightly or wrongly, with the name of the Viennese zoologist Paul Kammerer, whose claims were exposed in 1926. He had claimed to have caused two markedly different species of salamanders to acquire and inherit each other's characteristics, and to have caused the male midwife toad to acquire and inherit the pigmented thumb pads natural to some other toad species. As early as 1919 William Bateson challenged these results as not confirmed, and for several years sought to examine Kammerer's specimens but was always put off. Finally, however, G. K. Noble of The American Museum of Natural History, and Hans Przibram, Director of the Vienna Biological Experimental Institute where Kammerer worked, did examine the specimens and found that the "acquired characteristics" were faked, probably with India ink. Shortly thereafter Kammerer committed suicide, leaving a letter in which he admitted, "I find the statements of Dr. Noble completely verified," but disowned having taken part in the fraud, and declared his ignorance of the real culprit.

The sensational Kammerer exposure probably had some overall effect in clearing the air of the persisting assumption of the inheritance of acquired characteristics still held among at least the older biologists. Certainly among modern geneticists the old doctrine has been virtually abandoned. Of late, however, authentic reports have occasionally appeared of the inheritance of acquired characteristics, but in each case these turn out to be of single-celled organisms, in which there is of course no separation of body and germ cells, so that at least some acquired characteristics may well be transmissible by fission to the daughter cells. But this is beside the point and nothing new, Weismann himself having excepted the one-celled organisms from his denial of inheritance of acquired characteristics. He also made other obvious exceptions, as when reproduction is carried on by budding of body cells, or by cuttings, runners, tubers, etc., in which the germ cells are clearly not involved.

Superficially, Weismann's challenge may seem quite negative, a mere disproof of a prevailing mistake. This might, of course, be valuable in itself, even if it only led students to look elsewhere for better answers. But Weismann actually did more than that, for in pinpointing the germ plasm as the carrier of heredity and then emphasizing its continuity through the generations, he also indicated the very direction of promising research. At any rate, for the remainder of the nineteenth century, and largely because of his challenge, there was much questioning and active research in this field preliminary to a new scientific formulation of the basic laws of heredity. Francis Galton and Havelock

Ellis had earlier begun a statistical study of human variations, and now Karl Pearson, William Bateson, and Hugo De Vries were busily gathering data on variation throughout the living world. The last two were in fact arriving at the law of heredity when it was learned that it had already been discovered a third of a century before, only to be lost to science by mere failure to reach someone with enough understanding to recognize its fundamental importance.

The Resurrection of Gregor Mendel

The discoverer was Father Gregor Mendel, a monk attached to the monastery of Brünn in Moravian Austria, now in Czechoslovakia. For seven years, starting in 1857, he experimented in the monastery garden with the crossbreeding of the ordinary edible pea, altogether handling nearly twenty thousand plants. Keeping accurate records and making a sagacious statistical study, he derived a fundamental theory and law of crossbreeding, which he carefully checked by further tests. This basic formulation has become the very foundation of the modern science of genetics.

In a schoolroom on the evenings of February 8 and March 8, 1865, Mendel reported his findings to the Brünn Society for the Study of Natural Science before an audience of forty, among them botanists, an astronomer, and a geologist. They listened but asked no questions, did not discuss what they had heard, and then trudged stolidly homeward through the cold moonlit streets. No one apparently understood or appreciated the momentous revelation. But fortunately Mendel's long paper was preserved, published the next year in the Proceedings of the Society. No one, however, gave it real attention until the year 1900.

It is usual to ascribe the nonrecognition of Mendel's report to the unintelligence of his original audience and the obscurity of its place of publication. But a reading of the report itself suggests another, perhaps better reason. It was in all ways a model scientific paper, meticulous in its minute and careful array of details, and quite impossible for the nonspecialist to understand. Nowhere was there a simple summary of either the conclusions or the significance of his study at all comprehensible to his audience. Today we read back into the report our own modern understanding of the subject and find in it all the basic ideas. But to those who listened so patiently to him in that schoolroom, it must have seemed quite meaningless and uninspiring.

Even when he wrote to his friend the pioneer botanist Karl Wilhelm von Nägeli, his ideas were treated condescendingly as amateurish and inconsequential, probably because Nägeli was himself promoting an opposing but mistaken theory of hereditary momentum. Adding to his discouragement, Mendel's attempts at breeding the hawkweed went all awry, not confirming the clear law derived from his fruitful work with the peas. He did not realize that the hawkweed was self-pollinating, which of course upset all the crossbreeding tests he might make with it. He did do some experimental work with the honey bee, but all records of that have been lost. Then in 1868 he was promoted to abbot of the monastery and had no more time for mere garden experiments which seemed only idle to everyone else.

But publication, even though obscure, did preserve his important report, copies having been distributed in 1866 to libraries in both Europe and America. In 1869 his paper was referred to by the botanist Hoffman. Also it was listed in the Royal Society Catalogue of Scientific Papers. Then in 1881 Wilhelm Focke, in a book on plant breeding, mentioned Mendel several times but completely misunderstood him. Thirteen years later, however, L. H. Bailey copied this reference to the bibliography of his own book on plant breeding, and in 1900 Hugo De Vries ran down this reference and found the precious report. Thus by a seeming chain of accidents it finally fell into the hands of someone prepared to understand its full scientific worth and import. Or was it because current scientific development had reached that point of understanding? This is suggested by the independent discovery of Mendel by three men, De Vries of Holland, Karl Correns of Germany, and Eric von Tschermak-Seysenegg of Austria, all in the year 1900.

The Law of Heredity

Each multicellular plant or animal normally begins as a single cell, a microscopic speck of protoplasmic jelly. This divides into two, these two into four, and so on until there are billions of cells in the full-grown organism. Meanwhile the cells have taken various shapes, sizes, and jobs, each doing its small part, all cooperating in the big job of living.

Among them certain cells become set apart to reproduce the race. To do so among the multicelled, a cell of one individual must generally join with a cell from another individual to make the starting or fertilized egg cell. One of these joining cells is male, the other female. Obviously this thing called heredity must work through these two joining cells, and what is inherited must depend on what the two cells contain and how they combine their contents.

Close study under the microscope reveals within each parent cell a more opaque nucleus within which at one stage appears a number of short rods which we call chromosomes, the name indicating that they take a color stain readily. We know now that these chromosomes are the bearers of heredity. You will grow up to be basically what your chromosomes determine. And as they come from a combination of previous chromosomes, you will grow up to be not just a chip off the old block, but rather the collective slivers of many blocks, for each of us gets a mixture of many mixtures, some through the father, some through the mother, and from their fathers and mothers before them, down through the innumerable generations past. Thus the combinations are always changing through a constant reshuffling of their component elements. This, we shall learn, is of the utmost importance in the evolution of life forms. But for the moment we are here concerned with only one question: Can we find any rule in the way the reshufflings occur? In other words, can we foresee just how heredity will work? If we deal in averages, the answer is yes. There is a law of heredity. And it was this which Gregor Mendel had discovered.

Mendel did his work, of course, before much of this background knowledge was available. And he did his work with the facilities at hand, the poverty of resources of a monastery garden. And perhaps the nature of his experimental work was in good part determined by his own likings and aptitudes; at least he learned well the vital cares and skills of clean crossbreeding. But also he conducted his work with clear intelligence. He had sound background knowledge, for he was a thorough and keen reader of the authorities in his chosen field, among them Darwin. This we learn from the notes he wrote on the margins of his collection of books. And his historic paper reveals in detail how carefully and intelligently he chose and handled his experimental plants to assure significant results.

Thus he chose the garden pea for the practical reasons that its varieties showed simple contrasting characters such as tallness and dwarfness, greenness and yellowness of seed, smooth seeds or wrinkled ones, pairs of opposite character which he could study separately because he found they were inherited separately. A tall pea plant could thus have either green or yellow seeds, or the seeds of either color could be smooth or wrinkled, etc. Thus, he crossbred seven pairs of contrasting characteristics, studied the numbers of offspring with each characteristic as they appeared in successive generations, and found a rule running through his averages, the rule we now call Mendel's Law. Just what is that rule?

If you cross a tall pea with a dwarf one, all of the next generation will be tall peas, and you might think that the dwarf strain had been completely eliminated. But when you then cross these all-tall peas, you get one quarter dwarf peas in the next generation, showing that the dwarf strain is still there. The other three quarters are all tall peas. Then when you breed the dwarf peas among themselves, you always get dwarf peas, showing the dwarf strain is quite pure, unmixed with tallness. But now cross the three quarters tall peas. Only one of these quarters turns out to be pure tall, which always breeds tall. The other two quarters turn out to be mixtures of tallness and dwarfness, even though the dwarfness does not show at the moment. For when you breed them, they in turn give rise to both tall and dwarf peas, again three quarters tall, one quarter dwarf. And so through the generations, when you interbreed such tall peas as have a hidden strain of dwarfness, you get those same three-to-one proportions of tallness and dwarfness in the offspring.

Mendel explained that when you combine two opposing characters in crossbreeding, one will hide the other in the first generation of offspring. The one that appears he called the dominant, the other, which is hidden, the recessive. The one dominates, the other recedes, as far as appearance is concerned. But of course the hidden recessive strain will from time to time reappear with new reshufflings in later generations, for in one quarter of the cases chance will bring together recessive strains only, without dominant strains to hide them. Such recessive characters of plants and animals will always breed true, will always remain recessive. Some dominant plants and animals also have pure strains, unmixed with recessiveness, but to distinguish them from impure strains which look outwardly just the same, you must test by further breeding. If they always breed true, they are pure dominant (Figure 4).

Mendel thus found that tallness was dominant over dwarfness in peas, yellow seeds over green ones, and smooth seed coats

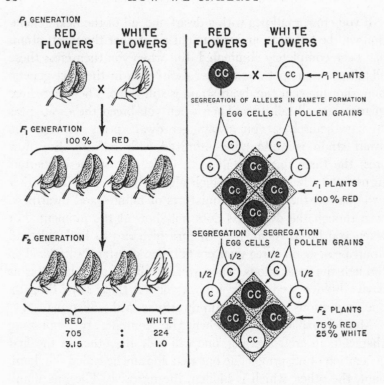

Fig. 4. Mendel's Law of Inheritance.

over wrinkled coats. Since his time we have extended our knowledge to a multitude of plant and animal characteristics but can cite here only a few. In wheat, immunity to rust is recessive, so we can easily and surely separate and get a rust-resisting breed. In maize, yellow grains are dominant over white, but purple ones are in turn dominant over the yellow. In cattle, hornlessness is dominant over the horned, so we can painlessly dehorn any breed we wish. Trotting is dominant over pacing in horses, which every breeder of horses should know. In the male cat, orange fur is dominant over black, but the female cat has it just the other way around. In human beings, curly hair is dominant over straight, dark hair over light or red, and brown eyes over blue. If the two strains are pure, the children of brown- and blue-eyed parents will have brown eyes, but in the next generation, three quarters will have brown eyes and one quarter blue. Blue-eyed parents will always have blue-eyed children, for the recessive strain never appears unless it is pure.

Practical Results

Obviously this law of heredity must be of great practical importance in plant and animal breeding. For example, European farmers had a kind of wheat which gave a large yield but had too much starch and not enough gluten. Also, it was susceptible to a destructive rust. After the rediscovery of Mendel's law, botanist Rowland Biffen of Cambridge University set about doing some practical recombining under the new guiding rule. He crossed the too delicate European wheat with the hardy Fife wheat of Canada, which gave a small yield but did resist rust. He got many combinations, none of which resisted rust in the dominant offspring generation. But he bred them again, and out came rust-resisting recessives, often combined with large-yield strains. Knowing his wheats and his rules, he knew just what to do, and in a few generations had a wheat which gave a large yield and also resisted rust, and bred true for both characters. Meanwhile, too, he had been picking his combinations to include a large gluten content, and so got just what he wanted in three ways, a gluten wheat of large yield which could fight off the rust. It took a few years to increase his few seeds to supply the European farmers, but he did it and thus added billions of dollars to the value of their crops, and the title "Sir" to his own name. And since 1934, millions of acres in the United States and Canada have been planted with Thatcher wheat, a hybrid combining the virtues of three older breeds, the Iumillo, Marquis, and Kanred varieties. The list of plants and animals thus improved by modern breeding guided by the Mendelian rules could be extended for pages. But to bring it literally "home," consider today's succulent turkey, meaty, flavorful, bred to sizes to fit any family table, and originally made to order at the Beltsville experimental station of the U. S. Department of Agriculture.

In working with such combinations of several pairs, it is possible to write formulas expressing the average proportions of the characteristic combinations which will occur. For each pair of pure opposing characteristics, the average ratio will be three dominant to one recessive, with two of the dominants mixed or impure. But for all the potential combinations of two or more pairs of characteristics, the possibilities become more numerous, and the proportions, according to the mathematical laws of probability, more complex. If we designate each pair by a letter of the alphabet, using capitals for the dominants and small letters for the recessives, we describe our several pairs as Aa, Bb, Cc, etc. If now we include only one pair Aa in our crossbreeding, we shall on the average get equal numbers of the combinations AA, Aa, aA, and aa. But if we use the two pairs Aa and Bb, we get more combinations, with the following visible: 9 AB, 3 Ab, 3 aB, and 1 ab. If, however, we use the three pairs Aa, Bb, and Cc, the following combinations will appear: 27 ABC, 9 ABc, 9 AbC, 9 aBC, 3 Abc, 3 aBc, 3 abC, and 1 abc. With still more pairs, the numbers of combinations become accordingly greater. And then there are still other proportions of combinations caused by crossbreeding impure strains with pure ones. The basis of all this Mendel worked out and presented in his report, using the resulting proportions as his own tests of the validity of the theorizing by which he explained the visible results of his experiments. Also, no doubt, he thereby greatly confused his bored audience in the Brünn schoolhouse, effectively denying them the thrill of feeling present at a momentous event in scientific history. For just these statistical tests, then and since, have in fact fully substantiated his theory.

This was quickly realized upon the rediscovery of Mendel's report in 1900. Furthermore, within two years Walter S. Sutton pointed out that the already-familiar chromosomes, in their observed divisions and fusions, actually behave in exact accord with Mendel's Law of heredity. Ever since it has therefore been accepted as basic to our modern science of genetics.

Chapter 6

HOW WE CHANGE

By Mendelian reshuffling of characteristics in crossbreeding, many seeming variations of form must occur in plants and animals. But they are not true variations of the characteristics themselves and are therefore not essentially new and different. Thus, with three pairs of characteristics we can get only eight visible combinations, and no more. The real source of the variations which make up evolutionary change has therefore not been touched by the discoveries of Mendel. That was one appeal of the Lamarckian Theory: it did seem to provide causes for variation by use and disuse, etc. Darwin and Wallace, however, had to take variation more or less on faith, merely as an accepted fact, the reason for which remained mysterious.

In common with plant and animal breeders generally, Darwin was familiar with the occasional "sports" or large variations, only now and then desirable, which could be preserved by selective breeding. But they were apparently too rare to help much in natural selection, so Darwin relied instead on many small variations accumulating over a long time. Later, however, such small variations were found to be apparently not cumulative beyond narrow limits, according to Wilhelm L. Johannsen (1903), who bred bean seeds experimentally for size.

But already in 1884 Nägeli had suggested evolution by jumps, though he ascribed them to a rather mystical urge to jump repeatedly in one direction. By 1894, Bateson published his *Materials for the Study of Variation*, mostly observations of animal abnormalities which led him to a belief in large variations. And De Vries, as early as 1886, had begun watching the odd behavior of the American evening primrose, which, growing wild in the fields of Europe, occasionally threw off half a dozen widely variant forms. In 1901 De Vries published his observations and ideas and rose to sudden celebrity. For he proclaimed that such large "mutations," because they were inherited, were the real raw materials of evolution, which could therefore be speeded up to meet the still-current objection of Lord Kelvin that astronomical time was much too short for evolution by minute variations as pictured by Darwin. But the Uniformitarian geologists were still demanding much more time, so that the whole matter remained quite unsettled.

Furthermore, it was later learned that the evening-primrose "mutations" were quite exceptional and not typical of most plants and animals, being due to accidental changes in chromosome numbers. In short, they were not true mutations at all, and De Vries, despite all his careful and honest work, "had pursued what seemed a reality and had found a phantom." But these facts did not come out for a score of years and so did not abate the popularity of De Vries' Mutation Theory and the hope that went with it.

Meanwhile, however, true mutations had been discovered through detailed studies of chromosomes in the light of Mendel's Law. This somewhat filled the need for a source of larger evolutionary variations. But in general these real mutations proved less promising, as many of them turned out to be injurious or even lethal, with but few of selective value for evolution of adaptive improvements. But given plenty of evolutionary time, these did provide a real basis for natural selection to work effectively.

The Fruitful Fruit Fly

Partly because Mendelian genetics is so obviously practical for selective breeding of useful plants and animals, it has been intensively studied ever since its rediscovery in 1900. All sorts of plants and animals have been subjected to such study, with emphasis perhaps on those promising most useful results. Crossbreeding experiments were of course carried on to determine dominancy and recessiveness of characters. But it was also soon realized that eventually the real background secrets would probably be found by more direct studies of chromosome details. So more and more the geneticists left the garden and barnyard to enter the laboratory with its microscopes.

The subjects of study have ranged from the one-celled forms to man himself, and much has been learned. Among other things it was found that each life form has its own distinctive number of chromosomes per cell, from a mere couple up to hundreds. Man has forty-six, or twenty-three pairs.

But for a really thorough study it was desirable to use some subject with few chromosomes per cell, which would simplify matters by reducing the number to be identified and watched. Also it should be some form with a short life-span, so that many generations could be crowded into a reasonable period of working time. There were of course other important considerations, such as clear pairs of contrasting characters, small size for easy housing and feeding, etc.

Thomas Hunt Morgan of Columbia chose the little vinegar or pomace fly and in 1906, with his students, began a study which was to prove classical. Most of us call this the fruit fly, while scientists dignify it as *Drosophila melanogaster*, which is Greek for "black-bellied dew-lover." It is a very minute fly, easy to feed, and also readily housed in jars in any assortment desired for crossbreeding. Its life cycle is less than two weeks and it breeds prolifically, so it provides plenty of experimental material with a minimum of delay in getting results. Its reproductive cells have four chromosomes, but there are hundreds of variant features which are inherited, with a goodly number of these easily recognized for convenient studies in crossbreeding and mutation. And as an extra bonus, there are certain larval salivary cells with giant chromosomes making detailed studies even easier and clearer. Of course, because of its minuteness, the fly itself must be studied through low-power microscopes and its chromosomes through higher-powered ones.

The studies with *melanogaster* fully confirmed the basic laws of heredity formulated by Mendel. But also they fruitfully added much more in new details and understanding. This is true also of the many other genetic studies using a wide diversity of experimental subjects, both plant and animal. We shall have space here for only the most pertinent results.

As the fruit fly has only four chromosomes per reproductive cell but hundreds of inheritable variant characteristics, we are sure that each chromosome must carry many such characteristics. Making us doubly sure, we find that the characteristics are inherited in groups, and we can even identify each group with its own individual chromosome. From this, and the fact discovered by Mendel that each character is also inherited individually, we must infer that there are distinct units within each chromosome carrying its own particular character. These units we now call genes. And while it is doubtful that anyone has ever actually seen a gene, all the evidence confirms its existence as a distinct unit. Important evidence of this is the remarkable fact that we can locate each gene within its chromosome and actually map the arrangement of the genes. To understand this, however, we must first look into the ways in which chromosomes and genes behave.

The Behavior of Chromosomes

When a cell divides, its nucleus undergoes a series of definite changes. First, the apparently mixed-up contents of the nucleus separate into distinct rodlike structures which, because they take color stains readily, we call chromosomes. Then each chromosome divides lengthwise into two chromosomes, each of which moves into its own half of the dividing cell body. Finally each chromosome group in each daughter cell merges into a new nucleus. This whole process of cell division is called mitosis.

Also when, in sexual reproduction, a male sperm cell fertilizes a female egg cell, the two nuclei merge. But if each nucleus contained its normal quota of chromosomes, the new merged nucleus would have a doubled number. And if this went on through several generations, the chromosome numbers per cell would soon multiply immoderately, and the net result would be something other than our little fruit fly. But in 1888 the German botanist Eduard Strassberger discovered that the sperm and egg cells actually have only half the normal number of chromosomes. So somewhere in the process of preparing for cell merging, there is a reproduction of the germ cell without a corresponding division of its chromosomes, thereby halving the number of chromosomes per cell. This process, called meiosis, keeps the chromosome number constant after merging, so the fruit fly remains a fruit fly, Man remains Man, etc.

Basic to Mendel's Law is the fact that when the male and female cell nuclei merge in fertilizing, the genes of the variant characteristics, such as tallness or dwarfness in peas, combine quite at random in all possible ways, dominant A of the male with dominant A of the female, dominant A of the one with recessive a of the other, recessive a of the first with dominant A of the second, and recessive a with recessive a, giving us the combinations AA (pure dominant), Aa and aA (impure dominants), and aa (pure recessive). Each combination is equally likely to occur, with the result found by Mendel that the statistical average is three dominants (one pure, two impure) to one recessive.

Mapping the Chromosome Genes

The first hint of gene grouping in the chromosome came from the commonplace fact that certain distinct characters normally occur together with each sex, these being then called secondary sex characters. And among the chromosomes, which otherwise occur in like pairs, we can usually identify those which determine sex. Thus, in *melanogaster* and Man there occurs one pair of chromosomes which are sometimes unlike, one called X, the other Y. When both chromosomes are X, the offspring becomes female; when both X and Y occur, the offspring

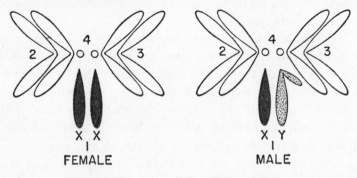

Fig. 5. Chromosomes of Fruit Fly.

will be male (Figure 5). It looks as though chromosome Y is the sex determiner, but that is not necessarily so. In grasshoppers, for instance, there are no Y chromosomes. So the preferred rule is, instead: Two X chromosomes makes a female, one X a male. But even this does not always apply. Among birds and moths, for example, one X makes a female, two X chromosomes a male, the same rule in exact reverse.

As we might expect, the secondary sex characteristics are also inherited through the sex chromosomes. So, too, with other chromosomes; each is a hereditary package containing its own group of genes linked together. So the genes from the two parents come together in any of the Mendelian combinations, but always in equivalent chromosome groups.

Naturally, in all this merging and dividing of chromosomes, accidents can well happen. Most common and usefully revealing are crossovers, in which there is an exchange of parts between pairs of chromosomes. Sutton had already realized in 1902 that the paired genes of any chromosome pair must be arranged in the same linear order to permit fitting each series to its counterpart. But the actual order of the genes was not known, and in 1910 Morgan and his associates began working on that problem. They found that when a pair of chromosomes joined in fertilizing and then separated in cell division, they sometimes traded end portions, coming apart as chromosomes with opposite ends from both parents.

They realized that in these crossover recombinations, genes far apart in any chromosome series are naturally more likely to become separated than genes close together. So by keeping a detailed record of the relative frequencies of their rearrangements, it was possible to work out the relative positions of the genes in each chromosome series. In short, the genes are strung together in a normal order along the length of a chromosome; this order can be mapped, and the linear maps we draw have proved both reliable and useful.

At Last, Real Mutations

Since Morgan began his fruit-fly studies in 1906, trained observers have examined between ten and twenty million specimens. From the very outset they occasionally came across some variant which was really new and not merely a recessive trait come out of hiding, for such recessive traits show up much more frequently. They were actually new variants and therefore true mutations, changes in the very genes themselves. The very first observed was white eyes instead of the normal red. That it represented a gene change was shown by its being inherited thereafter. Since then many hundreds of different gene mutations have been observed, but even so they are really very rare compared with the millions of specimens among which they originated. And even if we allow for many mutations which are not visible but manifest themselves in other ways, say by weakening or killing the offspring, we still find the incidence of mutations exceedingly low.

Why do such mutations occur? We could guess at any number of imaginable accidents changing the gene. But we had no real clue until Herman J. Müller, a student of Morgan's, reported in 1927 that he had exposed large numbers of *melanogaster* specimens to X rays, getting as a result a much higher rate of mutations, a discovery so illuminating he was given the Nobel Prize for it. Other radiations, such as cosmic rays, the gamma rays of radioactivity, and ultraviolet light, have been found thus mutagenic. So are several chemicals, among them mustard gas, organic peroxides, formaldehyde, certain iron and manganese salts, etc., with the list growing almost yearly. And as the rates of mutations prove proportionate to the radiation and chemical exposures, these are undoubtedly the causes for them. Furthermore, some radiations occur normally in Nature and are therefore assumed to be causes of ordinary natural mutations. However, there does not seem to be enough such natural radiation to account for even the low rate of normal mutations, so further causes are still being looked for.

But whatever array of mutation causes may eventually be discovered, it is now fairly certain that they work by disrupting the existing structural and chemical patterns of the gene units in the chromosomes. But where and when a radiation will strike and what its particular effect will be are altogether unpredictable, being in this sense quite accidental. And by and large, the result is more likely to damage than to improve, as is shown by the mutations actually observed in the ensuing offspring. They are far more often injurious or lethal than beneficial.

But whether occasionally good or preponderantly bad, these mutations are apparently the raw materials of evolution. Natural selection is then the sieve which sorts them out, tending to eliminate the injurious or ill-adapted, tending to preserve the beneficial, the better adapted.

The Rejuvenation of Darwinism

All in all, during the century since Darwin and Wallace presented it, the theory of natural selection has had, first its serious troubles, and then its modern rejuvenation. For the objections which Darwin could not meet, and therefore compromised with, have been one by one explained away by later discoveries.

Thus was met the objection of Lord Kelvin that Sun and Earth time had not been long enough for the evolution of existing life forms. Atomic fusion in the Sun provided energy for billions of years, and radioactivity in the Earth rocks permitted close datings of the geological record and of the fossils which marked the stages of life evolution. There proves to have been plenty of time for natural selection to have done its accomplished work.

Also with this extension of time, the need disappeared for large mutations as conceived by Bateson and De Vries. The actual mutations revealed by later genetic studies could be large or small, but they were accidental and random rather than directional or directed. But continuing environmental need could still give evolutionary direction by repeated natural selection of those accidental changes which from time to time did occur in the needed adaptive direction. After a far more thorough discussion of this whole problem, George Gaylord Simpson has summed up this important fact in these words:

> This process is natural, and it is wholly mechanistic in its operation. This natural process achieves the aspect of purpose, without the intervention of a purposer, and it has produced a vast plan without the concurrent action of a planner.

So, too, was met the objection of Fleeming Jenkin that any single variation in a life form would be inevitably overwhelmed and lost during crossbreeding by blending with the numerous nonvariants of its kindred. Mendel had shown that characters do not blend and weaken in crossbreeding, but remain intact as separately inherited units. Even when a blending inheritance does seem to occur, as when a mulatto results from a Negro-white union, it was later learned that several pairs of unit skin-color factors are involved, the intermediate skin shades then resulting from a multiplicity of gene units rather than any genetic blending.

Mendel also discovered that recessive traits (and we know now that gene mutants are generally recessive) can stay in hiding behind outwardly dominant traits. This means that a mutation can occur and hide, and so get a chance to spread widely through a species population without being prematurely eliminated. However, if the mutation proves to be an adaptive improvement, it will still appear often enough and get not just one chance but a multitude of chances to prove itself in the struggle for existence. And then, as a recessive, it can readily breed true and produce a numerous offspring untainted by the old discarded trait which it has supplanted by natural selection.

The results of all these studies by modern geneticists on the problems of heredity and change can be summed up in this sentence: We inherit through the genes within the chromosomes, and these come from the male and female germ cells which join to give us our start in life, the changes which can be inherited then originating by accidental alterations of gene patterns, with a natural selection by survival of the fittest in the struggle for existence, leading to adaptive evolution.

Until the time of Weismann it was quite universally assumed that those germ cells are affected by the other cells of the grown body, so that a change in the body of the parent can be transmitted to the child. Darwin even suggested a "gemmule" mechanism for doing this. But is it a fact that an injury to the parent body can be transmitted to the child? Or can exercise, like that which gives the blacksmith his strong arm, so influence the genes as to give the blacksmith's child a strong arm? Weismann questioned this, and all the carefully tested evidence since accumulated supports the answer of no. Instead, he pointed out that the germ cells proceed from generation to generation in a sort of physical immortality, but that the body cells, once separated from the germ cells, cease to take part in transmitting hereditary traits. That is why a mother's fright does not cause a birthmark on the child, a belief which some mothers still hold. That means also that you cannot, by wishing, or by reading good books and hearing fine music during pregnancy, make your child inherently better or literary or musical, that you cannot make it inherently anything but what the gene mixture provides, though you can help the child later by good food, hygiene, exercise at play, and education. Of course, the good wishing, reading, and music do the mother no harm and may later be transmitted to the child by example and education, but if we are to improve the human breed inherently, it must be through better selection of mates to get better mixtures of genes. There seems to be no way of acquiring a good hereditary strain but by picking our parents more wisely.

But this is not only quite impractical but also quite unfortunate, though it is certainly well-proven fact. For if we could but change ourselves for the better by effort, exercise, and education, and then have the betterment inherited genetically by our children, the human race could apparently be soon improved to approach perfection.

The Marxian Deviation

Unfortunately, the stubborn fact of the noninheritance of acquired characteristics is not universally recognized and taken into practical account. In the world of Communism the contrary belief took early root and still prevails, and has seriously blinded and hampered the realistic solution of vital practical problems. That world has been struggling to create a new economic order, in which it is believed that bettered social conditions will transform human beings for the better. And naturally shortcuts are looked for, such as the hope that the betterments of each generation can be made deep and permanent by inheritance.

But wanting things so does not necessarily make them so, and if it is a fact that acquired characteristics are not inherited, then any amount of wishful thinking to the contrary is wholly futile; it leads only to butting stubborn heads against the stone wall of Nature's realistic and inexorable ways. As Francis Bacon put it, we may "command Nature, but only by obeying her."

The founders of the Communist philosophy, Karl Marx and Friedrich Engels, were among the first to accept Darwin's theory of natural selection and his proofs of evolution. Like Darwin and the other Evolutionists of the time, they also assumed the inheritance of acquired characteristics. But when Weismann rose to challenge this belief, Marx was already dead, while Engels rejected him. However, it is obvious from their letters and published writings that their several biologic beliefs, this among them, were held largely for wishful reasons rather than on the basis of factual evidence. Organic evolution itself was acceptable as background for the human social development which was to culminate in Communism. The struggle for existence among lower forms was the basis for the class struggle in human society. But they rejected the Malthusian overpopulation idea given by Darwin and Wallace as reason for the struggle for existence. Unfortunately, Malthus had been misused by the economic apologists to justify the dire poverty of the English workers as due not to heartless exploitation but to population expanding faster than the food resources. Malthus actually protested vigorously against both the poverty and this apology for it. One must even doubt that Marx and Engels had actually read Malthus, for they also charged him with ignoring population increase among plants and animals, limiting it to human populations, though any reading of his work reveals that he actually began by describing such increase among the "plants and irrational animals" as the very cause of a crowding for space and a struggle for existence.

But whatever reasons there may have been for Marx and Engels accepting inheritance of acquired characters a century ago, there seems to be no excuse for the Soviet authorities. They do so of course on the authority of Marx and Engels, quite rejecting anything to the contrary learned since by the rigorously careful studies carried on over a century by the geneticists of the "capitalistic" world.

For the first few years following the 1917 Russian Revolution, science was wholly encouraged, supported, and permitted to develop freely. But Lenin had learned of the work of Ivan V. Michurin, a practical experimenter who had found a method of treating seeds to get early sprouting, most useful in the short growing seasons in many colder parts of Soviet territory. Lenin naturally encouraged such promising experimental work. But Michurin also thought that the effects of his treatment were inherited, for he got more of the early-sprouting seeds with each generation and apparently did not realize that a selective factor was at work, the natural selection of such seeds as survived the rigors of early planting. He merely assumed that it was all due to his special treatment, and was therefore a true case of inheritance of acquired characters.

The Michurinist Dogma

On this assumption, under Stalin, was then to be based a whole new doctrine of Michurinism, destined to outlaw the more factual and realistic genetic science based on Mendel, Weismann, and Morgan which had meanwhile developed among Soviet researchers. With the accession of Stalin following Lenin's death in 1924, the doom of scientific genetics became inevitable. The attack on it was perhaps delayed by the exposure, confession, and suicide of Paul Kammerer in 1926. He had been invited to continue his work in Russia and was already packing to leave when the blow fell. He was promptly made a Communist hero, complete with statue in Moscow. Even a motion picture was made of the exposure episode, making him the victim of intrigue, not by his scientific critics Bateson and Noble, but by connivance between a priest and a prince (both wholly fictional) intent on discrediting Marxian science.

In all that followed it should be remembered that Stalin was always a major participant. He sponsored and actively promoted Michurinism, both as Marxian orthodoxy and as a wishful shortcut to practical results, though the actual results proved disastrous to Russian agriculture. In 1939 he demoted N. I. Vavilov, the informed and able geneticist in charge of genetic and agricultural research and responsible for many important advances in these fields, then had him arrested in 1940 and sent to Siberia, where he died in 1942. In his place Stalin put Trofim D. Lysenko, whose pronouncements thereupon became the official biology of the Soviet Union but the laughingstock of the scientific world elsewhere. Finally, in 1948, scientific genetics was definitely outlawed, in both teaching and research.

Here again the heavy hand of Stalin showed plainly, for Lysenko, in his paper announcing the outlawing, put it bluntly:

Before proceeding to the concluding remarks, I consider it my duty to declare the following: I have been asked in one of the memoranda as to the attitude of the Central Committee concerning my paper. I answer: the Central Committee of the Party has examined my report and approved it.

And even more specifically, writing in *Pravda* (March 8, 1953) on the occasion of Stalin's death, Lysenko wrote:

> Comrade Stalin pointed out the paths for development of the theory of Michurinist materialist biology.
>
> That Comrade Stalin found time for the detailed examination of the most important problems of biology is particularly well known to me as a biologist. He directly edited the plan of my paper, *On the Situation in Biological Science*; in detail explained to me his corrections; provided me with directions as to how to write certain passages in the paper. Comrade Stalin paid close attention to the results of the August 1948 session of the Lenin All-Union Academy of Agricultural Sciences in which progressive, materialist, Michurinist biology triumphed over reactionary Mendelism-Morganism.

Inevitably the results of this outlawing of free scientific inquiry were disastrous. Several eminent geneticists immediately and publicly recanted their scientific convictions and abjectly swore allegiance to the biology of the Party line. Others played safe and kept silent. Those who stuck to their scientific guns were eliminated by demotion or discharge. Protesting, even by citing demonstrable fact, was futile as there were no avenues for publication or other reporting. So there was no way of detecting error and quackery, for frank, free scientific testing was barred in favor of sycophancy and conformity. To justify their employment, biologists had to show activity by reporting on work done, but in the face of an uncertainly applied Party line, wrote and taught with ambiguity and double talk. None dared venture anything clear or definite, certainly nothing novel and nonconformist. Naturally, the science of realistic genetics simply withered.

In 1956, however, a historic moment of truth arrived. Premier Khrushchev found it necessary to disown and discredit Stalin, including his works, and did so dramatically. But for freedom of genetic science it proved an opportunity missed, for although Stalin was charged with both mismanaging agriculture and slowing up progress in science by arbitrary dogmatism, Marxian orthodoxy and the wishful thinking of the Party line still prevailed officially. Although Lysenko was made scapegoat for failures in agriculture actually due to the political fettering of practical genetics, he remained as director of the Institute of Genetics and as editor of the journal *Agrobiology*. But dirt farmers from Russia have since looked longingly on the hybrid corn of our own midwestern American cornfields, with its 30 to 50 per cent higher yield, only to have it offhandedly poohpoohed by Khrushchev. Yet no nation so ambitiously striving for high productivity, enforced by insistent dissatisfaction, can forever ignore and reject the palpable results of free genetic research in high output and better products. Particularly in an intense struggle for economic survival, no nation can afford the handicap of dogmatic restriction on any part of its free scientific research.

Yet only with the sudden ouster of Khrushchev as Premier was the real downgrading of Lysenko begun, and an open attack made on dogmatism as impeding the development and application of modern biology. As this attack came from Dr. M. V. Keldysh, President of the Soviet Academy and appeared in *Pravda* on November 2, 1964 on the occasion of the forty-seventh anniversary of the October Revolution, it must be considered as the official attitude of the new Soviet authorities.

Unfortunately, the damage done by any such long period of dogmatic restriction persists more than we generally think, and cannot be undone by a mere legal lifting of restrictions. For first, the most useful minds, those most realistic and dissenting, have been inactivated by suppression and denial of public hearing. Lesser minds have yielded to wishful rationalizing and dutiful conformity to doctrinal orthodoxy. Nor will it fully help to translate and make available the findings of those who have meanwhile carried on free and realistic research elsewhere in the world. For merely to read what others have discovered does not give the working familiarity with facts and current thinking gained only by active and intimate participation in research. There still remains the irrevocable fact that Soviet scientists have for decades been barred from taking part in the extraordinary development of the realistic science of genetics in our modern world. What that development has given us in factual knowledge and basic understanding will appear in the next chapter.

Chapter 7

DECODING LIFE'S CIPHER

Embryology is the study of the development of the unborn or unhatched organism following fertilization of the female egg (ovum) by the male germ (spermatozoon). The ancient Greeks had begun its study, Alcmaeon of Croton (about 500 B.C.) among the earliest. They had hit on the idea of opening a series of hen's eggs at daily intervals to watch progress in the development, but didn't learn much because they lacked means for magnifying the minute details, so they mostly theorized. Aristotle believed that the female only furnished material while the male served as the efficient cause. And as in so many other matters, this teaching of Aristotle prevailed well into recent centuries.

Beginning the more modern development of this science, Fabricius in 1600 published observations on the forms of the organism before birth. In 1651 Harvey, who studied the chick embryo during incubation, believed that the ovum was a fluid from which the embryo arose by spontaneous generation incited by the "vital force" from the male. This differed from an older and then-prevailing view that the offspring from the very start was already performed in miniature within the parent body and merely had to grow in size, without essential change in form.

The Preformation Theory

More specifically, the believers in preformation held that each generation of parents contained within themselves the miniature preformed offspring, and that these in turn already contained other preformed offspring even smaller in size, and so on for each succeeding generation. But it was coming to be realized just what this implied: that all the offspring of our first ancestors, numbered by the millions down through the generations, must have originally existed, separately preformed, from the very beginning. And this meant, too, in the words of Jan Swammerdam written in 1672, that "all men are contained in the organs of Adam and Eve. When their stock of eggs is finished, the human race will cease to be."

Though the difficulties were increasingly recognized, the preformation theory was supported well into the eighteenth century by such important researchers and theorizers as Malpighi, Swammerdam, Albrecht von Haller, Leibnitz, and Bonnet. But meanwhile the theory had suffered a change, rather for the worse.

In 1677 Leeuwenhoek had announced the discovery of the male spermatozoon. A Mr. Ham or Hamm, a medical student from Leyden, had brought him a sample of semen from a man suffering with gonorrhea. In it, Ham's magnifier had shown moving animalcules with long tails which he suspected were the cause of the disease. Leeuwenhoek checked and experimented, then studied healthy human and other animal semen. It all contained spermatozoa, each of which proved to be a tiny bag or capsule with a long and actively whiplashing tail by which it swam.

This discovery led to a splitting of the preformist ranks into two disputing factions. On the one hand were the "ovists" or "ovulists" who argued that the preformed offspring resided originally in the female parent. Against them the "spermists" or "animalculists" insisted that the offspring were carried only by the male sperm, with the mother merely nourishing and bearing the offspring after it had first been implanted within her by the male. Leeuwenhoek shared this latter view but, writing in 1699, insisted that there was change of form during the prenatal growth from sperm to offspring, a growth "in what seems to us an irregular way." This observation, had it been followed up, could have led to recognition of a central fact of modern embryology. Instead, there prevailed a mixture of seeming spermist fact with a return to Aristotle's female material and male efficient cause. Whatever its merits, the spermist view proved more convincing, perhaps because it gave great satisfaction to the male sense of superiority.

Very soon the spermist view was further amplified by publication of drawings showing within the sperm capsule the crouching figure of a little man or "homunculus." This, we now know, was mere imagining, and perhaps, as Leeuwenhoek charged, Hartsoeker was just a fraud. But at any rate the latter did admit that "if we could see the little animal through the skin which hides it we might possibly see it as represented" in the drawing. Quite obviously, all such drawings were mere reversions to a medieval belief in the homunculus, which the alchemists had hopefully sought to create by their magic in a very special cucurbit or gourd-shaped flask.

The Realities of Embryology

No real advance in embryology was made for nearly a century, until Kaspar Friedrich Wolff in 1759 published an article in which he denied that the embryo was in fact preformed in miniature, asserting instead that it developed from a more or less formless germ substance, itself the result of a union of male and female germ substances, the union initiating that development. This sounds quite modern but unfortunately was merely theory on Wolff's part and based at that on two mistaken assumptions —first, that the ovum is a structureless substance, and second, that the male semen (or fluid), not the spermatozoon, is the fertilizing agent.

In fact, another seven decades were to elapse before the true story of embryonic development was to emerge, the direct result of improvements in the compound microscope which at last made possible the observation of minuter details. In 1829 Karl Ernst von Baer published his first studies of the actual development of the chick embryo, which rightly earned him the name of "father of embryology." He had found no initially preformed miniature, but instead a start from an unshaped speck which grew and differentiated into definite layers from which, step by step, emerged the shapes of the several organs which eventually make up the mature organism. At this date the cell theory was still a decade in the future, but von Baer lived on to take an important part in the further development of the new embryology which resulted from the added light which the cell theory imparted.

For the cell theory soon led to the conclusion that both the male spermatozoon and female ovum were cells. These then joined to contribute to the mixed characteristics of the offspring by forming the fertilized egg, itself a cell. This egg was often large when it contained a yolk, the reserve of foodstuffs in storage for further growth, a hen's egg being such a single cell, plus stored food. This egg cell began to divide, growing by feeding on the yolk, first becoming two cells, then four, and so on. In some cases the dividing cells became a small round mass (the morula), which soon distended into a hollow single-layered sphere (the blastula), one side of which then folded inward to form a two-layered cup (the gastrula), the outer layer being the ectoderm, the inner layer the endoderm. However, in eggs with considerable yolk the differentiation and development of the dividing cells might be modified, without clear blastula and gastrula stages. The two cell layers, ectoderm and endoderm, would still appear, but spread out rather flatly over the surface of the yolk.

As the developments of many different animal embryos were studied, a science of comparative embryology arose. This soon made it clear that the two initial layers were really basic to all multicellular animals. From the ectoderm were to develop the organs making contacts at the outer surface, while from the endoderm arose the strictly inner organs of the digestive tract. As we shall soon see, a considerable group of lower animals never did get beyond this basic two-layered stage.

But in the further evolution of animals there arose higher forms with additional organs—these from an intermediate embryonic layer, the mesoderm. But these three-layered kinds must themselves be divided into two broad groups in which the mesoderm originates differently. In one group the middle layer develops by a general splitting off of cells at juncture edges of the ectoderm and endoderm, while in the other there is a marked folding and budding off of endoderm pouches. This may seem a rather minor difference, but to the embryologist it proves of major importance, as the two methods turn out to be the great distinction between two broad classes of the animals. In fact, we shall find that this is a most decisive clue in solving the important and difficult mystery of the real ancestry of the backboned animals to which we ourselves belong. We shall, however, get to that later.

The Recapitulation Theory

But even before von Baer's study of the embryonic layers and the subsequent emergence of the cell theory, other facts of embryonic development were beginning to take on meanings which were gradually being pieced together. We have noted Harvey's early study of the incubating chicken egg in 1651. Shortly after, Swammerdam observed the development of the frog's egg up through tadpole to adult, though his magnifiers naturally did not show the dividing cells. In 1808 Tiedeman observed that the frog embryo seems to pass through stages similar to those of annelid worms, molluscs, and fishes, which observation Oken confirmed in the chicken embryo. Merkel found parallelisms in the development of the digestive tract, and Rathke in 1825 discovered fishlike gill openings in the embryos of birds and mammals.

Such discoveries were very suggestive, and by 1793 Karl Kielmeyer had already surmised some relationship between the embryonic development of the individual animal and its ancestral history. This same thought led von Baer to admit some evolution, though he always did reject the theory of descent. Before 1859 and Darwin's *Origin of the Species,* Louis Agassiz, an all-round biologist as well as a pioneer student of fossil fishes, taught that "The history of the individual is at the same time the history of the species." But after 1859, and then for religious reasons, he rejected evolution decisively.

But Haeckel, full convert to Darwin's theories, took up the idea that the development of the individual is a recapitulation of its ancestral evolution, called this the Biogenetic Law, and used it as a powerful argument for evolution by descent. He did realize that the embryonic recapitulation is much abbreviated, with shortcuts by omissions and a general slurring over of ancestral stages. But he employed this idea so enthusiastically that many modern biologists feel that he did not qualify the recapitulation nearly enough, but overemphasized both its application and its significance. Be that as it may, the recapitulation is nevertheless a broad general rule, subject to many detail reservations. So it still remains a convincing argument for the theory of evolution by descent, and is often helpfully suggestive in our attempts to trace the course of ancestral evolution.

And such recapitulation of ancestral history during individual development, however generalized and imperfect it may be, does call attention to a strange fact which must somehow be explained. Even in crude recapitulation the individual development through embryo and foetus is actually devious, presumably because the ancestral evolution was itself devious. Thus the unborn human foetus at one stage is quite fishlike, with tail and gill structures. The tail may be absorbed or may persist, but the gill structures alter to become bones of most unfishlike jaws and ears. Why this indirection in development? Biologic economy would suggest a more direct path to eventual results. It is quite apparent that such indirect and devious development is somehow an abbreviation in retracing an ancestral evolution which was itself devious, a fact we will later establish fully.

We realize today that the pattern of such devious development is part of our heritage, somehow contained and controlled in the genes which transmit that heritage. And from this it is also manifest that heredity involves much more than the final structures and workings of the organism, but includes all the transitory stages of growth and change to reach those end results.

The Bearers of Heredity

Coupled with this is another odd mystery—how the same sets of chromosomes, and presumably genes, produce different results in the various stages of development and the differing parts of the growing and matured body. For the chromosomes of all cells of an organism are apparently quite alike, being merely duplications of the original egg-cell chromosomes produced by repeated divisions. Yet they behave differently at each stage of growth and in each differing organ of the body. It is clear that somehow the genes act differently in various environments within the organism.

This particular problem still remains very much a scientific mystery, though it is being widely and vigorously attacked by experimental research. And facts which seem meaningful are beginning to accumulate, though the meanings themselves are not yet apparent. This then is a real frontier of current exploration.

And for those who love to contemplate marvels, there is something else about all this mystery. It is now obvious, of course, that the chromosomes and their unit parts, the genes, are the real bearers of all that life forms inherit. But having reached that clear and useful conclusion, we may well pause to consider what remarkable bits of matter these chromosomes and genes have turned out to be. Perhaps nothing brings this home quite so well as an estimate made by geneticist Herman J. Müller. Bearing in mind that a chromosome often strings together hundreds or thousands of genes, each controlling development of some feature of the growing or grown life form, and that a male sperm cell contributes twenty-three chromosomes (in the case of man) to the fertilized egg which starts each of us off in life, here is Müller's startling estimate: If we were to pack together all the spermatozoa responsible for the entire present human population of the world, some two and a half billions, they would together bulk no larger than an aspirin tablet. And the same would be true if we were to pack together all the chromosomes of all the female eggs from which that population was derived.

So it is at least manifest that mere physical size is not so important as we usually think. Much control can obviously be packed into a minute bulk. But of course such minuteness does mean difficulty in observing and experimenting. Ordinary optical microscopes are not nearly powerful enough; we must resort to electron microscopes magnifying hundreds of thousands of times, and even these do not make visible all the details we would like to observe. In fact, to get anywhere we must utilize a whole new battery of devices and methods, get our facts largely by indirection, and then theorize imaginatively, yet realistically, always with most careful checking. This is just what we have been doing in the field of genetics during the last few decades, with results most remarkable and promising. We have been able to do so by invention of a series of most ingenious experiments and equally ingenious new techniques and devices, not only the electron microscope itself, but the ultracentrifuge, chemical tests, stains and solvents, submicroscopic metal plating, separations by chromatography, use of radioactive and other tracer elements, X-ray diffraction, even virus dissection, to give only a partial list. By such means (to be explained as needed) we are now approaching a really tangible understanding of the nature and workings of life. But we had better proceed with the story itself.

The Nature of the Gene

In previous chapters we traced the unfolding of our understanding of the nature and workings of heredity and mutation. Toward the end of the nineteenth century Haeckel, von Kölliker, Strassberger, Hertwig, and Weismann had developed the idea that the chromosomes were the carriers of heredity and consisted of many unit determiners, later to be called genes. Roux inferred that these determiners were arranged linearly along the chromosomes, because these split lengthwise in cell division. Then after 1900, upon the resurrection of Mendel's Law of heredity, it was quickly realized that the law described exactly the behavior to be expected of such determiners; and all the experiments and observations, from Morgan on, fully confirmed this conclusion. But even to the present date no one has ever surely seen a gene, which would argue that it must be exceedingly minute.

Before 1900 Hans Driesch had speculated on the chemical nature of the hereditary determiners and concluded that they might be ferments, as enzymes were then called. And in 1915 Leonard T. Troland of Harvard, in his *Enzyme Theory of Life*, went beyond his sound disclosure that life processes are largely controlled by the catalytic action of enzymes, to maintain that enzymes reproduced copies of themselves, and mutated in their patterns, so as to control heredity and variation.

In 1921, however, Herman J. Müller pointed out that enzymes did not actually behave this way to reproduce and mutate, but that instead they were the products of genes of distinctive chemical character. For the moment he left open the question of whether the genes were of special genetic material or merely some type of protoplasm. But by 1926 he had decided in favor of a special genetic material. A few years later, from 1933 to 1937, he served as consultant on genetics in Soviet Russia, where he met the opposite viewpoint, represented by Alexander I. Oparin, who "followed the official Communist Party line by giving the specific genetic material a back seat." We have already learned why this was a crucial Communist attitude. And so inevitably, as the Party line hardened, the position of Müller as a Soviet genetics consultant became increasingly incongruous, and finally quite futile.

The chemistry of the chromosomes had of course been analyzed, during the nineteenth century in Germany by Miescher, Altman, and Kossel, followed by Phoebus Levene at the Rockefeller Institute. They were found to consist of largely simple proteins, nucleic acid, and an unidentified residue of about 5 per cent. Which was the genetic material? Early opinion rather favored the proteins because of their known biologic versatility, but the question remained entirely open until 1934.

Enter the Virus

In that year the chemist Wendell M. Stanley reported that after two years of purifying and concentrating, he had crystallized the tobacco mosaic virus. This was significant in many ways, among them because viruses were already known to behave like genes and had much the same chemical composition of proteins and nucleic acids. And in Stanley's crystals the 5 per cent residue had definitely disappeared, yet the virus was even more infective and still behaved like genes. So at least that 5 per cent residue was out as a genetic material.

Viruses were uncomfortably familiar to us all as causes of a wide variety of diseases. Following Pasteur, until 1898, everyone thought these diseases due to bacteria. Thus in 1892 the Russian bacteriologist Dimitri Ivanovski published a paper "On the Mosaic Disease of the Tobacco Plant," which he ascribed to the fluid toxin of a bacterium because it passed right through his filters, while solid bacteria did not. He did suspect, probably mistakenly, that his filter might be defective, but got no farther toward a sensible explanation.

Then in 1898 the Dutchman Martinus Willem Beijernick reported the same experiment with the same virus, but went much farther. Under the microscope he found no bacteria; on the laboratory food medium agar, he got no bacterial growth; and most important, the filtered fluid not only infected tobacco plants but actually multiplied itself in volume and so was apparently alive. And not knowing what to make of all this, he gave it a good resounding Latin name, *Contagium vivum fluidum*, meaning "living fluid infectant." But he also used the simple word "virus," meaning merely "poison." Later this usually became "filterable virus," a description justified until that day in 1916 when H. A. Allard used ultrafine filters which finally held the extremely minute virus particles. And eventually the supermag-nifications of the electron microscope showed them as particles, those of tobacco mosaic virus, usually abbreviated as TMV, being rod-shaped and much smaller than bacteria.

Many other viruses have now been studied, but only one other need concern us here, simply because it has proved so useful experimentally. This is the bacteriophage or "bacteria-eater," fa-miliar to experimenters simply as the phage. It is club-shaped, with a round head and a straight handle. It attacks a bacterium cell by attaching the end of the handle. The head must be hollow and the handle tubular, with contents which empty into the bacterium cell through the handle. But nothing appears to happen for a period varying from one to three quarters of an hour, depending on the type of phage. Then suddenly the bac-terium bursts and out come several hundred club-shaped phages. What has apparently happened is that the virus contents have acted like invading genes taking charge of cell activities, and directing the cell to manufacture more phages instead of more bacteria. Quite significantly, the phage cannot reproduce itself on its own, nor can any other virus, except by entering and utilizing some living cell, and it has often been argued from this that the virus is not actually alive in the accepted sense.

But what is the chemical nature of the invading virus gene? Is it protein or nucleic acid, or a mixture of both? About a decade after Stanley had crystallized the tobacco mosaic virus, answers began to come in. The bacteriologists Avery, MacLeod, and McCarty transferred an extract (mostly nucleic acid) from one bacterium to another, whereupon the second began repro-ducing, not itself but copies of the first bacterium, including its type of protein. And Hershey and Roper labeled phage protein with radioactive sulfur, and its nucleic acid with radioactive phosphorus, and later found that only the phosphorus-labeled nucleic acid had entered, with probably no protein. And finally Heinz Fraenkel-Conrat and others working under Stanley, and independently Gierer and Schramm, removed the protein by chemical means, and used only nucleic acid for infecting, and got reproduction of the phage, including its protein. This settled the matter: the infecting phage gene was nucleic acid, and only the discarded phage container was protein. So the genetic material was definitely nucleic acid.

The Chemistry of the Gene

In many ways the genes of chromosomes are not so easy to experiment with chemically as the genes of viruses, though gross chemical analysis has long shown them to be substantially alike. Chemically, they are broadly of two types, commonly referred to as RNA and DNA. These are convenient abbreviations for ribonucleic acid and deoxyribonucleic acid. Both occur in living cells, but in different places within them. Thus, DNA is found only in the nucleus, in fact only the chromosomes. Some RNA is found there, too, but most of it in cell structures outside the nucleus. Viruses, however, may have both, or all DNA, or all RNA.

An essential difference between RNA and DNA, as their full names suggest, is that one contains ribose sugar, the other deoxyribose sugar. This difference seems actually slight, as the molecule of the latter has just one oxygen atom less. But both are very peculiar sugars, being built on a five-carbon chain instead of the standard six-carbon chain of our familiar sugars. And as an oddity of history, both these sugars were first synthesized artificially by Emil Fischer, the ribose in 1901 and given by him an entirely meaningless underived name. Then in 1910 Levene found ribose in nucleic acid, and since then both these sugars have grown to great biologic importance.

In addition to these special sugars, RNA and DNA contain phosphates which, as the name tells us, are built about the element phosphorus. To explain the phosphates, we start best with phosphoric acid, the formula for which is H_3PO_4. Translated, this means that its molecule consists of one phosphorus atom hooked up with four oxygen atoms, and three of these with hydrogen atoms. Diagramed, it looks like this:

$$
\begin{array}{c}
O \\
\| \\
H-O-P-O-H \\
| \\
O \\
| \\
H
\end{array}
$$

If now one or more of the hydrogen atoms become detached, we get phosphates with free "hands" for attachment to each other or to other suitable chemical groups. In fact, that is just what they do in RNA and DNA. They join into phosphate chains, and also each with a ribose or deoxyribose sugar.

These sugars, in their turn, attach to other chemical groups in which nitrogen is present, but here there is more diversity. Broadly there are two kinds, the pyrimidines and the purines, the former with a single ring of carbon and nitrogen atoms, the latter with a double ring. In both RNA and DNA there are only two purines involved, adenine and guanine, the two differing in structural arrangement and in the number of oxygen and hydrogen atoms. There are three pyrimidines, however. Cytosine occurs in both RNA and DNA. Uracil is found only in RNA, and thymine only in DNA. Both uracil and thymine are alike except in one respect: where uracil has a single hydrogen atom, thymine has a methyl group of one carbon and three hydrogen atoms. But this slight difference seems to be very important practically.

Summed up, both RNA and DNA contain phosphates, the purines adenine and guanine, and the pyrimidine cytosine. RNA differs from DNA by containing ribose sugar and the pyrimidine uracil, instead of deoxyribose sugar and the pyrimidine thymine. All of this seems simple enough.

Structures of DNA and RNA

Unfortunately it proved altogether too simple. For at least the DNA of the chromosomes, and therefore the genes, presumably provided the genetic determiners of an apparently infinite number of inherited characteristics throughout the living world. And so somehow or other, chemically or structurally, the nucleic acids of genes must vary to produce such varying effects.

Early efforts to analyze the further details of nucleic acid makeup by chemical tests proved too rough on them, in the sense that these tender substances were damaged and could not be identified and measured. But in 1944 some English biochemists—A. J. P. Martin, R. L. M. Synge, and others—invented a more delicate method of separating chemical substances out of a mixture. Its common form is called paper chromatography. It uses a sheet of porous absorbent paper, a very clean variant of ordinary blotting paper. The mixture to be analyzed is first applied near an edge of the paper and allowed to dry. Then that edge is placed in a suitable solvent fluid, which by capillary action proceeds to travel across the sheet as through a wick. As the solvent moves through the deposit of chemical mixture, it dissolves and carries along the several chemicals, but at different speeds and to varying distances. Thus they become separated into bands, to which proper chemical tests can then be applied to tell them apart. The result, which usually comes out as bands of color, enables the chemist to judge rather closely the relative amounts of the several chemicals of the original mixture.

The inventors of the method first used it for separating amino acids, but it is now applied for all sorts of analytical purposes. Thus, in the hands of Erwin Chargaff of Columbia University it was employed to separate and estimate the relative amounts of the purines and pyrimidines in various samples of nucleic acids. From 1947 on, he was able to report some very significant facts. The proportions did differ in various DNA and RNA samples, but always the total of purines seemed equal to the total of pyrimidines, so that adenine plus guanine equaled cytosine plus thymine (in DNA) or plus uracil (in RNA). Also, the number of guanine units seemed to equal those of cytosine, and the adenine number those of thymine or uracil. This seemed suggestive, but just what it meant did not appear until 1953, when two biochemists at Cambridge University announced a revolutionary idea of genetic unit structure into which it fitted.

In 1951 James D. Watson went to Cambridge University to work on the X-ray diffraction study of myoglobin structure. But he soon dropped that, for there he met Francis Crick, who had distractingly interesting ideas about the structure of DNA. Between them, the American and the Englishman set about a creative collaboration of minds which resulted in a sharing of a Nobel Prize in 1962 with another Cambridge colleague, Maurice H. F. Wilkins. Already in 1951 Wilkins had taken some crystalline X-ray diffraction photographs of DNA. This showed that "DNA must have a well-defined structure. There was thus an answer for somebody to get."

In working out that answer, Crick and Watson began with "the necessity that the correct structure have the capacity for self-replication." And inspired by a just-published study by Linus Pauling on "The Nature of the Chemical Bond," they assumed that "neither long-range forces nor any form of mysticism" was involved, but "well-understood chemical forces." And during the next eighteen months they worked out an unexpected structure for DNA which has completely revolutionized all our thinking about genes and their workings. For one thing, the X-ray diffraction photos indicated an over-all helical or corkscrew structure, to which they added the idea of a double-strand helix, a happy idea which finally explained the mechanism of replication of the genetic patterns. But this deserves more detailed description:

First, the nucleic acid units, now called nucleotides, are connected by their phosphate groups into long chains or strands.

Second, these strands occur in parallel pairs connected crosswise as if by the rungs of a ladder.

Third, the cross connections are always from a double-ringed purine to a single-ringed pyrimidine, which keeps the lengths of the ladder rungs always equal, which keeps the strands parallel.

Fourth, the connections are always: cytosine to guanine; adenine to thymine. These cross-couples can therefore be abbreviated as C–G and A–T.

Fifth, along the lengths of the two strands, these several cross-couples not only vary in numbers but occur in any order, with the cross-couples placed with either end in either strand.

Sixth, these two strands are intertwined about each other into a double helix, or perhaps we should say the ladder is twisted into a double corkscrew.

In short, as we move along each twisted double-strand ladder, we come across C–G, G–C, A–T, and T–A couples at seeming random. And it was concluded that, to quote H. J. Müller, "It is the exact sequence of these nucleotides in line in the chain that must determine what chemical influence a given segment or region of the chain exerts in forming its protoplasmic products" (Figure 6).

This illuminating picture of DNA structure, which was largely theoretical in 1953, has been increasingly confirmed in the ensuing decade by experiments which have been well described as "elegant." The nucleic acids in phages have been tagged with radioactive elements and in bean chromosomes with the heavy hydrogen tritium, and as these multiplied by division, were found to behave exactly as this theory demanded. Best of all, this theoretical picture has fruitfully explained more and more of the details we have dug up in our studies of everything relating to the problems of genetics, as we shall see.

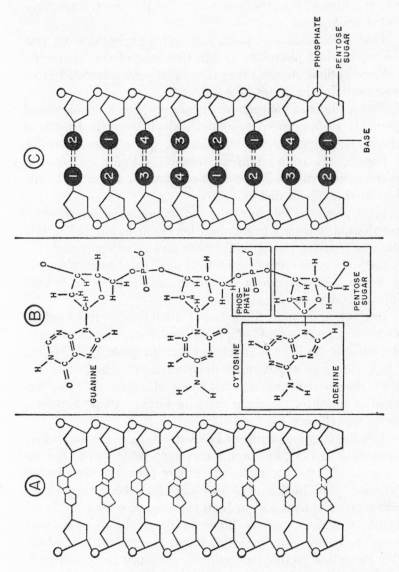

Fig. 6. Structure and Duplication of DNA.

The Replicating Mechanism

We now understand in chemical terms why C connects with G, and A with T, this being a matter of complementary chemical structures involving N and O atoms, which do not concern us here, and so-called hydrogen bonds, which do. For these chemical bonds are rather weak, and that is important. For it means that the two strands can rather easily untwist and come apart, perhaps step by step, starting at one end of the intertwined strands. What causes them to untwist and separate is not yet wholly clear, though we do have suggestive clues. It happens, of course, each time a cell divides and its chromosomes split, and is probably somehow related to cell growth.

But note what we get when such a double strand separates into two single strands. Where C occurs in one, G must have occurred in the other, and vice versa. Where A occurs in one, T must have occurred in the other, and vice versa. In other words, each strand is in all ways the exact complement of the other.

Furthermore, when thus separated, each strand can build its own attached complementary strand out of the supply of loose Cs, Gs, As, and Ts present in the cell substance surrounding it. Each C will pick up its complementary G, each G its C, and A its T, and each T its A. Meanwhile the phosphates will connect the complements lengthwise into a new strand intertwining with its pair into a fresh double helix.

Meanwhile, too, the second separated strand will have done the same, so we now have two like double strands where we originally had but one. This, then, clearly provides a basic genetic structure explaining how replication occurs, how replicas of gene patterns are formed as the chromosomes split and the cells divide again and again to multiply in numbers. Whatever the gene pattern may be, it is thus preserved with each duplication. In the multiplying of body cells, this means more genes

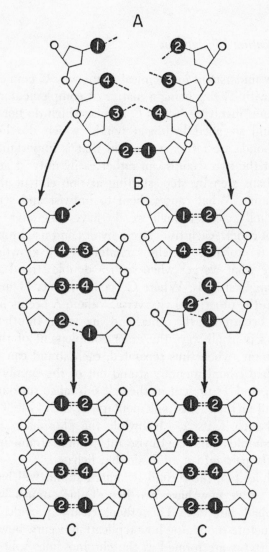

Fig. 7. The Replicating Mechanism.

like the original. And through the germ cells joining in the fertilizing of the egg, each contributes its share of reassorted gene patterns to the next generation (Figure 7).

Mutations are then readily explained as the result of alterations in the gene patterns, by the accidents of radiation hits, by chemical disturbances by mutagenic substances. How and where they will strike, or disturb, and what the effects will be, we so far cannot predict, so they seem quite random, are usually for the worse, only occasionally for the better, just as we observe mutations actually to be. But once a pattern has anywhere been changed, that change will be replicated with each dividing of a double strand and each rebuilding of its duplicate. So the mutation will be inherited, of course unless and until it is discarded by natural selection as disadvantageous.

The Genetic Code

So now we have a clear and tangible picture of how a given genetic pattern can replicate itself, on occasion mutate, and take part in the constant reassortment of genes which is behind the observed facts of inheritance expressed in Mendel's Law.

But there still remains a vital mystery: How does the determiner gene determine? The DNA of a gene has but four nucleotide components—C, G, A, and T—and they come in only two combinations. RNA also takes part, as we shall see, but it, too, has only two pairs of only four components—C, G, A, and U. But we can get very few combinations by arrangements of only two pairs of only four components, while there is a virtual infinity of inherited characteristics which they manifestly determine. It is like trying to make up an infinity of words out of an alphabet of only two pairs of only four letters. In short, the possible chemistries of so few nucleotides seem altogether too limited to explain the huge multiplicity of effects.

But the new picture offered by Crick and Watson changed all

that. The possibilities of variety increased immensely. For the nucleotide couples come in long double chains, and manifestly an infinity of arrangements in order are possible, if only the chains are long enough, which they were soon found to be.

But what a forbiddingly intricate problem that seemed to present! Here is an infinity of effects, determined by an infinity of arrangements in order of nucleotides. How possibly can their relationships be worked out—unless there is some simplifying system running through at all?

So system was looked for and, let it be said, was fortunately— and triumphantly—found. As we have long known, the stuff of life, the protoplasm of the living cell, consists of proteins in seemingly infinite variety. But they are all compounded from a limited number of unit compounds, about twenty amino acids. With those few basic units, combined in sufficient numbers, and varying orders, and three-dimensional configurations, Nature provides the infinite variety of all the proteins. So what is needed, after all, is merely enough distinctive groupings of nucleotides to determine formation of the few basic amino acids, of course in proper orders and combinations for building the needed proteins of protoplasm. Here, then, is possibly a comparative simplicity capable of producing the infinite complexity and multiplicity of the observed end results.

Fortunately this proved to be another magic right idea which clarified everything it touched. A Spanish-born American biochemist, Severo Ochoa, suggested a way to make up nucleotide strands consisting entirely of uracil, the pattern of which was necessarily UUUUUUUUU. And soon it was found that this caused production of the amino acid phenylalinine. With that start, several teams of biochemists set to work to trace the connections between other combinations of nucleotides and the several amino acids. The procedure was to mix a few nucleotides from another uniform chain and watch the results, gradually working out the combination which resulted in each of the other amino acids. It meant some very tricky juggling, and sounds almost fantastically impossible, yet today, step by step, at first tentatively but more and more certainly, the code relating nucleotide combinations to given amino acids is emerging. In fact, at this writing it has just been announced by the biochemist Richard V. Eck that the patterns of nucleotides themselves fall into an over-all pattern which enables us to predict code items which have not yet been fully verified. The proof of this will of course be their final verification. His table embodying this pattern is given below, and it will be interesting to watch whether further determinations will actually verify this table or disprove it. It will be a tangible and useful illustration of how the scientific method is applied to gain new truths.

It was evident from the very first that groups of nucleotides were required. Four nucleotides, taken singly, could hardly determine some twenty amino acids. Even arrayed by twos, there were not enough combinations for that number of amino acids. But groups of three or more could do it. There was a temporary problem whether those triplet or larger groups could overlap, sharing nucleotides at the overlaps. But that placed serious limitations on what group could follow what group, and therefore seems to be ruled out. Furthermore, current research now indicates that separate sets of three actually determine production of the several amino acids, with some uncertainty about the part played by the middle unit of a triplet set. But at the rate things are now moving, it should not be long before we will complete our code table with relative certainty.

All these research successes, those in progress and those accomplished, indicate clearly enough that the Crick-Watson picture of 1953 has been fairly well confirmed. The nucleic acids of genes consist of helically intertwined double chains of nucleotide pairs coupled together ladderlike in definite orders which vary with particular genes. These structures can separate in cell division, but in so doing replicate their patterns and so transmit by heredity the characteristics they determine. Radiation or chemicals may alter the patterns, however, and thus cause mutations, and these are then replicated and inherited, subject to natural selection in the struggle for existence. By sexual intermixing through fertilization of egg by sperm, the characteristics are also reassorted from generation to generation, with notable effects on the processes of selection and evolution.

Within the Cell

Earlier in the chapter we asked the basic question: How do the hereditary determiners, the genes, actually determine? Notice that we have not yet really answered that question.

We have already explained how DNA can replicate its genetic pattern by separation of its double and complementary strands, with each strand then building its complement by chemical selection from materials ready in the cell substance.

On the other hand, in our code table relating the triplet groups of nucleotides to amino acids produced, notice that U for uracil appears often, but T for thymine not at all. That means that at this point we are dealing with RNA only, and not with DNA. What, then, is the relation between DNA and RNA? Or more specifically, how is the genetic pattern (inherited through DNA) then transferred (through RNA) to the amino acids and the proteins they form in the offspring organism?

Emphasizing this same question, we find DNA only in the chromosomes of the nucleus and not in the portions of the cell where proteins are actually produced. We do find RNA in slight amounts in the nucleus, more in the cell substance outside the nucleus, and abundantly in a multitude of minute particles called ribosomes in which we find that proteins are in fact produced.

We do not yet have the full answer in all details. We are still gathering the pertinent facts by ingenious experiments and interpreting them by cautious theorizing. The facts are not always clear, often seem conflicting, and we are admittedly groping our way to understanding. But as of this moment of writing, and omitting the highly technical details, the following picture seems to be emerging.

The business of DNA is twofold: first, to replicate its own pattern to transmit that pattern by heredity and to duplicate it in cells as they multiply by division; and second, to transfer a corresponding derived pattern to the RNA of the cell.

This second bit of business is evidently done in the nucleus (which the DNA never leaves) and accounts directly for the RNA which is found in the nucleus. This transfer of patterns is evidently done by two chemical changes: (1) substitution of each uracil for a thymine, which may mean merely replacement of a methyl radical by a hydrogen atom; and (2) substitution of ribose for deoxyribose sugar, perhaps involving only the adding of an oxygen atom. But what triggers the changes, just how they are done, we do not yet know. Whether it is all done by both DNA strands, or just one, and whether the resulting RNA is single-stranded, or double, is not settled, and may in fact differ with various organisms.

Evidently the resulting RNA soon moves out of the nucleus and through the cell fluids to the ribosomes, becoming a messenger carrying a pattern determined by the DNA which produced it. That pattern consists of at least one strand of nucleotides (grouped probably by series of three) which finally guides production of amino acids (in proper order for production of given proteins) at the ribosomes.

The experiments indicate that there is much RNA already present in the ribosomes when the messenger RNA arrives. It may or may not be somehow combined or involved with ribosome proteins and all ready to go into amino-acid production under control of the messenger RNA.

There is, in fact, evidence that a messenger RNA strand does its job of control several times before it degrades and disappears. James D. Watson pictures it as similar to a movie film negative with its series of picture frames in proper order. It slides over the surface of a ribosomal RNA unit, each frame (of three nucleotides) imprinting its effect to cause production of an amino-acid unit. And the frames being in proper order, the amino acids come in proper order for building up the predetermined protein molecule. Meanwhile the RNA strand is already moving over a second RNA-ribosome unit, to produce a second protein molecule, and a third, fourth, etc., until it gives out and other messenger RNA strands arrive to carry on.

This is a tentative picture of DNA-RNA action. It may be modified at any time, for this is a most active present frontier of research, where new facts, new theories, and new tests are every day adding clearer and surer understanding. Nothing should be considered final, except perhaps that whatever picture does eventually emerge as proven, it will quite surely be based on understandable physics and chemistry without benefit of magic or mystery or miracle.

Chapter 8

THE BARREN PRIMAL
EARTH

When life first appeared upon the Earth, conditions must of
course have been suitable for it to survive. However, both the
early life and the early Earth were probably very different from
what they are today. For all the evidence suggests profound
evolutionary changes in both, during which the two must have
continued sufficiently compatible for the life to persist without
interruption.

So we are necessarily here concerned with the origin and consequent state of affairs of the early Earth, since it must have
conditioned the appearance and continuance of life upon it. The
over-all story, as progressively worked out by modern astronomical and geophysical studies, has varied considerably during the
last century, a history which has already been told in my earlier
book, *Our Emerging Universe*, and need not be fully retold here.
But as its changing aspects have direct bearing on our present
problem, that history should be at least outlined as background.

Throughout the nineteenth century the Nebular Hypothesis
of the Frenchman Laplace prevailed in astronomical thinking,
though serious theoretical difficulties kept mounting and finally
forced development of new ideas. First of these was the Encoun-
ter Theory of the Australian Bickerton in 1878, but it was overlooked and forgotten, and not until 1900 did its broad counterpart, the Planetesimal Theory of the Americans Chamberlin

and Moulton, appear and win general approval. Both featured the tidal action of a passing star tearing enough matter from the surface of the Sun to form the planets and secondary matter of the solar system. This was then modified in details, first by the British astronomer Jeans, then by the British geophysicist Jeffreys. But in the early 1940s the German physicist von Weizsäcker, followed by the American astronomer Kuiper, returned to a nebular theory, in which our Sun and its family of attendant planets, satellites, comets, and meteoric matter all arose from a general condensing of an original blob of swirling gas, dust, and general rubbish, probably dark and low-temperatured, such as we observe scattered here and there amid the glowing nebulae of the Milky Way. Much of the parental blob condensed into a central globe to become the Sun, which by that condensing and gravitational fall finally superheated until it became a nuclear reactor maintaining its own energy production, as do other shining stars, by converting hydrogen to helium, quite in the manner of our H-bombs.

Some of the rotating blob remained, however, as a turbulent disc of gas, dust, and other rubbish revolving about the Sun as center. Most of it was hydrogen, helium, and other light gases which soon largely dissipated into space, leaving a concentration of the much rarer and heavier elements. These then gradually aggregated into a number of planet and satellite globes, which constantly grew as they gravitationally attracted and swept up residual rubbish in their orbit paths. One of the lesser globes, third out from the Sun, was the protoplanet destined to become the Earth. Like the other protoplanets, as it gained in mass, it increased its gravitational pull and ability to gather up more matter and to settle down to increased compactness.

The original Nebular Hypothesis of Laplace was rather indefinite about the initial temperature of the Earth. The several tidal theories from Bickerton to Jeffreys all involved an origin from the superhot surface of the Sun, but the Plantesimal Theory definitely assumed a cooling of the scattered material and its slow aggregation into planets and satellites without appreciable crustal heating. The subsequent tidal theories were less definite about this, but the concurrent studies of the interior of the Earth led to a belief that the fall of matter during aggregation and its shrinkage to greater compactness would heat it and so melt and soften at least the interior as to permit a gravitational assortment of its materials. The heavier metals, such as iron and nickel, would settle downward to the core, where they seem to be concentrated now. The lighter granitic and basaltic rocks would float upward to form the surface crust on which we now live. And the rocks of intermediate densities would shift to become the series of mantle shells which our studies indicate lie in between the core and the crust.

Then in the summer of 1949 Harold C. Urey, Nobel Prize winner in chemistry, gave a course at the University of Chicago on "Chemistry in Nature," and thereby became interested in the origin of the planets, and by 1951 gave the series of Silliman Lectures at Yale on that subject, following the next year with a book entitled *The Planets, Their Origin and Development*. In general he concurred with the ideas of von Weizsäcker and Kuiper, but also concluded that the Earth globe had passed through an early transitory period of superheating, raising temperatures even at the surface to several thousand degrees. This would have involved two most important effects: any incipient life would have been completely burnt out; and any existing accumulation of atmosphere, and probably surface waters, would have been lost by dissipation into space. The Earth would have been both barren and airless.

Adding to the probability of such early superheating is the presence of considerable radioactive material even in the present Earth. The very heaviest elements, such as uranium and thorium, are unstable, and by slow breakdown convert into helium and lead, meanwhile releasing much heat energy. The process stretches out over billions of years, during which there would be a gradual wasting away of the original amount of such materials and a resulting decrease in the rate of radioactive decay and heating. And taking into consideration a number of other radioactive elements which break down faster and have consequently now practically disappeared, there must have been far more radioactive heating going on in the early days of the Earth's existence. There is some question whether much radioactive matter ever existed deep in the Earth's interior, but that is a secondary problem, as it would after all be the superheating of the surface crust which would drive off any original atmosphere and burn out any incipient early life.

The New-Moon Story

Somewhere, too, our Moon must have entered into the early story, but just how is still rather unsettled. One older theory had it born of the Earth itself by a breaking in two of the swiftly rotating original Earth globe. (This was discussed fully in my former book, in both its details and its persisting difficulties.) Another idea was that the Earth-Moon pair had formed together at the outset as gravitationally bound twin condensations from the original disc of preplanetary rubbish. And still another theory was that they had been separately formed, but happening to orbit near enough together, had "captured" each other gravitationally to become a permanent planet-satellite pair. (But how this last method might be related to the observed present features of the Earth and Moon had not been developed and made known until after my earlier book had already appeared.)

Actually such a theory had been developed in mathematical terms as early as 1955 by a German high-school teacher, H. Gerstenkorn, who then properly published an account of it in a German astrophysical journal, only to have it ignored and forgotten. But early in 1963 it was revived in a paper by the Swedish physicist Hannes Alfven, published in the British science magazine *Icarus*. Without entering into the mathematical details of the actual capture, some time in the course of events the Earth and Moon orbited so closely that the tidal pull of the Earth tore the Moon globe apart. The critical distance at which this would inevitably occur was already theoretically known to be somewhat less than ten thousand miles, measured center to center.

What became of the disrupted substance of the original Moon? About half of it probably fell to the surface of the Earth, presumably to form the present granitic continents of the crust, perhaps also the underlying crustal layer of basalt on which the continents now float. Their combined average density (2.75 times the density of water) approaches fairly closely the average density of the Moon (3.34), if we allow for some present compacting of the material within the Moon's interior, and some gravitational sorting of the Earth's crustal material.

Another portion of the disrupted Moon substance would simply recongregate into a smaller Moon globe, necessarily at a somewhat greater distance avoiding another disruption. But much material would also be scattered into miscellaneous orbits about the Earth. Much of this would then be swept up by the reborn Moon itself, some of it even after the Moon had settled down into a fairly solid globe with a well-cooled crust. Such material, falling back late to the Moon, would then account for the innumerable crater scars which pockmark its present surface. Most of that scarring probably occurred a billion or more years ago. But also some such old Moon material may still be present in the Earth-Moon region, some falling to Earth from time to time even now as meteorites. But some meteorites may have another origin, as we shall learn shortly.

Tidal Side Effects

All of the side effects of such a Moon capture and disruption, with a dumping of Moon material upon the Earth, have not yet been worked out fully by the professional scientists. But give them time. And meanwhile we can have a try at some effects which seem most obvious and inevitable. Thus, it would seem that the recongregated Moon would be orbiting quite near the Earth, and would then slowly recede to its present mean distance of about 240,000 miles. In fact, this much of the Earth-Moon story had already been surmised by earlier workers in this field, as fully explained in my former book.

But at first, when the two globes orbited so closely together, their tidal effects upon each other must have been enormous. Gravitational theory demands that the Earth should have been rotating upon its axis in a few hours, and the Moon revolving about it in a day or two, besides itself rotating upon its axis in some short period. All of this, plus their nearness, would result in huge tidal pumpings. The Moon, that close, would raise ocean tides miles deep sweeping over the whole Earth's surface, continents and all—if there were any or enough ocean waters to do so. But also there would be deep tides within the Earth mass itself, an elongating distortion with two waves sweeping westward around the Earth in the few hours of its much shorter day. And the much more massive Earth would tidally distort the Moon shape even more, with a double tidal swell sweeping around the Moon each time it rotated relative to the Earth.

Such huge, rapid, and continuous rotational tidal pumpings must have had enormous braking effects, causing slowing of the rotations of both members of the pair. And the internal distortional movements within the viscous interiors must have involved tremendous frictions transforming into heat to raise interior temperatures in both bodies. The braking action, by a rather odd transfer of angular momentum from the Earth to the Moon, would also cause a slow receding of the Moon farther and farther from the Earth, with a lengthening of the month of Moon revolution about the Earth. This last effect has already been explained in my previous book.

By a couple of billion years ago the rotation of the Moon

about its own axis relative to the Earth must have come to a stop, and with it the major tidal pumping and heating of its own interior. Surface cooling then must have soon resulted in a solid crust which could preserve the crater scarrings inflicted by meterorites. But even then interior heat could have caused huge extrusive lava flows playing a major part in forming the level Moon plains we now call maria.

For in 1962 Zdenek Kopal, astronomer of the University of Manchester, England, pointed out that even today there must be a residual tidal pumping going on to cause internal heating of the Moon. However, this is due not to Moon rotation but to its monthly revolution about the Earth in an eccentric orbit. At the nearest point, the Earth pull is about 30 per cent greater than at the farthest point. As the Moon always turns its same face toward the Earth, there is a normal bulge of 165 feet of this face due to Earth pull. But according to Kopal, because this pull varies, the bulge heaves up and down by some thirty-three feet in a pumping action causing internal flowage and friction sufficient to maintain the Moon's interior temperature at about that of a blast furnace, several thousand degrees Fahrenheit.

Of course the tidal pumping within the Earth still continues as it rotates daily relative to the Moon and the Sun. The heat from friction of the fluid ocean tides is very minor and is so quickly lost into space that it does not accumulate. However, there is also a tide of some fourteen to twenty inches twice daily in the Earth mass itself, and as this works against the very viscous interior, the frictional heat production must remain considerable. Yet it is now really negligible compared with what it must have been in the early days of the Earth-Moon pair. We must therefore recognize that in those early days, one or more billion years ago, there was this further source of great Earth heating. So considering all the heating factors, fall of matter from space, global shrinkage, radioactive energy release, and tidal pumping friction, the resulting high Earth temperature at that stage, even at the surface, must have definitely barred the formation and existence of life and even the retaining of any atmosphere or surface waters which may previously have existed.

A New Mephitic Atmosphere

But eventually, we do know, the Earth's crust did cool to virtual solidity, and in due time to a surface temperature below the boiling point of water. That meant that any new supply of water could settle down as fluid into lower surface basins to form permanent oceans and lakes. That water supply would have to come largely from the Earth's interior, where it had remained entrapped as steam, or mixed with rock matter, or even in solution in molten lavas. Some would be driven upward toward the surface by heat and seepage, or released by cooling from extrusive lava flows, or expelled as steam in volcanic eruptions. The gradual filling of the ocean and lake basins therefore presented no real difficulty.

The renewal of an atmosphere was also no real problem. There were plenty of interior gases which seeped to the surface because they were light, or were released from solution with cooling of lavas, or were among the expelled matter from volcanic eruptions.

But the resulting atmosphere was, to say the least, a peculiar one compared with that of today. Undoubtedly it was so mephitic that very few present life forms could have survived in it. For it was marked by the virtual absence of free oxygen. There was actually no lack of oxygen, as it makes up about half the substance of the crustal rocks. But it was not free and available for breathing by life forms. For it quickly combined with accessible free hydrogen to form water (H_2O), or with carbon to form carbon dioxide (CO_2) or carbon monoxide (CO), or otherwise oxidized the surface rocks. In short, any free atmospheric oxygen would be quickly used up, and could not accumulate. Only later, when plant life kept renewing the oxygen supply, could enough of this vital element be kept free in the atmosphere to supply the needs of modern life forms. But that could only occur after life itself had already been in existence. Life must therefore have first appeared while this early atmosphere prevailed, and must itself have been such as to permit survival in that same atmosphere.

The composition of that early atmosphere therefore becomes important to us. The lighter gases, such as helium and neon, or any free hydrogen not locked up in chemical combination, would inevitably escape by dissipation into outer space. There would be a growing percentage of free nitrogen, though some would be combined with hydrogen to form ammonia (NH_3). There would also be methane (CH_4) and perhaps some hydrogen sulfide (H_2S). Important, too, would be the content of water vapor being ever renewed by evaporation from all water surfaces. At the outset the oceans would be much warmer, the evaporation rate higher, and the air extremely humid. And no doubt the oceans absorbed a considerable portion of such atmospheric gases as were water-soluble. The surface waters therefore shared somewhat in the mephitic composition of the atmosphere. And shortly we must obviously face the problem of how life could possibly originate and survive in such a seemingly poisonous environment.

But meanwhile, due to the mere existence of an atmosphere and surface waters, there began an important new era of surface changes. The evaporation, largely from ocean waters, and the transportation of water vapors over land surfaces by the circulating air meant the beginning of the cycles of erosion and deposition which kept altering the Earth crust both above and below the sea levels. Driven largely by differential heating by the Sun, plus the Earth's rotation, atmospheric winds carried moisture from ocean areas to land areas. The higher land elevations meant cooling and precipitation of water as rainfall, wetting down of the continental surfaces, filling of upland lake basins, and the feeding of downhill draining streams gathering into rivers, all eroding the mountains and lesser uplands and carrying both chemically dissolved and physically suspended and bottom-swept mineral matter down to final deposition as ever-deepening sedimentary strata in shore waters. Thus mountain ranges were slowly leveled and new land areas built up, all accompanied by sinkings and risings of the Earth crust in a series of vast alterations of the very face of the Earth already fairly well deciphered by our science of historical geology. It all took several billions of years, and somewhere, sometime, somehow, life began in its initial, simple, and inconspicuous first form, probably so soft and unidentifiable that it left no recognizable fossil record of its presence.

Transplantation Theories

Starting with an originally sterile Earth, there seem to be but two ways of explaining the arrival of life upon it by natural means. One is that life arose spontaneously here on Earth by physicochemical processes out of existing nonliving materials under the then existing conditions. The other is that life already existed somewhere outside the Earth and was then somehow transplanted to it.

Obviously, any such arrival from elsewhere merely puts off the problem of the original origin of life. It places this problem off on some unknown elsewhere in an unknown past where conditions were probably even beyond guessing, leaving any solution quite beyond our scientific research.

This of course was not objectionable to Vitalist thinking, which already implied the belief that some eternal vital essence pervaded the entire Universe. And though Wöhler had struck a mortal blow at Vitalism by his synthesis of urea in 1828, his good friend and brilliant pioneer in organic chemistry, Justus von Leibig, though himself a declared Mechanist, could, as late as 1861, express the kindred idea that "the atmosphere of celestial bodies as well as of whirling cosmic nebulae may be regarded as the timeless sanctuary of animate forms, the eternal plantations of organic germs."

Yet in science the theoretical possibility that life might have arrived on Earth from some outside source could not be ruled out entirely. But the special problem then arose how germs or spores could travel and survive on a trip through space, say from planet to planet. In 1874 von Helmholtz offered a suggestion that simple life forms might be carried through space by meteorites. This fitted into a suspicion that had been held for many decades that meteorites were fragments of a broken-up planet. In 1801 Piazzi had discovered the asteroid Ceres, first of more than a thousand known to circle the Sun in orbits largely between those of Mars and Jupiter. Olbers, who had discovered the second asteroid, Pallas, in 1802, and the fourth, Vesta, in 1807, advanced the theory that they were the larger pieces of a former planet disrupted by getting too close to the massive Jupiter. And the suspicion grew that meteorites were merely smaller fragments scattered widely during this disruption. The compositions of meteorites gave partial support to this theory, some being heavy iron and nickel—as if they came from the metal core of a planet—though most were stone—as if they came from a planet mantle or crust.

With such ideas abroad, it was inevitable that searches would be made in meteorites for traces of lowly life. And in 1932 Charles Lipman thought he had found bacteria or spores in a meteorite, but as they proved identical with forms already present here on Earth, they could very well have moved in after the meteorite landed.

But back in 1864 a meteorite had been seen to fall and burst near the town of Orgueil in southern France. Some twenty fragments were immediately sent to museums and laboratories for study, with the chemists (including Pasteur himself, it is said) finding that they contained some 6 per cent of what was judged to be organic carbon. This meteorite was of a rather rare type, being a carbonaceous chondrite, of which only about a score are known. And recently, in 1961, this and three others of this same rare type were studied at Fordham and New York universities in collaboration with an Esso laboratory, and in them were found what looked like microscopic primitive organisms, but this time unlike any known existing life forms.

Yet all of this is of course inconclusive, and nothing will really be settled until a meteor-borne germ or spore is literally caught in the act of transplantation, arriving by a freshly fallen meteorite uncontaminated by Earth life, then observed to move out to grow and reproduce in an Earth soil, which is exactly what must have happened if this theory be true. But as all this presumably occurred a billion or more years ago, when the Earth was young and the other planet only freshly broken up, perhaps this is too much verification to hope for now, as it would demand survival of the germ of life, under most unpropitious conditions, over an utterly unreasonable span of time.

Travel by Light Pressure

But in 1871 another possibility of space transport was opened up, though it was not realized at the time. James Clerk-Maxwell, the Scottish physicist, predicted from physical theory that light should exert a slight pressure as it fell upon any surface. This was confirmed in 1900 by the Russian P. Lebedev, and shortly after actually measured by Nichols and Hull in this country. They found the pressure very feeble, the total for noonday sunlight on a square foot of the Earth's surface being only about a ten millionth of a pound.

However, within a couple of years the Swedish physical chemist Svante Arrhenius explained that even this slight pressure would be enough to drive very minute particles, such as bacteria or spores, outward into space at high speeds. It would all depend upon their sizes. If they were small enough, their surface areas would be so large relative to their masses that the light pressure (acting on areas) would exceed the gravitational pull (acting on masses), and the particles would fly away from the Sun. You can illustrate the idea quite simply with a slice of bread. When you blow against the whole slice, its weight prevents any movement. But now break up the slice into crumbs. Obviously it now exposes much more surface, though the total weight remains the same. Again blow on it, and the crumbs fly away.

At any rate, Arrhenius thus explained how spores and bacteria could be driven from the upper reaches of the Earth's atmosphere outward through space, perhaps to Mars. He also pointed out that if the particular speck of life got stuck to a somewhat larger speck of dust, too heavy for light pressure to predominate, then the gravitational pull would take over and carry it sunward, say from Mars to Earth. Thus, two-way travel could be provided, either inward or outward, and any planet could be seeded with life from any other.

The Perils of Space Travel

However, the problem still remains: Can a spore or bacterium survive such a space trip? For it will be traveling naked through space, without benefit of pressurized cabin or air-conditioning or even cruder natural covering. Arrhenius carefully considered at least two phases of this problem: the extreme cold of interplanetary and interstellar space, and how long a time it would take. He argued that such simple life units, if thoroughly dry, could survive mere cold for hundreds, perhaps thousands of years. This may be possible, having been recently partly confirmed when a sample of blue-green algae, preserved dry for over a century between paper sheets in the herbarium of a Florida museum, was taken out and wet, whereupon it began to grow and even reproduce. Arrhenius further argued that at maximum speeds possible with light pressure a particle could travel to another planet within weeks or months, get out of the solar system in a little over a year, and even reach the very nearest star and a possible planet system in about nine thousand years.

But though that made such transport seem possible to Arrhenius, a far more serious difficulty has since arisen, as we have learned more of the effects of ultraviolet light. We have found this short-wave radiation a most effective germ and spore killer, and use it systematically for sterilizing purposes, effective even with only short exposures. Here on the surface of the Earth we are fortunately protected from the intense ultraviolet radiation given off by the Sun, for we are shielded most effectively by certain ionized layers in our upper atmosphere which absorb almost all this deadly radiation. But in airless outer space there would be no such shielding, and we can be quite certain that no spore or germ would have any chance of staying alive during even a short journey of weeks from one planet to another, and certainly not during the thousands of years for any trip from one solar system to another. So now the real objection to any theory of transplantation of life across space is the presence there of the virulent killer, ultraviolet radiation. And to that we must now add other deadly killers more recently discovered. There are the cosmic rays, violent in their energy crossing space, stepped down in violence only as they make their way down through our atmosphere. And our space probes have revealed X rays from bursts of solar flares, powerful and frequent enough to catch and destroy the life of any spore or bacterium in unprotected transit.

Also we must not overlook the fact already noted, that in any case the Transplantation Theory still does not answer our basic question: How did life originally originate, either here on Earth or elsewhere on some more or less distant planet? All it does is to put off the problem to some indefinite and inaccessible place where we cannot study it at all. It therefore offers no satisfaction to anyone, unless perhaps as a way of stalling off to avoid facing a really troublesome and disturbing problem here on Earth. But that, of course, would be just a bit of escapism.

Chapter 9

THE EMERGENCE OF LIFE

The word "emergence" in the title of this chapter is used in a rather specific sense. Apparently it was first so used in 1875 by the science philosopher George Henry Lewes in a book on *Problems of Life and Mind*. By the word emergence he meant any appearance of higher attributes and behavior as the result of new working combinations of lower units of matter and energy.

To use a modern illustration, two basic kinds of units, the lightweight electrons negatively charged and the heavyweight protons positively charged, in variant working combinations give rise to differing atoms of the several elements, which then behave chemically and physically in their distinctive ways. The higher-stage atoms *emerge* from combinations of lower-stage electrons and protons.

In their turn, the several atoms, in various working combinations, give rise to molecules, ranging from the simplest inorganic compounds to the most elaborate organic compounds, each with its emergent attributes and behavior. And these, in suitable working combinations, chemical and structural, give rise to life units with new attributes at an even higher emergent level. And so on, at still higher levels emerge units which consciously perceive, and which think reflectively, and even develop such general conceptions as emergence.

Emergence, however, is not a magic word which by itself explains everything or anything. It is merely a convenient term for summing up the undoubted fact that in the workings of Nature, units at any level do, in suitable combinations, give rise to units higher in level of attributes and behavior. The task still remains of explaining how and why each combination, by virtue of its own inherent attributes working together, does give rise to the different higher-level attributes and behavior.

Explaining, of course, comes more easily at the simpler lower levels. Thus, we are apparently approaching basic understanding of how the properties of the atoms of the elements arise from their subatomic compositions and structures. But at the next level of properties arising from compounding of atoms into molecules, explanation becomes difficult. Why, for instance, should two invisible gases, hydrogen and oxygen, combine into water, a visible liquid with the property of wetness? And we certainly cannot say much for our understanding of the emergence of life from the chemistry and physics of organic materials and structures. Here our far more complex and difficult puzzle is so far only partially solved. But here, too, as at each lower step of emergence, our scientific experience assures us that we are dealing with causes we must call "natural." Nowhere, at any stage of emergence, need we rely upon the touch of any magic wand.

Some idea of the reasons why variant combinations of protons and electrons produce variant elements can be gathered from Chapter 4. And how they were originally formed in the million-degree temperatures of star interiors or celestial explosions is told in my chapters on "In the Beginning" and "The Stars in Their Courses" of my earlier book, *Our Emerging Universe*. But at the next-higher emergence, the chemical compoundings of atoms into molecules go on only at temperatures ranging from a few thousands of degrees downward, and so occur only on star surfaces and among the still-cooler globes and stray materials scattered through their planet systems and in outer space. And at still another emergent stage, the units of life can carry on only within the narrow temperature range between the boiling and freezing points of water, though some can temporarily survive dry and frozen, and others can maintain body heat above the freezing point even when the surrounding temperatures are lower.

Life from the Nonliving

After 1859 and Darwin's success in convincing the scientific world that life had actually evolved, an inevitable consequence was a derivative conviction that life must somehow have originated from nonliving matter, presumably by some natural process.

But also, after 1862 and Pasteur's thorough disproof of the spontaneous generation of even lowly bacteria, scientific opinion settled down to an opposite attitude so overwhelming that it literally became a negative dogma, expressed therefore very properly in Latin, *Omne vivum ex vivo* ("All life comes from life").

A clash of opinions (both scientific) became inevitable. But the stalwart Evolutionists, while recognizing the force of Pasteur's proofs, began looking for reasonable exceptions. Thus, Haeckel in 1866 held that in some remotely early stage of the Earth's history, when conditions were suitably different, life of the very simplest possible kind—"homogeneous, structureless, amorphous lumps of protein"—could have arisen by processes which today we cannot describe because of sheer lack of factual data. But by 1878 he was imagining the simplest living thing, the "nonnucleated moneron," crystallizing out mechanically from suitable inanimate matter.

Huxley, on the other hand, in 1868 was describing present particles of protoplasm without nuclei, peopling "an immense extent of the bottom of the sea," and was presently to suggest (and later abandon) an origin in a deep-sea bottom-living slime which he called bathybius.

Less cautious was Henry Charlton Bastian, who in 1872 began defying Pasteur's proofs, asserting that life must somehow have had to originate from nonliving matter by natural processes, and indeed probably can and is doing so today. But his eager experimental efforts to prove this were rather unconvincing, as Pasteur and others readily proved them carelessly done. His related chemical theories were also rather dubious, and he finally retreated to invisible submicroscopic sizes for his new life forms. But he did fight on stalwartly through four decades to keep alive the vital basic idea which eventually did prevail that living matter must have been born from nonliving matter by entirely natural processes.

Meanwhile there were others who acquiesced in this general assumption, and theorized, usually nebulously, and unrealistically, on how life could have begun. Thus, E. Pflüger, in 1875, started from cyanogen (CN), built up in a red-hot stage of the cooling Earth, but went on to an impossible protein chemistry. In 1899 F. Allen employed completely unknown causes and a most indefinite chemistry. Even August Weismann, in 1902, offered minute "biophores" originating under novel conditions not even defined. The fact was, of course, that not enough was then actually known of the conditions of the early Earth, nor of the detailed structures and chemistries of the lowest life forms which had to come into being. This lack would take decades to fill, and is frankly not completely filled even today.

So Henry Fairfield Osborn, writing in 1917 on *The Origin and Evolution of Life,* found this same lack of essential background knowledge. He tried to keep his own approach fresh by abstaining from reading current writings of others on the subject. Yet he did not have enough fresh materials of his own, and could not escape being misled by two important ideas then prevailing on the history of the Earth. One was the Chamberlin-Moulton Planetesimal Theory of an Earth born cold. The other was Lord Kelvin's low estimate of the age of the Earth at less than a hundred million years. The first theory led Osborn to conclude that the "primordial atmosphere . . . contained free oxygen" and that "the earliest forms of life were probably dependent on atmospheric oxygen," though he did note extant doubts by others on both points. Kelvin's low estimate he called "a conclusion very unwelcome to evolutionists." As a leading authority on paleontology, he concurred with other biologists that a much greater age was necessary for the evolution of existing life, but he nevertheless yielded to Kelvin's great authority and even dismissed as unreliable the first results of age determinations by radioactivity methods suggested by Rutherford, though they already indicated the long age needed by the Evolutionists, since decisively confirmed as at least forty times the maximum allowed by Kelvin.

Emergence of the Preliving

But in 1929 the rather iconoclastic British biologist J. B. S. Haldane broached the fresh idea that life must have begun in an environment lacking in oxygen. And in 1936 the Russian Alexander I. Oparin, in his book *The Origin of Life*, stated this possibility, but without drawing any critical conclusions from it. But finally, as we noted in the preceding chapter, Urey had concluded by 1951 that the Earth globe had passed through an early period of superheating, with loss of any original atmosphere, and on subsequent surface cooling had acquired a new atmosphere, lacking in free oxygen but containing nitrogen, ammonia, methane, carbon dioxide, carbon monoxide, hydrogen sulfide—some or all. And the surface waters would dissolve some of these, thus sharing in their obviously mephitic character. Into this seemingly forbidding environment, and out of such dubious raw materials, the first life must have been born. The elements composing them were right enough, but their compounds sounded forbidding.

However, with such raw materials in mind, Urey suggested an experiment which his student Stanley L. Miller proceeded to perform, reporting on it in 1953. Through mixtures of just such raw materials he ran electric charges for periods of about a week, in some experiments using a silent discharge, in others a high-frequency 60,000-volt spark discharge. The end products varied somewhat, but most important, careful chemical analyses revealed that significant amounts of several amino acids, plus simpler organic compounds, had been formed. And as amino acids are the building blocks of the proteins, the characteristic constituents of living matter, the experiments demonstrated one way by which the raw materials quite surely present in the early Earth could, by natural means such as electric discharges, have been built up through a first crucial step toward living matter.

Confirming experiments have of course been performed by others. And those further experiments have been revealingly varied. Thus, ultraviolet light has proved even more effective than electric discharges, and because the early atmosphere lacked in oxygen, more ultraviolet light could have penetrated to the Earth's surface to become an important factor in producing the supply of preliving amino acids. Even the obvious objection that such radiation would then kill any proteins produced could be overcome if those living substances were then submerged more or less deeply in water, mud, or soil.

Evidently, the next step would be the building up of such proteins from the available amino acids. One possible way was by applying heat, and trying this, another fruitful discovery was made in the laboratory directed by Sidney W. Fox at Florida State University. Not only did heat help build up combinations of amino acids, but it also produced new and needed amino acids. Important, too, it disclosed a series of chemical steps closely paralleling known chemical pathways in the living processes of existing organisms. While the details are of course understandable only by the expert biochemist, the broad facts do suggest that existing chemical pathways in present-day organisms may prove to be really useful clues in tracing the processes involved in the originating of primitive life. Also, it is evident that heat may have been the most important over-all factor at several stages in that original transformation of non-living raw materials into living matter.

Some such heat may have been provided in the initial cooling of the Earth crust to the point where atmospheric water vapor first condensed and settled down into ocean and lake basins as hot fluid water. Or it may even later have been heat of hot springs derived from subterranean volcanic lavas. Such hot springs even now often abound with simple life forms such as algae of the most primitive types. Or the heat may have been that of shallow waters of pond or shore pool nearly dried out, in which a concentration of preliving matter, perhaps in a natural laboratory of moist mud or clay, went through the critical transformation into the proteins of the first life.

It should perhaps be noted that only the first of these sources of heat depended upon a "hot stage" of the Earth crust, the other two being quite consistent with even a "cold Earth" origin. And only the first demands a very early origin for the initial life. The other two give a much wider range of time for all the steps involved, right up to the very present.

The Build-up of Proteins

Another suggestive discovery from these Fox experiments with heat was the effect of the presence or absence of water. Because of the large content of water in all living cells, and the fact that all known primitive organisms live in water or at least some moisture, it had always been assumed that life must have begun in the waters of the ocean or some lake, pond, or pool loaded with suitable raw materials, such as minerals in solution and a sufficient supply of amino acids or other preliving compounds, all of which Haldane has described as a "hot dilute soup." But now Fox found that important steps could better occur by application of dry heat (150° to 200° C), well above the boiling point of water but not hot enough to char.

His problem at the time was to build up assortments of amino acids into peptide chains simpler and smaller than the elaborate proteins of life. As early as 1907 Emil Fischer had succeeded in synthesizing an eighteen-unit proteinlike compound out of two kinds of amino acids, a pioneer achievement followed by others. And the Fox effort was directed toward building up even more complex composite chain molecules (polymers) under conditions which could have existed in the ancient natural environment. With the dry heat applied to mixes of common amino acids (predominantly aspartic and glutamic acids, already artificially produced and quite common in living proteins) he succeeded in producing a polymer made up of eighteen different amino acids, which was then found to be like natural protein in at least ten of its properties.

This does not mean that he had produced living protein. He had merely begun a probably long series of hopeful experimental tries during which he or someone else might be lucky enough to hit on some combination which spelled life or near-life, all of which would take much time and innumerable experiments. Nature, of course, had had millions of years of time and no end of variant environmental circumstances to achieve the same start. And once the happy right variant had produced the first unit of life, raw materials enough were surely present, plus time enough, for that unit to absorb and grow, divide and multiply its kind, and change to better chemistries and structural forms on a course of differentiating and improving evolution. In all of this the first step seemed exceedingly important. For as someone has quoted approvingly and hopefully, the old Chinese proverb says, "A journey of a thousand miles begins with but a single step."

But Sidney Fox was too informed and realistic to rely solely on expectations based on a single crucial step. He knew very well that the problem was not likely to prove as simple as that. For one thing, he was familiar with the many ideas broached in an already-extensive literature reporting the work of others. And in August 1957 he had been one of a strong top team of American researchers who took part in the Moscow Symposium of the International Union of Biochemistry on the subject "The Origin of Life on the Earth." And that must have been a most informing and stimulating, yet humbling, experience.

The 1957 Moscow Symposium

The conference on "The Origin of Life on the Earth" had been initiated in 1955 by the International Union of Biochemistry, which also suggested Moscow as the meeting place in recognition of the active interest in and important research work done by Russian scientists on this problem. This was no doubt coupled with a growing respect for Russian scientific capacities and achievements as demonstrated by their independent development of the A- and H-bombs. That respect was to be further enhanced, within a couple of months following the conference, by their projecting the first Sputnik into a space orbit.

The Academy of Sciences of the USSR issued the invitations and organized the program, and academician Alexander I. Oparin, himself a pioneer student of the problem, opened the six days of reports and discussion. More than a hundred scientists from seventeen countries, including astronomers, geologists, biologists, geneticists, and particularly biochemists, contributed papers and otherwise took part in covering all phases of the subject. All were experts in their fields, and many had done special work on this particular problem. The symposium began by considering the astronomical and geological origins and conditions on the primal Earth, following with the many possible origins and evolutions of preliving substances, then of proteins, nucleo-proteins, and enzymes, of organic structures and functioning, and finally of photosynthesis, thus covering every aspect of what seemed at all pertinent. Never before had such an array of competent and informed specialists been brought together to attack this problem so thoroughly.

Yet in the background it was reported that one could sense a feeling of unease. Until the year before, the Russian biologists had been under the tight political restraint of the Communist Party line, which required the acceptance of Michurian inherit-ance of acquired characteristics, and the rejection of Mendelian genetics as developed by the free research elsewhere in the world on the basis of chromosomes, genes, and DNA. Only in 1956 had Premier Khrushchev, while disowning Stalinism, implied a freeing of Soviet genetic science. The Russians were therefore just emerging from a period of intellectual restraint and con-ditioning and were still uncertain of their freedom to think and to speak. At the 1957 symposium, out of courtesy at least, the guest Mendelian geneticists had to be listened to with respect, and several bolder Russian scientists took occasion to declare themselves in agreement. Only one mild attack was actually made on "the chromosomal theory of heredity," by alleging that the geneticists had dismissed "the gene as a corpuscle of a chromosome" and "put forward the molecule of DNA as the unit of heredity, ascribing genetic properties to it," as if DNA were not obviously the chemical description of the gene. Others among the Russians, less bold or more devious, but apparently favoring the unorthodox "chromosomal theory," threw sops to orthodoxy by ambiguously favorable references to Michurinism or by approvingly quoting Engels' dictum of 1878 that "Life is the mode of existence of albuminous bodies," a statement which actually merely expressed his acceptance of the prevailing biologic opinion of his day, though it has since been elevated by implication to an original discovery and overtly to a Party dogma because of its "materialist" connotations. But despite such hedgings, let it be said that no one who took part in the conference failed to realize that the problem of hereditary replication was very much a vital part of the general problem of the origin of life.

Yet any critical reading of the 656 crowded pages of the published transcript of the reports and discussion gives one the impression that much, perhaps most of the material presented will eventually prove to be beside the point. Not that anyone can conclusively say, at this present stage of scientific development, what will or will not remain ultimately pertinent. We can only expect, as the multifarious research goes on, that key discoveries will disclose just what is significant and what is not, enabling us to concentrate attention and work on those fewer factors and subproblems which are surely and directly meaningful. But even now, with the knowledge and insights we already have, there appear certain aspects which must obviously be included in our own less technical coverage of the problem of life's origin.

The Individuation of Life

The interest and activity of the Russian scientists in the problem arose largely under the leadership of Oparin. As early as 1924 he began writing on the subject, and his 1936 book on *The Origin of Life* became the classic study of the problem for the next couple of decades. He is still a leader whose recent books represent vanguard thinking on the subject. In his *Life; Its Nature, Origin and Development* (1960) he did retain some Michurinist addictions. But in his *The Chemical Evolution of Life* (1964) he seems at last fully realistic and open-minded.

His scientific reputation really rests, however, on an outstanding idea broached in his 1936 book. That idea is here described as the Individuation of Life. Oparin had been following the 1931 and later reports of the Dutch colloidal chemist H. G.

Bungenberg de Jong on his experiments with what he called coazervates, formed as droplets when he mixed certain organic colloids. Basically, colloids consist of particles suspended in some medium (usually liquid or even gas) because they are so small that they are bounced about by the impacts of the moving molecules around them, and therefore cannot settle down and separate out. If, in addition, the particles have electric charges which are alike and therefore repel each other, this helps keep them in permanent suspension. What de Jong had done was to mix organic colloids with particles of opposite electric charges which attracted each other and caused a clumping together into larger coazervate droplets. And while the materials with which de Jong was working were not those involved in the chemical origin of life, Oparin became interested because here was a natural method by which proteins could also be aggregated into separate life units. Some experimental work does tend to confirm this possibility, but it must also be admitted that there seem to be several factors involved in such aggregating and individuation which are not too well understood even today. Thus Sidney Fox, in recent experiments with heat used in polymerizing proteinoid combinations of amino acids, unexpectedly got minute spherules—round, oblate, and irregular in shape and suggestively in the bacterial range of size. So individuation can apparently be brought about in several ways which (to quote Fox) "could have occurred on the primitive earth, before the establishment of science apparatus supply firms; only the natural geological crucible would have been required."

One feature of the Fox spherules is particularly significant: they act as if they were osmotic. When they are immersed in a strong solution of ordinary salt, they shrink in volume, which suggests that the interface boundary between each spherule and the solution is semipermeable as the membranes of living cells are, and acts as they do. This means that it is permeable to water but less so to other substances, such as the salt molecules, large protein molecules, etc., so that the flow of such substances into and out of the spherule is controlled by the ordinary physicochemical factors of osmosis operating in a living cell. Thereby suitable groups of biochemical capabilities can be packaged into and operated in separate and individual units. The units have thus become individuated.

Oparin, following de Jong, had called this process coazervation, but his great central contribution was that he first realized and stated just how significant it was practically in the originating and evolution of life. Unfortunately, however, he did not sum this up in a clean and plain phrase or sentence but scattered it, almost as an incidental idea, over several pages of technical talk, mostly chemical, which almost hid it from sight.*

Summed up (it is hoped more neatly) that idea was:

The formation of individual and separate self-contained unit packages of substances reacting physicochemically with the environment *for the first time made possible the operation of natural selection* to evolve those units toward stability, permanence, and other improving. It was therefore the true beginning of the evolution of life forms.

Oparin, despite his diffuse statement of it, did recognize the importance of this, for he considered it the stage at which life began. And his distracting talk was largely to explain just how it was important, of which more as we go on.

Let us start with any sample of Haldane's "hot dilute soup," containing a suitable assortment of preliving substances. As a soup in some hollow of the Earth surface, it was an unstable and impermanent entity. The Sun's heat might evaporate and thicken it, even dry it out; or rain might thin it and cause it to overflow and drain away. Or it might intermix with something else and lose its identity. It lacked continuity because it was not wholly self-contained. It is hard to think how natural selection

* Pp. 190–95 in the English (Dover, 1953) edition of *The Origin of Life.*

could possibly have progressively improved its chemical and structural organization.

But comes the moment when heat (or any other natural factor) causes the amino acids not only to polymerize into proteins but to aggregate into spherules enclosed in osmotic membranes. Now each is a self-contained and discrete unit, surviving or not on its own. If its chemistry or internal structure is not right for continuing operation, it stops operating and dissolves away. If both of these are merely right enough, it may or may not go on, depending on external conditions and competition for raw materials needed. If it contains or absorbs a mineral catalyst or happens to form an enzyme-protein which helps speed up its chemistry, its chances for survival are increased. If it changes (even accidentally) for better or worse, its chances for survival are made better or worse. If it absorbs food well and grows and then divides, either by mechanical breakup or by internal tensions, it becomes two of its kind and doubles the chances for survival, and doubles them again and again with each succeeding generation. On the other hand, every time it changes, it may be for the worse, so stability in what has already survived is most likely to be for the best. Yet change will occur, and natural selection must pick and sort, inevitably causing evolution and improving fitness for survival, which at this stage usually means better internal chemistries and operating organizations and structures. And very soon (within some millions of years) it will become a remarkably efficient, and compact, and most mysterious cell laboratory, the basis of all life to come.

Note here that organic evolution has started. Where it will go we shall learn later in the book.

Life's Processing of Energy

We identify that cell laboratory as the unit of life, lived either singly in microorganisms or as collaborating multiples in larger organisms. But being alive, just what does it do? In another form, this is obviously again the old question: what is life? But in the answering, this calls for description, rather than definition.

Essentially, the life unit draws in substances which possess chemically stored energy, and then extracts and uses such energy in its processes and activities. Some of the substances are retained as building materials or are altered, with everything unusable then eliminated as waste. In all of this, however, the life unit maintains its operative continuity, though it may change in form, grow in bulk, and multiply itself by replication.

The very first life forms must have derived whatever energy they used from substances built up by natural chemical processes without the aid of any previous life. Also, free oxygen was probably not available for either building up or extracting energy from such substances. That all of this is possible and likely is evidenced by the existence even today of lowly anaerobic bacteria which can live only when oxygen is absent, and must therefore draw upon the energy from simple compounds composed entirely of other elements. Until life appeared to start consuming it, the accumulated supply of such compounds was probably plentiful in the Earth's surface waters, often much concentrated in evaporating ponds or shore pools, and then perhaps held conveniently upon the catalytic surfaces of clay or soil particles or crystals.

But the accumulated and currently replenished supply of such anaerobic-energy sources would be limited and, with the multiplying of life units, in due time exhausted. Besides, the extractable energy in such substances was meager, quite insignificant compared with another potential source of inexhaustible energy continually pouring in upon the Earth in the form of radiations from the Sun. Any organism which could avail itself of this supply of energy would have an enormous advantage in the struggle for existence, living and growing abundantly while others might starve, and so multiplying its kind without limit.

The solar radiation arrived in varying wave lengths and frequencies. One broad band of longer, low-frequency waves came
through as heat, which, as we have seen, may have played a
major role in both activating and giving individuate form to the
first life substance. Another band of short, high-frequency waves
arrived, mostly as ultraviolet radiation, which may have been
the real activator of life, but was also a potent destroyer of life
and therefore suspect as too dangerous. But also, in between,
came a band of visible light, colored by wave lengths and
frequencies to reds and oranges. And this band, perhaps because
it was neither destructive to life nor burningly hot, proved best
for absorption by the organism as a source of usable energy.
Or perhaps the energy packages were just right in size and timing (there being talk at this point of a resonance factor) to lift
the chemical compounds involved to higher energy levels. At
any rate, we know that the life cells must in fact have mutated
to be able to absorb these red and orange waves, while rejecting and reflecting away those not used, which discarded portion
of visible light comes back to us as the greens of our vegetation.

The Capture of Sunlight

This process of energy capture is carried on by a green-reflect-
ing substance called chlorophyll giving color to chloroplast
granules within the plant cells. The process itself is named
photosynthesis, from the Greek meaning "light build-up." It
utilizes water (in land plants from the moist soil) and carbon
dioxide from the air, and out of these builds up carbohydrates
composed of carbon, hydrogen, and oxygen. Examples of these
are starch ($C_6H_{10}O_5$) and the simplest sugar ($C_6H_{12}O_6$),
which are readily converted one into the other merely by adding
or subtracting a water molecule. Given off as by-products are
oxygen molecules (O_2) and, surprisingly, water. By other and

later additions, the carbohydrates are built up into lipids (fats) and proteins.

Already in the early 1600s the Flemish chemist van Helmont, by growing a willow tree for five years in a pot of soil, during which the tree became 164 pounds heavier while the soil lost only two ounces, discovered that the plant drew its food supply not from the soil, as everyone had assumed, but, he guessed, from the water he had added. In 1727 the English physician Stephen Hales found that carbon dioxide from the air was also needed, a gas which ironically van Helmont had discovered. This was confirmed in the 1770s by Joseph Priestley, the English Unitarian minister and chemist, who was followed in 1779 by the Dutch physician Jan Ingelhousz, who assumed that the carbon dioxide was split up, and accordingly worked out the formula for the chemical reaction in producing starch by photosynthesis, in effect thus:

$$6CO_2 + 5H_2O + \text{light} \rightarrow C_6H_{10}O_5 + 6O_2$$

This seemed altogether right until 1938, when the American biochemists Samuel Ruben and Martin D. Kamen, using a traceable heavy form of oxygen (O^{18}), discovered that the carbon dioxide does not split up at all, but is incorporated into the carbohydrate directly. Instead, the water molecules are split up by the light energy. Half the resulting oxygen is then released into the air, while the corresponding half of the hydrogen joins the carbohydrate. The other halves then reunite again as water, but in doing so release energy which is then used to build up a transitory substance, ATP (short for adenosine triphosphate), which is a high-energy package now very familiar to biochemists in many processes, serving in this instance to activate formation of the carbohydrate which stores the energy for later use by the plant. So the modern over-all chemical formula (leading to a sugar instead of starch) reads:

$$6CO_2 + 12H_2O + \text{light} \rightarrow C_6H_{12}O_6 + 6O_2 + 6H_2O$$

The steering agent in all this is a pair of complex substances, together the green chlorophyll, closely related chemically to the hemoglobin of red blood cells, but with a magnesium atom at the center instead of an iron atom. The photosynthetic process occurs in two principal stages—first, the breakup of water activated by sunlight, and second, a locking up by carbohydrate formation of the energy released by reuniting part of the water. The first process of course needs light. The second can be done in the dark.

Much current research is now being directed to synthesizing chlorophyll artificially in the laboratory, not only to advance basic understanding but also in the utilitarian hope that we can somehow shortcut the production of foodstuffs, without the heavy labors of farming. There are even some claims that this marvel has already been done, but in such minute quantities that so far any backyard gardener can do much better. Yet the scientific importance of such a synthesis cannot be overemphasized.

But the big fact is of course that in the world of Nature the achievement of photosynthesis by the plants, at a very early stage of evolution, had several highly revolutionary effects. First, the plants themselves gained a virtually limitless source of energy for carrying on their own life and increase. Second, the release of oxygen by the breakup of water eventually gave our atmosphere its present abundant supply of that precious element in free and usable form. Third, a side effect of this was conversion, high in the atmosphere, of oxygen into ozone by absorption and stopping of the ultraviolet light, thus largely shielding the life below from this deadly radiation. Fourth, the increase of plant life provided an ample supply of energy-packed foodstuffs for a new world of animal life. And fifth, the supply of oxygen made possible the easy and sufficient energy release necessary for the highly active lives of those animals.

The Extracting of Stored Energy

Back in the 1770s Lavoisier realized that animals derived the energies they used by a process akin to ordinary combustion, in which oxygen combining with carbon and hydrogen produced heat and other energies. The oxygen was breathed into the lungs, and carbon dioxide and water vapor breathed out. This and the energy extractions which go on in between are now described broadly as respiration. Heat was produced, for the body warmed up. And other energies were expended in physical movements. But just where in the body the combustions occurred and why they were not the hot flames of burning were details not understood until recently.

Today we realize that plants, too, despite their seeming inertness, use energy to carry on their physiologic processes of chemical change, growth, reproduction, etc., and that they derive such energy by essentially the same process as the animals, basically a process of oxidation akin to combustion. The green plants, however, first store that energy by photosynthesis within themselves and then draw upon it as needed, while the animals, directly as herbivores, indirectly as carnivores, parasitically consume such plant stores of energy as foodstuffs. A few degenerate plants have also descended to similar parasitism upon green plants, but remain vegetatively inert instead of becoming active and alert in the animal fashion.

It is obviously a prime advantage to all life forms that they do not extract the energy they use by a process of hot combustion, which would mean only consuming destruction in burning flame. But how is this managed? What makes possible what we may call "cool combustion"? The answer lies in the previous storage of energy by the chemical building up of complex carbohydrates and derivative fats and proteins.

When life first began, there was probably present in the atmosphere and surface waters a considerable supply of the hydro-carbon methane (CH_4), an excellent energy source. It is, for instance, an important ingredient of our everyday fuel gas. Why could not the first life have drawn upon it for needed energy? Apparently because it oxidizes (burns) with a hot flame. And the reason for that is its simple molecular composition, which only permits oxidation to occur in one single step. The carbon and oxygen simultaneously combine with oxygen to form carbon dioxide and water, and all the energy is released in one hot instant.

Carbohydrate storage of energy for life use is quite another matter. The carbohydrate molecule is a complex of many atoms which can be taken apart bit by bit, releasing small portions of energy step by step, and under positive controls such as enzymes which prevent any runaway combustion in one hot and disastrous step. In the end, of course, by the complex total process of respiration, the carbohydrate is completely taken apart and oxidized to its eventual molecules of carbon dioxide and water.

In contrast, a lowly yeast cell, immersed in a sugar solution, can take the sugar molecules only partially apart by a controlled but limited process we call fermentation. The yeast extracts only about 5 per cent of the total energy stored in the sugar, but while that is distinctly an uneconomical use of available energy, it is plenty for the needs of the yeast, which has nothing to do but live on, grow, and reproduce itself by simple fission. It does not even make use of the alcohol it leaves, though we do. So the yeast seems of more purpose to us than to itself, as it has nothing whatever to do in life beyond keeping its kind alive, but doing that is enough to have caused natural selection to preserve and evolve it.

Another probable reason for storage of energy in complex carbohydrates is so they can then be built up further into derivative fats and proteins otherwise essential for life itself. But an even more direct benefit doubtless arises from the ease with which they can be altered and adapted for various uses in the organism. Thus, in plants insoluble starch ($C_6H_{10}O_5$) can be effectively stored but also readily altered to soluble sugar ($C_6H_{12}O_6$) by adding a molecule of water, when it can be transported, wherever needed, by the juices of the plant. The same sugar, glucose, in the animal bloodstream, travels freely to any spot in the body and enters or leaves any cell through its membrane. But it is readily altered to starchlike glycogen and stored in a liver reserve, or locally in a muscle cell, ready to be converted back to glucose for oxidation and release of its energy to contract the muscle or do other bits of physicochemical work elsewhere in the body.

But originally and basically, the evolutionary reason for complex carbohydrate storage of energy might well have been to permit multiple-step extraction of that energy for living use, while avoiding single-step combustion by burning flame.

Conserving by Replication

Evolution is a process in which we are prone to think more of the changes and rather belittle the conserving of the continuing stabilities. Actually those stabilities represent fitnesses already achieved by earlier changes, embodied in an organism continually maintaining its tested working coordinations. Changes do come into that continuity by random mutations. Most, we know, are harmful, but some few either add to fitness under old environmental conditions or adapt to fit altered conditions. Natural selection is accomplished automatically by a discarding of the unfit and a preserving of the fit in the struggle for existence. But from there on the retaining of the fitnesses, old and new, in working coordination, becomes necessary. This is of course done by faithful replication of all that has been attained by the process of reproducing the successive generations.

We already know much of how that is done by the genetic substances DNA and RNA. While surprisingly simple in basic plan, they are most intricately variable in detail setup, and must necessarily be so to control replication of the equally intricate details of living matter. But how did they evolve, both the living matter and the replicating controls?

At present we can only guess. For the record of the ancient beginnings are completely gone. And in the face of deadly competition from higher life forms, there can now go on no comparable prolonged evolvement of equivalent forms of primal life, in part because the critical preconditions have undoubtedly also changed. So we have nothing really to go on, and can only hope that in our laboratories, or perhaps on some younger world out in space, we can someday observe life in the actual process of thrilling emergence.

Undoubtedly the beginning was the simplest possible physically and chemically, and went on with provoking slowness toward the elaborations we now observe. We can think of a first unit of life, self-contained by an enclosing membrane, drawing in needed matter and energy from an ambient "soup," yet stably self-continuing in chemical composition and processing. That unit, just by growing, might become too big in bulk for its surface of membrane and so be held back in functioning until it divided, either by accidental mechanical breakup or by internal tensions from its oversize, thus multiplying in numbers of units of feasible working size, yet remaining the same chemically in both substance and processing, all without any special means of genetic control. To that, in time, first simple, then increasingly elaborate genetic controls could have been progressively added.

So no doubt the initial stability and functioning of any primal life were at the outset very low, but step by step, taking all the time needed, the improving elaborations of substances and processes, of genetic and enzyme controls, would be added to make the forms of life more fully fit and variantly adaptive. Individual adaptive fitness was always the prime need, but because in general the most fit life forms tended to prevail over the less fit, there resulted an incidental and broad upward evolution of life forms. That evolution toward higher life forms was, however, full of exceptions and retreats, so that only by and large would it have been progressive.

In that upward climb of life all the truly primal forms seem to have been wiped out. Or if some do in fact survive today, they are apparently too simple for us to identify as living. At least all the recognized survivor forms are essentially complex. Even those we consider most lowly, such as bacteria and blue-green algae, which have not yet concentrated their genetic matter into a central-cell nucleus, nevertheless have genes of DNA or RNA as means for stably continuous replication. Even a virus, so incomplete that it cannot feed itself, and which only intermittently seems to come alive in some living host cell, still has complex genes, from which fact some strongly suspect that it is not really a lowly life form, but an advanced one which has parasitically degenerated by discarding some of its functions. In short, none of the unit forms we know and can identify as living, however lowly we may regard them, is truly primal in simplicity but all are, in fact, already "fearfully and wonderfully made."

This is a background fact which should perhaps be remembered, if only dimly, as we now go on to trace the evolutions of the forms of life we know.

Chapter 10

OUR POOR RELATIONS

Our early relatives were a rather low lot, living by makeshift means and seemingly surviving only by sheer luck, prolific breeding, and predaceous habits. Also they were a motley crew, of many diverse forms, from the very simplest on to those of increasing complexity. As yet, of course, there were no higher forms of life, and even in our day they and their nearest kin comprise the great majority of living forms, both in numbers and in kinds. Because they are so many, it will be impossible to describe or even name them all, lest we compile a catalog rather than tell a story. Those few we do mention will somehow always be key characters in our story, chosen because they illustrate developments pertinent to our long ancestral climb.

In a very real sense, all of these early forms represented a number of rather basic experiments in ways and means of survival under the conditions then prevailing. One could say more vividly that they were Nature's first tryouts of ideas fitting for survival. But when we give Nature that capital N, we must be careful not to give it also human form, with the flowing whiskers of age and wisdom. As meant here, Nature consists of certain ways of physical and chemical behavior observed in things as they are, and does not imply a planning mind, a will to do, nor supernatural powers and direction. So when the words "experiment" and "tryout" are here used, they mean only this: Each new generation of a life form is broadly like its parent generation, but not exactly so, varying a bit here and there. Then automatically, in the struggle for existence, each variation must prove itself. If it gives advantage, it tends to survive with its possessor; if not, it tends to destroy its possessor and itself. If it gives advantage and so survives, it will tend to be inherited by the generations which follow. In effect, this is a selection for fitness, resulting in evolution by changes aiding survival. But such selection is wholly *natural*, and in it there is no need for a controlling conscious mind, no need for wisdom and planning, no will or purpose involved, nor supernatural powers and guidance. It is instead quite automatic, indeed inevitable.

And if we keep this process of natural selection in mind, we can abbreviate all our further discussions considerably. For it will be sufficient if we merely note that a given change or adaptation gives advantage. This may then be taken as the reason for its appearance, survival, and development. In short, the mere fact that any structure or function adds fitness for survival can be considered sufficient "reason why" for its existence and persistence. We have of course learned that there is much more behind it: the accidental and random mutations of genes, the natural selection of those proving advantageous, the preservation by transmission through heredity of those adding to fitness, the accumulation in time of added fitness, etc. But from here on, for our purposes there is no need to repeat this background enumeration and explanation. It will be enough if we can show that any given change has advantage in the struggle for existence; that is its sufficient reason for appearing and being.

Some few of the adaptive ideas "tried out" in early life forms proved so basic that they soon prevailed quite universally and still persist in higher forms of life. Others were more special and resulted in broadly differing groups of living beings, such as plants and animals, invertebrates and vertebrates, etc. Many more were so limited that they resulted in lesser groups, each divided into further subgroups, etc. Ever since Darwin convinced the scientific world of the fact of evolution, such groupings of life forms have been conceived on the basis of kinship through descent, in effect tracing and reconstructing in more or less detail the branching family tree of life. This is fundamentally what we are attempting here for our own ancestry, but it will not always be easy, particularly for those early ancestral relatives of ours.

Tracing Our Ancestry

Broadly we use three basic methods of tracing such kinships and lines of descent. One is by noting the family resemblances which distinguish each group of relatives from other less related groups, a comparison which goes into every detail of their structures and, on occasion, chemistries. The second is to trace the individual development of each being as it grows from its original egg cell on toward its final adult form, that development presumably following broadly the ancestral evolution and often indicating kinships not otherwise clear. And third, and a very important way, is to trace the evolution of ancestral life as preserved in the actual fossil remains found in the rock layers of the Earth crust. As we proceed with our story, we shall use all three methods, employing each as it proves revealing. Yet on occasion all three together will not be enough, and we shall find ourselves at a loss, with unfilled gaps in both the general family tree and in our own direct ancestry. Fortunately, however, the gaps will be minor except for a couple which are really important and difficult.

At the outset we face just such a major gap if we depend only on the fossil record of our earliest poor relations. But we know that all the multicelled organisms, both plant and animal, including Man himself, start their individual careers as single cells, and from that we reasonably infer that they all began their ancestral evolutions as single-celled organisms. Also, we find that the simplest plants and animals now existing are just such single cells, or near-cells such as bacteria. So almost certainly our earliest ancestors also were single-celled, or nearly so. But because such organisms are necessarily minute, usually soft-bodied, and often quite shapeless, they are not at all likely to leave meaningful impressions in the primeval mud later to become stratified rock. Yet we have found some rare fossil bacteria of early geologic dates, and now and then deposits of bog iron or of carbon in the form of graphite, all probably formed by bacteria, as well as ancient formations of limestone similar in structure to some now being produced by living plants, the single-celled algae. But these remains are not very illuminating, so for present purposes the useful fossil record of the earliest organisms can be considered as practically missing.

But in the course of ages some of the single-celled forms secreted hard coverings of lime or silica, such as the foraminifers and radiolarians (animals) and diatoms (plants). These coverings, on the deaths of the organisms, sank slowly through the waters to form fine bottom oozes. Also, in due time the single-celled aggregated into multicelled organisms, ever-increasing in size, and often these too formed hard and tough coverings or other parts of lime, silica, chitin, or cellulose. Occasionally these could themselves be preserved, or petrified by mineral replacement, or leave casts or impressions, giving a readable fossil record. Favoring fossil preservation of these early forms was the fact that they all lived in water, freely floating or anchored to the bottom, or crawling over or through its mud or sand. Then when they died, their chances of being buried in the mud and sand to be preserved as fossils were fairly good. It was because of this, and their own great profusion, that we now find their shells and other hard remains in great and revealing abundance. Yet there are still some major gaps in the record, due to the many land uplifts and erosions over intervals of millions of years, repeated again and again ever since these oldest of our good fossils of early life were formed.

Fossils as Time Markers

For the child playing on the shore, the shells he picks up and then casts aside are merely curious and pretty playthings. Even for the adult bather on the beach, such a shell is probably only dimly identified with a creature that lived and died in the nearby waters. Even for the avid shell collector it may be only a name and a possible specimen for his collection. But for the scientist unearthing these and other fossils from exposed rock beds, these are the relics of life that was lived in ancient days, and therefore full of meaning. Usually they are likely to be old acquaintances adding little knowledge that is new. That little may, however, be rather important. For if the familiar fossil is one known to have lived only in a limited period, it serves as a "time marker" or index fossil for identifying rocks of that period. If, on the other hand, the specimen is really hitherto unknown, its finder feels most lucky, and it becomes an object of intense interest, to be studied in every detail for anything significant. If it is found with index fossils, or bracketed between rocks dated by such fossils, it, too, can be dated on the geologic calendar. Least useful, perhaps, are those fossils not limited to any period but persisting down through the ages, for they have little time-marking value. An outstanding example is the lamp shell Lingula, still with us and hardly changed at all from its ancestors of half a billion years ago. It serves only as an ultimate example of ultraconservatism in the ever-changing world of life. Its real mystery is what combination of conditions and simple but seemingly adequate adaptation enabled it to survive so long unchanged.

Fossils vary a great deal in the detail and perfection of their preservation, ranging from mere footprints in the mud or castings of mere outer shapes to fine imprints of every detail, as of a leaf or an insect's wing, and mineralized preservations of every microscopic detail of plant or animal tissue. Obviously, finds of such rare perfection are real buried treasures delighting the scientist, who can compare them in detail with living forms and get a complete knowledge of the ancient creatures, not only in their structures, both gross and minute, but often of their very ways of life. It is by such comparative studies, in every detail possible with the materials at hand, that he then proceeds to piece together the evolutions and kinships of the forms of life, and so provides us with the family tree and the calendar of the long past. Here, simplifying the technicalities and sticking to essentials, is the resulting story he tells. Note, however, that as he tells it he now and then hesitates, frankly makes a guess, and even skips a bit when gaps in his known facts break the continuity of the full story he is trying to tell.

At the Threshold of Life

In a previous chapter we recognized the emerging of individual coazervate droplets as perhaps a first step in the transforming of nonliving to living forms, though we may question whether they should properly be called alive. We considered also some possible chemical steps induced by natural conditions (which we can perhaps duplicate in our laboratories) in an evolution from nonliving to living chemical compounds, and of the physical structures to go with them. We had a look at the viruses as a possible step forward (or perhaps backward) in chemical and physical evolution, but again had to question their being properly alive as they show no signs of life outside the living cells of some host organism, though they do grow and multiply in numbers after the fashion of real life, and do mutate after the manner of genes, which certainly belong in the realm of life.

But now we come to bacteria, next upward at least in the scale of size, roughly ten times the diameter and therefore a thousand times the bulk of the virus particles. The bacteria do grow and multiply outside of living tissues, and so can be considered as independently alive. They were first seen in 1683 by Leeuwenhoek through his fine magnifiers, but their real study began two centuries later when Pasteur proved their importance in causing disease. Since then they have been intensively studied and found both beneficial and harmful to mankind. Thus helpful are the decay bacteria which break down and dispose of dead tissues to form simpler chemical substances which can again be utilized in building living tissues. Such, too, are the various nitrifying bacteria, which either fix atmospheric nitrogen or modify unusable nitrogen compounds, making them usable by life in building needed proteins.

Bacteria are not only small but also of very few simple shapes: the spherical coccus (berry) forms; the rodlike bacillus (stick) forms; and the twisted (corkscrew) spirillum forms. They have little visible internal structure—the nuclear material, for instance, perhaps being diffused throughout the substance. A bacterium seems, in fact, to be hardly more than a bit of protoplasm of simple but definite structure (Figure 8). If conditions are favorable, it grows (which implies feeding by surface absorption) and quickly divides (on the general average about every twenty minutes). Its activity is normally simple and single, but its rapid multiplication in numbers makes that activity potentially great in harm or benefit. The bacteria thus represent recognizable life in an early, if not the earliest, form.

At this point that intriguing question arises: Are these early forms of life plants or animals? Because of their normal inertness, the bacteria are usually classed as plants, though some few do squirm about a bit, and none of them has chlorophyll. But many other undoubted plants also lack chlorophyll, and some even move about, at least in some early stage of development. So the line between plants and animals is not always clear, and this is so especially among the simpler life forms.

One solution of the problem is to accept them as in between and give them a class name that is neutral and noncommittal.

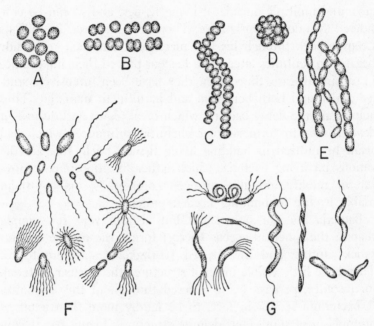

Fig. 8. Shapes of Bacteria.

Such a name has been provided for the next higher group of living beings, the one-celled organisms. They are called protists, from the Greek meaning the "very earliest," though this may prove to be a misnomer. Furthermore, this name does not always satisfy the scientific gentlemen who do classifying (they call themselves taxonomists). They are not just being contrary or fussy, however, for they often are quite right in placing a given protist among the protophytes (meaning "earliest plants"), or among the Protozoans (earliest animals), there being just no question what it is. But often, too, classifying quite as rightly, they thus manage to break up families made up quite obviously of close kin. And there still remain some few protists which are real puzzlers, dubiously right on the line between plants and animals. We shall have to return to this subject a bit later.

Amoeba, the Minimum Animal

Obviously among the simplest of the undoubted protozoans is *Amoeba proteus*, living in the bottom slime of stagnant pools and ditches. It is a tiny bit of naked protoplasm, a single cell without wall of fixed shape. Its substance is a transparent semifluid, viscous, and denser than the water in which it lives, and able to change its shape slowly as need requires. Without special organs of traveling, it can yet travel, simply by pushing out a part of its substance, then flowing into it, thus taking what we may call a step. That momentary protrusion has even been graced with the name of pseudopod, meaning "false foot" because it is obviously not a foot at all. When Amoeba comes upon a particle of food, say a bacterium, it merely flows about it in lieu of swallowing, proceeds to digest what it can use, and then flows away from the waste remains. Or it comes upon a grain of inedible sand, or something chemically damaging, whereupon it backs away in slow flowing retreat (Figure 9).

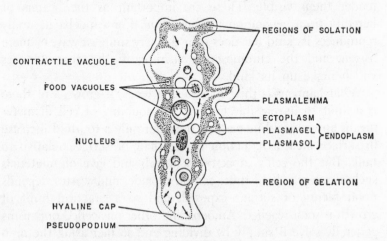

Fig. 9. The Protean Amoeba.

In its primitive way, Amoeba carries on all the basic activities characteristic of animal kind. Thus it breathes just by absorbing oxygen through its surface, combining it with the carbon and hydrogen of its food, and giving off the resulting excess carbon dioxide and water. Water is also absorbed, and could soon thin out its protoplasm damagingly if it were not gotten rid of. This is done by a so-called pulsating vacuole, a sort of bubble helping to discharge wastes and excess water from the cell, thus being in effect a precursor of kidneys. That pulsating vacuole is in fact just one of several structures visible within the cell, for despite its primitiveness and apparent simplicity, the Amoeba is a somewhat organized unit of cooperating parts. There are no proper organs, for organs are defined as composed of many cells, but there are equivalent cell parts, called organelles because of their smallness, which do the several jobs involved in cell living. Most conspicuous is a nucleus, visibly denser, which exercises a central control over the cell activities. There are various granules, some with jobs we know about, others functioning we know not how. And identified with the nucleus, there are chromosomes, so named because they readily take dyes which render them visible. These are important as the bearers of heredity from generation to generation. For Amoeba naturally reproduces its kind but does it in the very simplest way, by mere fission, and the chromosomes then carry the characteristics which make up its kind.

What happens is this: As Amoeba feeds, it grows. But there is a limit to its possible growth, for doubling of cell diameter means an eightfold increase in bulk but only a fourfold increase in surface area, a reduction of one half of surface relative to bulk. But the cell's capacity to absorb and give off materials such as oxygen, foodstuffs, carbon dioxide, and wastes depends upon plenty of surface exposed, and so a practical limit of growth is soon reached. Amoeba and other one-celled organisms generally solve it simply by dividing and so increasing the ratio of surface to bulk. Such division at least looks very simple, though the process is actually not so simple as it looks. Nucleus and chromosomes must also divide, and other involved things do happen which we need not linger on here. The result of the fission is obviously two daughter cells made up of the very substance of the mother cell. And they in their turn will, of course, pass on their substances to four granddaughter cells, and so on forever. There is a continuity of substance here which could be called immortality. At least we can say that no Amoeba ever dies of old age, though death by violence is common enough.

One-Celled Diversity

In contrast with shapeless *Amoeba proteus* is another much more organized protozoan, Paramecium, also found abundantly in stagnant pools. It is several times larger than Amoeba, about a hundredth of an inch in length and sometimes visible to the naked eye as a moving fleck of light. It is elongated, flat, and a bit twisted, well described by its popular name, the "slipper animalcule." Its flat shape means that its surface is somewhat larger relative to its bulk, which may well be a reason it grows larger than plump Amoeba. But there seems also to be another reason, for Paramecium takes its food by a definite mouth opening on one flat side and eliminates wastes by another definite exit, so that surface exposure becomes less important. Food particles are swept toward the mouth by water currents created by fine waving protoplasmic hairs called cilia, a real improvement in getting enough food. Its whole surface is covered with such cilia, which also serve to drive it through the water, swimming forward or backward, bustling about in an apparently aimless twisting course (Figure 10).

Here is evidently better organization and greater cell complexity. Within the cell are two nuclei, one small, the other large, and two vacuoles. When Paramecium divides, it does so much

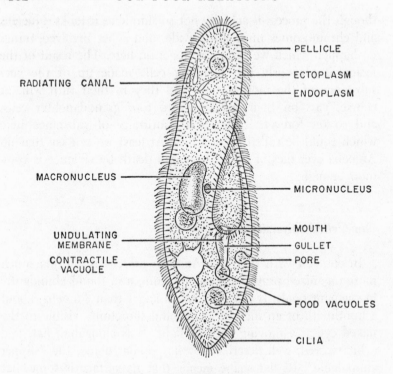

PELLICLE

ECTOPLASM

ENDOPLASM

RADIATING CANAL

MACRONUCLEUS

MICRONUCLEUS

UNDULATING
MEMBRANE

MOUTH

GULLET

CONTRACTILE
VACUOLE

PORE

FOOD VACUOLES

CILIA

Fig. 10. The Organized Paramecium.

like Amoeba, but of course each half must grow a new full and normal organization. And a further innovation in reproduction is also introduced by Paramecium and some of its kin. Repeating fission does not go on forever. Occasionally two Paramecia join temporarily in an act of conjugation, during which their small nuclei undergo meiotic division, some of them moving to the other Paramecium to fuse with a counterpart nucleus. The excess nuclei disappear, the result being two Paramecia, each of which in due course starts another series of normal divisions. The process of conjugation is our first inkling of what is to become sexual reproduction, there being an apparent fertility difference between the two Paramecia which conjugate. When we return to the subject of sex and heredity, we shall find that conjugation is quite useful, both in invigorating the racial stock and in preserving advantageous variations for adaptive progress. But here and now we shall stick to our immediate subject, the evolution of our early one-celled poor relations.

Much of that evolution was largely diversification. We have already noted the one-celled forms which developed tough coats of limestone, silica, and cellulose. Among these are the diatoms, which are plants with chlorophyll, and the foraminifers and radiolarians, which are animals, all with hard coats of often intricate and beautiful designs. Another interesting group are several protozoans, ciliated like Paramecium, but with a stalk end for attaching to some firm foothold, and a mouth end surrounded by cilia to gather in food, common examples being Stentor and Vorticella.

The Flagellate Mystery

But even more pertinent here is a protist group called the flagellates, named from their whiplike flagellae, of which there may be one, two, or many attached at one end of the elongated single-celled body, which swims by their lashing undulations. They seem simpler than Paramecium, but an advance on Amoeba. Yet there is a soil Amoeba named *Naeglaria gruberi*, which is ordinarily a shapeless Amoeba, but on occasion becomes temporarily a full-fledged flagellate. Which form is really ancestral, we just do not know.

Even greater is another flagellate mystery. Most flagellates are distinctly animals, in their feeding, digesting, and other characteristics. But there are some exceptions, among them *Euglena viridis*, quite common in our fresh-water streams and ponds. It seems to be both animal and plant. As an animal it swims about, has a mouth opening for feeding, and digests its food the animal way. But the *viridis* of its name means "green," for it also has chlorophyll and can build up its substances the plant way. So what is it, animal or plant? Or is its group just at (or near) the parting of the ways where plants began an evolution of their own? Or were things the other way around, with the animal flagellates branching off from the plant flagellates, themselves descended from such ordinary unflagellated plants as the primitive one-celled blue-green algae? Specialists in this field have suspected close kinship between the bacteria and the blue-green algae, both having members which do nitrogen-fixing and apparently lack cell nuclei. But that would mean quite another line of ancestry for the plants as a whole. For it is fairly certain that from these simplest blue-green algae have come the more complex algal forms, the green, brown, and red, and from the green algae the still-higher plants. It would help a lot if we had a really good fossil record going back to the early days when the plants and animals parted. But as things are, we can only compare their simple descendants after half a billion years of much change and weeding out, and thus try to trace the illusive kinships the best we can.

Parting of the Ways

Though so far there is no sure picture of the lines of descent, we are very certain that back in those early one-celled forms, plant and animal did part and go their separate ways. However, in adapting to similar conditions, they sometimes confuse us by taking on forms and functions very much alike. Just because they lived together in the same world, they often entered into various interactions and interdependencies. Their ways were different, but their world was one.

The plants acquired chlorophyll and the ability to capture sunlight energy and store it chemically in foodstuffs synthesized from materials abundant in the ever-present atmosphere, waters, and soil. With all their raw materials at hand, the plants had little need for movement, so inertness and lack of a nervous system and musculature became the general rule. They did, however, need some tough substance to protect, support, and firmly bind together the plant organization, and for this they developed a secretion of cellulose (itself dead) to become cover and structural matrix. Their shapes became adapted, in part for absorption of raw materials, but predominantly for exposure of much surface to sunlight.

The animals, on the other hand, fed on the foodstuffs which the plants provided, and on each other. That meant moving to their food supplies, and moving to escape becoming food supplies themselves. Survival became a matter of alertness, strength, speed, and all manner of special adaptations for attack and capture, defense and escape. That also demanded development of more effective senses for receiving urgent stimuli, and nerve paths, incoming and outgoing, for transmitting impulses for triggering muscles to responsive actions, and some central coordinating unit for organizing effective actions. So shapes and functions, of body and parts, were adapted to facilitate a life of movement, and the internal chemistry was evolved (largely through faster-acting enzymes) to speed up reactions and movements.

But again we are getting ahead of our story. Before any such development could go far, another great step had to be taken by our lowly forebears. They had first to escape from the limitations of the one-celled structure and become many-celled. For that we must obviously start another chapter.

Chapter 11

BIGGER AND BETTER BODIES

Before life could go on to better things, it had to get bigger bodies. For size does give advantage. For one thing, it is the broad rule (with exceptions) that the large overcomes and preys on the small, Amoeba eating bacteria, Paramecium eating Amoeba, the multicelled eating Paramecium, ad infinitum. But perhaps the primary limitation of the one-celled is that mathematical rule, already familiar, that with increase in size, the ratio of surface to bulk constantly decreases. Basically, the single-celled can solve that restriction only by growing, then dividing. Thereby, also, they get a greater chance of survival by prolific numbers, but no advantage of larger size.

Then, too, single-celledness restricts the possibilities of advantageous differentiation of parts and effective division of labors. True, the one-celled have done fairly well in this respect, but only by exhausting every apparent possibility. But even so the possibilities are actually very few, nothing comparable to those available to the multicelled organisms. Becoming multicelled was therefore the needed next step toward new and practically unlimited freedom for variety in improvements.

The transition to the multicelled began by simple and easy stages. The very first was for the one cell to grow and divide into two, which did not then separate. Examples are the blue-green algae cells, and diatoms, and some flagellates, kept together in some shapeless colony, often by an enclosing blob of jelly.

More definite, among the algae, are the four-celled colony of *Gonium sociale*, increased to sixteen cells in *Gonium pectorale*, on to Eudorina with thirty-two cells on the spherical surface of a gelatinous core, to the spherical multicelled colony of Pandorina, and finally to the *Volvox globatur* colony of tens of thousands of cells arranged in a layer about a central core of water or thin jelly. Other algae string together in loose chains of cells, up through gradations of longer, heavier, and branching filaments to the great floating strands of the seaweed kelp reaching lengths of hundreds of feet. In contrast, among the animals, probably because of their active and predatory lives, the mere clusters of like cells did not long persist, but gave way to definite and diversified forms more precisely adapted to their more strenuous ways of survival. Let us follow some of the more basic developments.

Units with Differentiation

Perhaps most basic is the development which converts the merely loose colony of individual cells into a single unified organism acting as one. *Gonium pectorale* shows a beginning of such integration. Its sixteen cells are slightly separated and arranged into a flat disc, but they are also connected by short protoplasmic strands. That these are more than mere mechanical connectors is shown by the fact that the cells, each of which has two flagellae, work in definite cooperation in swimming through the water, turning the disc to face the light, etc. Volvox then illustrates a further step in integration, its cells being themselves in direct contact, and also closely connected by a network of protoplasmic strands, the means for coordinating the activities of Volvox as a whole. This network is clearly the beginning of a nervous system, a subject which will be more fully pursued in due course.

Another basic development of the multicelled was the differentiation of the cells themselves, in physical form and in chemistry, too, for doing specialized jobs by a more effective division of labors. In the end, both plants and animals developed many such kinds of diversified cells, ordinarily grouped into suitable organs specialized in function. Such development, however, really begins among the bacteria and protists, for when conditions become unfavorable for active living, being too cold or too dry, it is quite usual for the normal cell to shrivel up and secrete a tough coat, and go into a resting stage, thus surviving until warmth and moisture return to revive it, be the time short or perhaps even years in duration. Such resting cells should perhaps not be considered as reproductive cells, but early in the development of multicelled organisms, true differentiated reproductive cells do appear. Thus, in Volvox some are merely enlarged wall cells which move to the interior of the sphere and there multiply into masses of cells, the starts of new Volvox spheres. But also in Volvox another method of reproduction exists, in which the cells from a portion of the wall differentiate more radically. Some enlarge into eggs and become inactive. Others become small flagellated free-swimming sperm cells. When one of these reaches an enlarged egg cell, its nucleus enters and fuses with the egg nucleus, thus fertilizing it for further development. The egg then secretes a tough wall and becomes able to live through adverse conditions. Finally, when right conditions return, the egg starts developing into a new multicelled Volvox sphere. We have here a true case of sexual reproduction, even though the fusing male and female sex cells both come from the same Volvox individual.

The Two-Layered Kinds

Another broad division of labor which turned out to be of lasting and basic importance was one between outside and inside cells. In a hollow sphere such as Volvox, the cells are all outside, well exposed to exchange foods, gases, and wastes from and to the surrounding water, but also exposed to every injurious contact. Developing a thick protective coat would of course interfere with effective exchanges. But if two layers are formed, one of protective cells outside, another of absorptive cells inside, the problem is simply solved, if the inside cells are somehow kept in contact with the surrounding water. This can be done, for instance, if one side of a hollow sphere of cells proceeds to cave in to form a sack of two cell layers, with an opening to the outside. This is the rough plan of two groups of primitive animals, the sponges and the coelenterates, the latter named from two Greek words for "hollow" and "intestine," and comprising the corals, sea anemones, jellyfishes, etc. In fact, their development as individuals from the original egg cells follows exactly the course described. Each egg cell divides into a multitude which form a hollow sphere (the blastula), and this proceeds to cave in on one side to form a hollow two-layered sack (the gastrula). From the outer layer then develop the exterior parts; from the inner layer, the food-cavity parts.

Of these sack animals, sponges seem to be the most primitive. There are several thousands of fossil and existing species recorded, and therefore many variations on the basic sack structure. The early presponges were not sacklike at all, but shapeless colonies of peculiar "collar cells." This kind of cell began among the one-celled flagellates and has a cup- or funnel-shape opening outward, with one or more flagellae thrusting out centrally from its bottom. By slow rhythmic movement the cup sucks in minute food particles and thus feeds itself. In the first true sponges the colony was spherical, held together by needles of silica secreted between the adjacent cells. The collar cells faced inward toward a water-filled space connected to the outside by a multitude of pores through the sphere wall. By the lashing of the cell-flagellae, water was drawn through these pores, bringing in the food particles. In the course of time the sponges became anchored to the sea floor, developed an exit opening at the top of the central chamber, but were still fed through the myriad wall pores. One division of the family still has the silica framework, another has lime for support, and the softer sponges of our households are the skeletons of a horny material called spongin. Despite the half billion years that have passed since the sponges began, they are all still very primitive, without an integrating nervous system, each collar cell living more or less independently in the jumbled community.

Better organized, and more definitely sacklike, are the coelenterates. They divide broadly into two types: the medusa type such as the free-swimming jellyfishes, and the polyp or hydroid type such as the hydras, corals, and sea anemones, usually attached at one end to some firm foothold. The polyps are normally cylindrical, with a mouth end often surrounded by tentacles which draw in food. The medusae range from bell- to disc-shaped, with a fringe of tentacles about the edge, and a central mouth underneath. The medusae are soft-bodied, often transparent or colored, in contrast to many of the polyps which form hard limestone coverings or supports, sometimes living in such vast colonies that they build great coral reefs. Though fundamentally of two-walled sack structure, they develop forms of wide variety, from the simply single sack of Hydra to the intricately branching colonial forms. They vary, too, in reproductive method, from simple asexual budding to definite sex cells which conjugate, often with a life cycle of polyps and medusae in alternating generations. Oddly, they are all alike in one seemingly minor way: they all have stinging organs, sensitively triggered capsules for throwing out poison darts, both to kill food and to protect against enemies. More basic, there is also a simple nervous system, a ring about the mouth opening, connected with a loose nerve network spreading through the sack body (Figure 11).

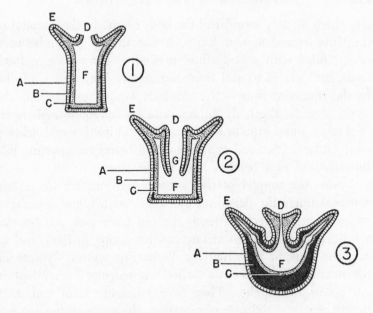

Fig. 11. The Sack Animals.

The Three-Layered Kinds

The sponges and the coelenterates never did develop beyond the basic two-layer sack stage, though jellyfishes do grow a mass of jelly-ish cells between the layers. Evolving a third intermediate layer represents the next step upward, as all the higher animals have it, starting early in the embryonic cleavage of the egg into many cells. That new cell layer, the mesoderm, is destined to be the source of several in-between organs. It would almost seem that the two original layers, ectoderm on the outside, endoderm on the inside, were already fully allocated, and an additional layer was required for the new extra organs. These, in due time, developed within a new cavity of the body, placed between the now-separated inside and outside layers, which we may simply call the body cavity. In the simplest of the three-layered animal forms, it was merely the in-between cavity, filled with a body fluid needed to carry oxygen, foodstuffs, and wastes to and from the organs, both new and old. In the course of time better conduits would be installed (the blood vessels), the body fluids would be driven through faster by a force pump (the heart), and the fluid itself would develop more efficient chemical carriers to do a better transporting job. But most of that belongs later in the story.

Among the simpler of the three-layered animals are certain worms, namely the flatworms and roundworms, and some near relatives, the rotifers. In them the old body sack has become a tube, with the mouth at one end for taking in food, and an exit, the anus, at the other for discharging wastes. Typical are the microscopic rotifers or "wheel animalcules," abundant in our ponds and ditches. They have a definite front end, with mouth, eye, and a cluster of vibrating cilia for both feeding and swimming. The tail is long, forked, and retractable, and able to attach as a stalk for temporary anchorage. Inside the rotifer, despite its minuteness, are all the essential organs of the simpler worms, even to a primitive brain knob at the front end of the simplest possible nerve thread. In the flatworms this nervous system becomes a ladderlike network culminating up front in a modestly enlarged brain and a pair of eyes. The body now has two sides, left and right, and also differing upper and lower surfaces with the mouth underneath. There are many variations in form and structure, depending a good deal on where and how the worm gets its living, either as a free-swimmer making its own way or as a parasite vegetating within some higher animal from whose foodstuffs or substance it draws its own sustenance. Many of the parasitic worms, such as the flukes, pass through amazing cycles of stages in successive animal hosts, having taken opportunistic advantage of such hosts as became available during the courses of their evolutions.

These more primitive worms are important in our story in their development of the basic tubular, front-and-rear, left-and-right, top-and-bottom structure. In a word, they had become bilateral, inside and out, and very likely gave rise to all the higher forms which (with a few seeming exceptions) are also thus bilaterally symmetrical. Some of the seeming exceptions appear among the molluscs, such as the octopuses, or among the echinoderms, such as the starfishes. The former are fairly lumpy, the latter five-pointed in their symmetry.

Mollusc Miscellany

The molluscs as a whole divide into several groups, the three most important being the gastropod (stomach-footed) snails and slugs, the bivalve or pelecypod (ax-footed) clams, oysters, and mussels, and the cephalopod (head-footed) squid, octopus, cuttlefish, and argonaut group.

Because of similarities in at least outward structure, we suspect kinship between flatworm and snail or slug, though you should be warned that the kinship is very uncertain. It is quite incidental that the snail developed a shell to retire into, even though snail shells are important to us as fossils for dating geologic formations. As the fossil record clearly shows, the shell itself changed much in shape and detail pattern, but essentially it was always merely a house which the individual kept outgrowing, and therefore progressively enlarged by adding more material at the edges of the opening. If the shell grew into a long straight tapered shape, it was most awkward to lug around. But if the growth was lopsided, the shell would curl into a flat spiral or twist into a compact cone, both much easier to carry about. As shown by the abundant fossil remains, the molluscs tried all types of shell shapes, with the twisted cone very popular among the snail folk. One result is that they are now sorted out by the classifiers into many thousands of distinct species, very largely on the basis of variant shell shapes.

We may well guess that the snail type represents the middle stem from which the two other broad branches of the molluscs developed. One branch acquired two half shells, hinged right and left, with elastic bands and muscle bundles between them for opening and closing. With the shells a bit apart, water bearing oxygen and foodstuffs were drawn in through so-called gills, really a filter for trapping food particles. The muscular foot, protruding between the open shells, is used by the clams and oysters for digging a path through sand and mud, and by the cockles to jump. Some oysters attach themselves as adults to rocks by tufts of adhesive threads. The active scallop, on the other hand, swims about by a pumping action, opening and closing its shells, guided by a row of bright eyes just inside the shell rims. On the whole, however, the bivalve tribe are an inert and dull lot, not at all blessed with brains.

Quite in contrast, the third great branch of the molluscs, the cephalopods, are active, alert, and somewhat brainy. They are named "head-footed" because the so-called foot surrounds the beak-jawed mouth as a ring of writhing tentacles armed with powerful suckers, the squids and cuttlefishes having ten tentacles, the octopuses and argonauts but eight. The captured prey is bitten and pumped full of a paralyzing digestive juice which dissolves it into a soup which its captor then sucks in. Living such an active predatory life, the cephalopod movements become swift and aggressive, with alertness and clear vision important. And so, for lowly molluscs, they have today rather superior brains and incredibly perfect eyes, though both brain and eyes do differ importantly from our own. Back in the early geologic times they, too, carried a wide variety of shells, very useful to us in dating those times. But with increasing swiftness of movement, those shells became both unnecessary for protection and real handicaps as awkward encumbrances, and so today have disappeared or been reduced to mere remnants.

But despite their real geologic importance, all the molluscs are of little interest in our tracing of our own ancestry, inasmuch as they are definitely a side branch, far removed, on our family tree.

The Segmented Kinds

At any rate, we must perforce return to the lower reaches of that family tree, namely to the worms. Only now we are concerned with some higher worms, if we may properly speak of any worms as "higher." But of course what we mean is that these worms, the annelids, have taken another important step forward. That step was a segmentation of the body length into a number of duplicating structural units. A centipede is a good example of this type of structure, though somewhat higher on the tree of evolution. Between it and the true segmented worms we find another caterpillarlike creature, Peripatus by name, most important as the sole living survivor of the original ancestors of the most numerous and diversified of all the animals, past or present. This great group is called the arthropods, meaning literally the joint-footed, and includes the crustaceans (lobsters, crabs, barnacles, and shrimps), the king crab (survivor of an ancient group related to the extinct trilobites and eurypterids or sea scorpions), the true scorpions, the spiders, and the insects. In their evolution several things happened. As we pass from the simple segmented worm (say an ordinary earthworm) on through Peripatus and the centipede to the full-fledged arthropods, we note changes such as these: From segments nearly all repetitiously the same, we find increasing differentiation, until none are quite the same; indeed, all may be radically different. Thus from a beginning of stiff bristles for worms' feet, through unjointed but flexible stumps (one pair for each segment) of Peripatus, we arrive at elaborately jointed legs, and these then changed to appendages used for entirely different purposes, such as the nineteen pairs of specialized tools with which a lobster is blessed. From a soft skin covering the worms, we move on to a hard, jointed outside skeleton for body, legs, and appendages (but no internal skeleton), with a muscular system within its hollows, familiar enough to anyone who has struggled with taking apart and eating a lobster. The nervous system changed but little except in details, a brain swelling up front over the gullet, connected on both sides to a ladder chain of nerves with segment swellings under the digestive tube. But something rather odd happened to the blood system, a seemingly backward step. Already in the segmented worm there was a primitive circulating system of blood vessels, but in the true arthropods the blood is back in the body cavity, though some still have a bit of pulsating tube doing the pumping job of the heart. This change, in fact, takes place in the individual life of Peripatus, the go-between, and testifies strongly to a backward step of evolution in this feature of the arthropods.

So again it appears that we are off on another side branch of our family tree, and that the arthropods and their near ancestors are only our remote cousins. But even this is not entirely certain, as we shall see when we consider a theory that the arthropods may actually be more directly in the family line than most of us think.

Completing the Roll Call

But before we attempt to trace that early family tree, let us complete the roll call of our poor relations with two groups known as the molluscoids and the echinoderms. In neither case will outward appearances help in the least. Thus the molluscoids, as their name indicates, look outwardly much like molluscs, though internally they are very different. Their main group, the brachiopods or lamp shells, have two shells like the bivalves, but their shells are not right and left, but front and back, on an animal organized internally altogether differently from a clam or oyster. Similarly, the outward shapes of echinoderms are unlike anything else in the animal world, being not generally bilateral but radial in arrangement, the five-pointed starfish being typical.

But when we look into their life histories, we find that in both groups all pass through a free-swimming stage closely similar to that of the segmented worms and the molluscs. Assuming that their individual developments at least roughly parallel their race histories, we conclude that far back before our fossil record began, a lowly wormlike common ancestor gave rise to these diverse animal forms. In imagination we can reconstruct it as a soft-bodied sacklike organism with a bilateral symmetry, but variant top and bottom, and already possessed of rudimentary head, with eye spots and primitive skin protuberances adapted for swimming. Some of its kind in due course developed back and bottom shells and, thus burdened, settled to the water bottom and anchored themselves by stalks, becoming the lamp shells, a tribe which flourished greatly for a couple of hundred million years, later revived for another period of tens of millions of years, and is even now represented by a few forms, among them that ultraconservative Lingula mentioned earlier. Also belonging here, as rather disguised relatives of the brachiopods, are the colonial bryozoans or moss animals, another unimportant group of ancient lineage.

From that same wormlike ancestor, the echinoderms were apparently also descended. For even the five-armed starfish begins life as a larva of the bilateral type, and only later grows the extra parts to complete the radial shape. Together with its kin, the sea urchins and sea cucumbers, it developed very distinctive organs, such as the rows of tube feet hydraulically operated, used for both holding and traveling. The name "echinoderm" means "hedgehog skin," but the covering spines are better described as jawed snappers, used both for defense and for cleaning itself. It is evident that the echinoderm is one of

Nature's most radical experiments, both in general form and in details of structure, and was worked out with several variations, all but one group on the radial plan. That exception is the sea cucumber, which looks like an animated sausage, but bilateral rather than radial in basic plan, crawling over the sea bottom on a belly, with the mouth up front and the anus at the rear.

All in all, Nature did much experimenting in these lowly poor relations of ours. As we look them over, we find a few basic structural plans by which we can sort them out into broad groups, but with much diversity within each group. Sometimes, indeed, in separate groups we find parallelisms which often prove confusing—for instance, those superficially double shells of the bivalve molluscs and the really distinct lamp-shell brachiopods. Such parallelisms are usually only equivalent adaptations to like conditions of life and may therefore be only surface resemblances independently evolved. In fact, it is often said that the outside of an organism merely tells where it has been, while the inside tells where it came from. At any rate, in tracing kinships, we look more for internal similarities than those merely external.

Which Is Our Ancestor?

But as we search among these poor relations for the ancestors of the higher, backboned animals, we face the immense task of studying in sufficient detail both the internal structures and the embryonic and larval histories of an aggregate of diverse forms numbering something like a million. Even picking out the likely key characters among them for necessary intensive studies demands some knowledge of structural and developmental detail. And though an enormous amount of such work has been done in the century since Darwin and Wallace started the scientists on that search in real earnest, there are still many gaps and much uncertainty in tracing the kinships among these most ancient and primitive progenitors of animal kind. Yet if we view the known facts in broad historic perspective, we do find an over-all progress in ancestral evolution represented by rather marked stages of basic achievement.

First, perhaps, is an initial formation of individual coazervate droplets or their equivalents, preliving and yet capable of competition for survival and therefore of improvement by natural selection. There must have been a progressive chemical organizing of preliving to primitive living substances. Then there must have been a gradual evolution of single-celled protists in both chemical and physical organization, and the evolving of chlorophyll by the plants to make them self-sufficing. Thereby they separated from the parasitic animals, with resulting divergence of modes of living, inert for the plants, active for the animals, with subsequent evolutions along divergent yet everinteracting careers. A major development was the overcoming of the handicaps of minuteness of the one-celled by the joining of cells into multiple communities, the differentiation of cells into organs with divisions of labor for higher efficiencies and closer organic unity. One necessary result was the evolving of the primitive two-layered sack structure, improved in the three-layered tube with body cavity, new organs, and blood fluid bathing all internal parts. And finally, the evolution of the basic bilateral, front-and-rear, top-and-bottom form preparing for the emergence of the next higher group, the backboned kinds.

Progress, we shall discover, normally begins slowly and gradually speeds up, probably because of increased competition between those most nearly alike both in forms and needs. Certainly it is true here that the early basic evolutions took much time, the later ones less. Thus it is probable that something like a billion years must be allowed for the organization and evolution of one-celled life, more than half a billion for the multicelled poor relations before the vertebrates appeared, half the remaining period before the warmblooded birds and mammals arose, and finally a very small and recent fraction of all this time before Man himself emerged. Yet even now in this age of vertebrates, mammals, and Man, the poor relations still predominate in both sheer numbers and diversity of kinds. Only when we measure by brain development and versatile capacities to do and to control can we properly speak of Man and his nearer kin as dominating the world and its life. But at this early stage of our story that dominance is far, far in the future, as the culmination of several most important evolutionary achievements. At this stage we can only ask: From which of the poor relations did the backboned vertebrates descend, and how was this done? The answer to that is not wholly clear, but some probabilities will appear as we proceed with our evolutionary story.

Chapter 12

GETTING A HEAD

A most important step in getting ahead was getting a head. Even the primitive two-layered flatworms, roundworms, and rotifers had already taken that step and acquired what deserves to be called a head. The reason is simple enough: they were all forward-moving. This, of course, does not mean that they were vigorously progressive, but merely that they moved physically in one direction which we describe as forward. As a result, one end (namely the front end) took most of the bumps and made the first and therefore important contacts. So the entire organism was organized on a front-and-rear basis, organized to move forward, with a concentration of contact equipment up front, so making that end a head.

We ordinarily call such contact equipment the sense organs, such as eyes, nose, ears, tasters, feelers, etc. But they are not always up front, each being placed on the animal quite consistently where it makes its contacts best, as feelers on fingers, tasters within the mouth, but mostly at the head end where the contacts of forward movement are ordinarily made.

Another reason for head-end sense organs is the presence there of the mouth. For the sense organs are primarily dedicated to rather slavish service to the mouth, food being quite the first concern of the primitive animal. The mouth itself is usually up front because the animal does its moving chiefly to feed that mouth, and among the forward movers the food contacts are made best up front. So for feeding the face, and detecting what is ahead, be it food or danger, forward movement produces a front-end assemblage of sense organs, mouth and accessories. This assemblage, however grotesque it may sometimes be, we must call a face. Of that face and its equipment we shall learn more in later chapters, after we have gone into the problem of general bodily shape. Enough here that among the forward-moving animals that shape is normally elongated fore and aft, divided (with variations) into head, body, and tail, and as speed is acquired, becomes streamlined for swift and aggressive movement, but with flexibility to swerve right and left. These, however, are later concerns.

Our primary concern is really with what is inside that head end, what brain there is, what connections it has to the organism as a whole, and of course how it all works. In short, we are here concerned with the evolution and operation of the first nervous systems.

Reactivity Evolves

One of the very first pages of our family album shows that simple-looking fellow *Amoeba proteus*. He is only a speck of living jelly, microscopically minute, and unshapely because quite formless. He, at least, is without head and tail. He would be a regular lazy bones if he had bones, for he just pokes around until he meets a dinner (which he leisurely surrounds) or a danger (which he leisurely avoids). He is nothing to brag about as an ancestor, though we did learn that in chemical and physical makeup his one cell is far from simple. Yet in the vital matter of brains, senses, and behavior he is certainly down near the very bottom, and in trying to read his simple mind, we find very little to go on.

Yet we know that he has sensitivity (though not of the prima-donna type), because he does respond to outside stimuli, even if somewhat sluggishly. He even discriminates, between food and danger, engulfing the one, avoiding the other. That, however, does not have to mean any conscious discrimination, but only a physicochemical reactivity.

That may mean more if we turn for a moment to that more active protozoan, Paramecium, the slipper animalcule, to illustrate the point. For its greater activity gives us better opportunity for experiment. Its normal life is one of bustling about, making many outside contacts. It clearly discriminates between those contacts, but rather simply. From solids it withdraws. Fragments and soft objects it consumes, but with equal avidity whether they are usable as foods or quite inedible. Its only avoiding reaction is a simple backing away, followed by renewed forward movement. But because of its twisted-slipper shape, each advance is at a new angle, the corkscrewing backing and advancing being repeated until the solid object is finally cleared. In the same trial-and-error way, it avoids regions of too great acidity or alkalinity, saltiness, heat, and cold. Bacteria are a usual food and give off a mild acidity. Guided by this, Paramecium is led toward them, and arriving, settles down to browse. Too great acidity, however, drives him back. Thus, if a drop of acid be put into the water, all the Paramecia will move to the distance of comfortable acidity and there form a ring about the drop. All this of course indicates no more than a physicochemical reactivity and does not imply any conscious mind and choice.

This is obviously a fundamental reactivity of Paramecium, but also there seem to be secondary ones. Thus, it shows a proclivity for swimming upward toward the water surface, and this involves some up-and-down orientation. The control has been traced and found to depend on particles resting on the bottom of its food vacuoles. For if we trick a Paramecium into engulfing finely powdered iron and then hold a strong magnet over it to draw the particles upward, the Paramecium will turn upside down and swim downward, completely fooled by the impulses which normally start from the bottom of its food vacuoles.

Other ingenious experiments with this and other single-celled animals have revealed a rather important fact—that the physicochemical reactions to stimuli, which we may call impulses, move in definite directions through the animal. Thus, in Paramecium the impulse movement is from front to rear, or from the bottoms of the food vacuoles to the proper swimming cilia. In the funnel-shaped Stentor the impulses move from the mouth toward the foot stalk. Even in shapeless Amoeba there are temporary impulse paths inward from the pseudopod of the moment. Ordinarily there is nothing visible, even in the protozoans of fixed form with presumably fixed impulse pathways. But in the actively swimming protozoan Diplodinium, structures are visible as an inner ring about the mouth opening, connecting by fine fibers to the feeding and swimming cilia and to the retractile strands which act like muscles. In other words, there are definite channels for conducting impulses along definite routes to special organs for reacting. We are of course tempted to call these channels nerves, and in any multicelled animal would certainly do so. Only then the nerve unit is always itself a complete and separate cell we call a neuron, having its own headquarters body with nucleus, etc., but extending by extremely long fibrous processes capable of transmitting a nerve impulse, again always in one direction only. In Diplodinium, obviously, these fibers are merely specialized parts within the single cell (Figure 12).

Nerve Nets and Rings

With the coming of the multicelled animals we naturally expect big improvements in nervous organization. At first, however, we face serious disappointment. Thus, in sponges, which we found earlier were essentially single cells living more or less independently in a jumbled community, we can detect no

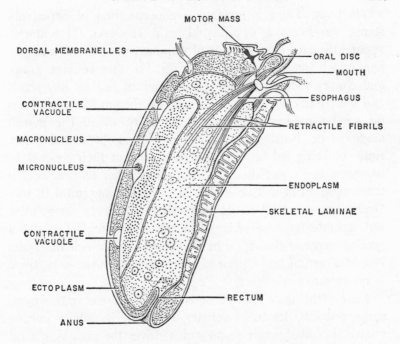

Fig. 12. Impulse Paths in Diplodinium.

nervous system at all. Each cell seems to be just a bit of contractile life put to work by direct stimulation, without the intervention of any connective nerve tissue.

For a first bit of improvement we come to the sea anemones. They are coelenterates of two-layered construction, and sack-shaped, with one general opening for taking in food and ejecting wastes. They attach to rocks by adhering foot discs, by which they can also slowly creep. About each sack mouth is usually a circle of tentacles reaching out to find and seize food and bring it to the mouth. When the animal is touched anywhere on its surface, it usually pulls away by a quick general contraction which reduces its size. This is done by wall muscles controlled by a nerve net which spreads all through its substance and carries the touch stimulus as a general alarm to its whole body. There is nowhere a concentration of nerve substance corresponding to a central brain. However, the tentacles apparently have local systems of response, more direct and perhaps much like those of sponge cells. For they contact, grasp, and convey food to the mouth without stirring up any alarm and body retraction. Also, a tentacle can be cut off and still go on seizing food and passing it along to where the mouth ought to be. Furthermore, one tentacle can be fooled a few times by being fed bits of inedible paper, but then "learns" to recognize and reject them. However, any other tentacle of the same animal can still be fooled in the same way, until it, too, "learns" to reject all on its own. All the evidence shows local but separate response systems for the several tentacles, plus a general response through a nerve net spread through the body. But of a central brain, even of the most elementary sort, there is no evidence whatever.

Among the near relative of the sea anemone is the more active jellyfish. Its main activity, however, is only a pulsing contraction of the bell shape which drives the animal upward through the water. Then it rests and floats gently downward like a parachute, capturing smaller animals with its tentacles as it descends. These activities are controlled by a nerve ring within the margin of the bell, with branches extending down its tentacles and central mouth tube. There are even marginal sense organs of various kinds, serving apparently as balancers, primitive eyes, and chemical reactors. But again any semblance to a central and coordinating brain concentration is quite lacking.

Another example of the uncentralized nervous system is found in the starfishes. Here there is a nerve ring about the central mouth, and from this ring one nerve branch extending out into each of the five body rays, with a simple eye at each tip. Each nerve branch seems to be a control unit which acts almost independently. Thus, if an arm is cut off from the starfish body, it can carry on by itself, crawling about on its tube feet. But also it would seem that each arm can take charge of the whole animal in turn, raising its eye in the direction of movement and setting all the tube feet of all the arms marching together in one direction. Or if the starfish is thrown on its back, all the tube feet of all the arms start struggling to get some grip for turning over. But when one arm does get a grip, all the other arms cooperate by quitting their own efforts. If, however, the central nerve ring is cut between the several nerve branches, all cooperation ends and each arm takes independent action in walking, turning over, etc. So here again there is no central brain, though some coordinated control is taken over by any nerve branch as occasion demands. In other words, the starfish has five possible directions of forward movement, and in effect five heads taking their turns at going ahead. But unfortunately for the starfish future, five heads are just four too many. For forward evolution, one head and one direction of forward movement are to prove much better (Figure 13).

The Brain Central

Perhaps we should point out that this story is not being told in strict chronological order. Instead, representative stages, earlier or later in actual time, are picked and presented in the general order from lower to higher, and probably in the general order of evolution. Thus long before the sponge animals collected into loose colonies, and sea anemones, jellyfishes, and starfishes developed nerve nets and nerve rings, even some of the protozoans, early kin of Paramecium and Diplodinium, had already developed an elongate form with a forward-moving head end, and acquired an assemblage of equipment which we might call a face. With development of equivalent forward-moving head ends in multicelled flatworms, roundworms, and rotifers,

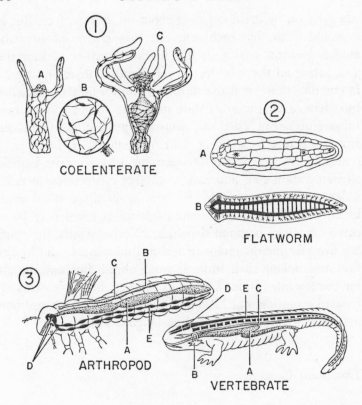

Fig. 13. The Evolving Nervous System.

this main-sequence evolution had already advanced by a really basic step.

Our primary concern is still with what was happening within the head end and the body which it controlled. Particularly important were the beginnings of a central coordinating brain and a system of body nerves extending largely rearward from it. A main factor in locating the brain was the position of the eyes. They are normally placed forward-looking and upward-looking, though of course in neither the progressive nor the pious sense. They looked forward to see what the animal was running into, food or trouble. They looked upward to keep the eyes from grubbing into the bottom mud and to detect interceptions of the light flooding down from overhead. And because the eyes were placed forward and upward, so was the brain, to which the eyes were important fact-feeders. With only rare exceptions, such as snail eyes on the ends of stalks, eye and brain are normally kept well together.

On the other hand, the body nerves of the invertebrates were kept down low, perhaps largely because the important contacts were originally made there as the primitive animal forms crawled over sea and lake bottoms. The result was a brain swelling or ganglion up front over the mouth and gullet, and a ventral or belly nerve cord extending rearward, with a pair of nerve bands around the gullet to connect the brain ganglion above to the nerve cord below.

In the watery world which early life forms occupied, up and down were very different. Gravity pulls down, toward bottoms on which to rest and crawl. Light comes from above, and most of the primal world of water is above, to be reached only by a climbing effort or some equipment for floating. Front and rear also became importantly different by reason of habitual forward moving. Left and right, however, were quite the same, being only two directions for swerving aside. For the active forward-movers, head and tail had to be different, but left and right could be the same. So generally they acquired a two-sided symmetry and, in due course, paired feet and other appendages, paired sense organs such as eyes, ears, nostrils, etc., and a basically paired brain and nervous system, bilateral left and right.

In the previous chapter, in tracing the evolution of the worms, we noted an important advance by the segmentation of the elongated body into a number of duplicating structural units, well illustrated in earthworms, Peripatus, the living fossil, and the centipedes. We noted also that they progressed from primitive forms with segments all alike to higher forms of crustaceans, trilobites, scorpions, spiders, and insects, with increasing differentiation of the body segments themselves and of their appendages. With this general body segmentation there was an equivalent segmentation of the nervous system, represented by a series of paired ganglions or nerve swellings connected like a ladder with cross rungs. This became the basic pattern for all members of the widespreading arthropod group, the largest division of the great invertebrate tribe. In due time, however, because of the fusing of the ganglion pairs, the ventral cord came to look like a single string of ganglion swellings from which minor branches extend to left and right into the paired appendages, sense organs, and other structures. All in all, the resulting great advance was the multiplication and eventual differentiation of body parts under a unitary control dominated by a centralized brain.

The Outside Skeleton

Along with this vital achievement, the arthropods made another great advance, the evolving of a framework for supporting the entire body structure more effectively. This, as it happened, was on the outside, serving also as a protective armor. That protection may well have been the real reason for its original development. And the protection may have been twofold, partly against physical attack by hungry enemies, partly as a waterproofing to withstand drastic changes in migrating from salt to fresh water, or vice versa. Later, also, it probably enabled the arthropods to lead the other animals in the exodus from water to land, by helping prevent too rapid drying out in the air. But whatever the reasons, the arthropods became the very largest and most diverse animal group in the world, with well over half a million species.

This supporting framework, called the exoskeleton because it is worn on the outside, is the outstanding feature of the arthropods, though they also had other peculiarities which need not concern us here. That exoskeleton is composed largely of chitin, with sometimes a bit of lime. Chitin is a tough and inelastic substance, chemically stable but variable and complex in its composition. It forms a very effective coat of mail, inside which the arthropod lives. Strictly speaking, that covering is not just hardened skin, but a separate layer added by skin excretion. The arthropod body is normally divided into head, thorax, and abdomen, with often an extension like a tail, properly called a telson. However segmented the covering may have been originally, the portion over each body part is often fused into a single roughly tubular section, with flexible joints between sections. This is particularly true of the jointed appendages, kept flexible by elastic material between the tubular cover sections. The telson segments may also fuse, as in the spiked tails of trilobites and horseshoe crabs and the sting of the scorpion. Or they may remain segmented and flexible, as in the flattened tail paddle of the lobster.

While obviously the arthropod exoskeleton serves primarily as protective armor and mechanical support for the soft body, its several hard tubes, flexibly jointed to each other, provide rigid levers for the muscles to attach to and pull on. Only the muscles are all inside, which somewhat restricts their sizes, positionings, and actions. Furthermore, the muscles (or tendons) and nerves, as well as all other body connections and conduits, must pass through inside the joints, which necessitates open joints between tubular structures, itself a mechanical complication and disadvantage. But, as we have already noted, the exoskeleton gave several notable advantages—making the arthropods adaptable to a wide range of conditions, making them successful beyond all previous animals in multiplying both their numbers and their kinds.

Arthropod Drawbacks

Though the arthropods did succeed in overcoming the mechanical difficulties of the outside skeleton sufficiently for practical purposes, it remained in one way very seriously restrictive: it did hamper growth of the individual animal. Once encased in its hard and unyielding integument, the animal could not grow steadily larger and more powerful. The mollusc, which grew a hard shell for housing the soft body, was not thus restricted, because it simply added a new and larger extension to its house as it grew larger. But a growing lobster or trilobite, being completely encased, had to discard its whole covering by breaking and molting it. This it did periodically, doing its growing while uncovered, then excreting a new hard covering to fit its enlarged size. But meanwhile it was as helpless as a medieval knight without his coat of mail and had to retire from open activity to avoid its natural enemies, to which it could fall easy prey.

Another interesting phenomenon common among the arthropods also probably arose because of this exoskeleton restraint in individual growth. This is the life cycle made up of several stages differing in form and activity. Such cycles vary a good deal among the arthropods but can be illustrated by the life cycle of the butterflies. The adults, which are male and female, eat merely a little nectar and that only for energy, as they do not grow. Instead, they flit through their brief butterfly existence merely to fertilize and lay their eggs. These hatch not into butterfly form but into soft-bodied caterpillars equipped with strong jaws and voracious appetites, eating and growing rapidly until needed size is attained. Then they attach themselves to suitable supports, hang there naked, or spin themselves protective cocoons, or grow temporary coverings and rest as pupae while gradually changing in body structure from caterpillar to arthropod butterfly. Part reason for all this is probably to escape from exoskeletal hampering of body growth, as all growing is done during a separate unhampered stage of the life cycle.

But there are probably other factors also involved, such as inherited individual reliving of the ancestral evolution from segmented worm to integumented insect. Among animals in general, we often see such transformations through several life-cycle stages which are obviously combinations of reliving ancestral evolutions with adaptations to special circumstances. It is thus understandable why the amphibian frog lays its eggs in water and these hatch into tadpoles adapted for water life, with gills for breathing and tail for swimming. The tadpole stage is occupied with eating and growing, meanwhile developing legs and absorbing the tail and gills in preparation for the lung-breathing land animal, the adult frog. It is thus also clear why such stationary animals as corals and sponges which live, feed, and grow in fixed positions give rise to larvae which are free-swimming so they can travel to find less crowded spots elsewhere for settling down, thereby spreading the species and increasing the chances of survival.

But let us not digress too far. We have here been primarily concerned with the serious disadvantages of the arthropod exoskeleton. As a protective armor it was of course valuable in a number of ways. And as a mechanical support for soft body parts it had proved adequate up to eventual limits of size often disadvantageous in an increasingly competitive world. The most serious disadvantage, however, was restriction upon individual growth. One solution was repeated moltings, involving dangerous periods of unprotected exposure to predatory attacks. Another was resort to complicated metamorphoses through some cycle of differing stages, again with multiplied difficulties of survival.

For mere mechanical support, the obvious alternative to an exoskeleton was an internal framework of properly jointed and muscled hard parts. This was to be attained by the vertebrates.

It could be supplemented, as needed, by protective exterior coverings, such as armor, scales, fur, or feathers. Very importantly, it did not involve the narrow limitations on size or the restrictions on individual growth imposed by an exoskeleton. Altogether it was a drastic innovation opening many new possibilities and, for reasons to appear, was quite certainly not attained by descent through an arthropod ancestry. It did permit a central brain and nerve stem in an elongated bilateral body, but as this turned out to be above the digestive tube and not below it, and intimately associated with a dorsal skeletal axis, it was probably independently evolved from some more primitive ancestor not yet committed to the very different and specialized arthropod structure. What that ancestral origin actually was, in the light of the known facts, is our next very vital problem.

Chapter 13

BACKBONE BEGINNINGS

The internal backbone of segmented unit vertebrae is of course what gives name to the grand division of vertebrate animals. It is the axis of the skeletal framework on which their forms are built and supported.

Another basic distinction of this higher animal tribe is that the main axis of its nervous system is dorsal instead of ventral, above the digestive tube instead of below it. The central and coordinating brain is still up front and above, but now continues directly rearward as the dorsal nerve stem. On the whole, it is a basically better brain and is destined to become a very superior one, of which more later.

The axis of the skeletal framework is intimately associated with the dorsal nerve stem, for which it early becomes a protective housing. And it seems quite probable that these two originated together, internal backbone and dorsal nerve stem.

An incidental feature of the vertebrate structure is a fundamental elongate segmentation of the body. This is most apparent in the fishes, lowliest of the vertebrates, where the segmentation of even the muscle bands is very plain. But also in the higher vertebrates, segmentation is clearly retained in separate vertebrae making up the flexible backbone, in the rib structure, and in the branchings of nerves from the main nerve stem. Whether such segmentation is inherited from some invertebrate ancestor or is a new adaptation for body flexibility can probably not be decided until we learn more positively the actual origin of the vertebrate stock.

What is that origin? Which, among the invertebrates, was the ancestor of the vertebrates? And how did the changes, both basic and detailed, come to occur? All these questions pose one great problem. Next to that of the origin of life itself, this is undoubtedly the greatest problem of organic evolution which has not been clearly and fully answered. There is this difference: that as to the origin of life we have too few clues and tangible ideas, while the clues and ideas on the origin of the vertebrates seem too many and hard to choose between. We will, of course, examine the clues and ideas we have, but to do so fruitfully we must first state our problem more fully, particularly as to the nature and advantages of the vertebrate innovations, the internal backbone and skeleton, and the dorsal nerve stem and its branches.

The Internal Skeleton

In two ways the vertebrate internal skeleton serves the same purposes as the arthropod external skeleton. First, they both provide the supporting framework for soft flesh and viscera which without them would slump down into a formless and unworkable heap. Second, they provide the jointed mechanism of pivoted levers to which muscles attach to move the body parts for locomotion, eating, handling, and all manner of other practical purposes.

But otherwise the vertebrate skeleton is different. It is made up principally of bone, with here and there some softer cartilage, as in the padding between the bony vertebrae making up the spinal column. In the young the skeleton is first composed of cartilage, later replaced by (not converted into) bone. In the more primitive fishes (sharks and their kin) the adult skeleton is only cartilage, never bone. In chemical composition, bone is mostly calcium phosphate, with some calicum carbonate or lime, essentially dead matter, though deposited originally by living cells. Cartilage is a more complex mixture of organic materials, somewhat flexible and elastic.

The familiar vertebrate skeleton consists of the main skeleton and the appendage skeleton. The first is the segmented axial or spinal column, from skull to tail, plus two attached girdles, the front for attachment of the front fins or limbs, the rear for the attachment of hind fins or limbs. The appendage skeleton consists of the bones of arms and legs, including hands and feet, or their variant equivalents in the fishes, birds, seals, and several specialized forms. In addition, among the fishes and preverte-brates, there is also a visceral skeleton supporting gills and related structures, some of which persist, much modified, in higher vertebrates, as bones of the lower jaw, the inner ear, etc.

One important advantage of the inside skeleton is that it does not hamper individual growth as the outside arthropod skeleton does. The vertebrate, living outside its skeleton, can expand by growing all the muscles and other tissues it needs. Very helpful, too, especially in the infant and childhood period of rapid growth, is the fact that the skeleton itself can grow, first as cartilage, later by replacement by bone, and even by some replacement of the bone itself.

One result of such unhampered growth of the individual is to prove of immeasurable importance in later animal development, the fact that the young can start small and then grow to the mature adult size without substantial change in form. The young can be hatched small from an egg or born small, not in a different larval stage to permit free growing, but in close semblance to the adult, needing only growth to fill out to the mature form. How much this can mean will appear later in our story when we trace the origins of human intelligence and social instincts.

For the present, however, we must stick to the immediate mechanical advantages of the inner skeleton. Being inside, its hard members can be solid instead of tubular, and therefore more compact, a much simpler framework than one consisting of tubes and open joints. As it does not have a large outside shell for enclosing and protecting, it needs much less substance, only enough for physical strength, adequate support, and mechanical leverage. Its joints, being between solid instead of tubular members, are mechanically simpler and firmer, yet more flexible. More and larger operating muscles can be attached, with more freedom in their placing and action. Such freedom adds new possibilities in versatile appendages able to do a variety of things, as compared with the tubular appendages of many diverse forms, but each doing only its one specialized job. The lobster needs nineteen pairs of diversified appendages, while Man needs only one pair of legs with feet for traveling and one pair of arms with hands for all his handling jobs.

Pros and Cons of Armor Plate

Obviously, however, inside bones cannot do one useful thing which the arthropod exoskeleton does very well: it cannot provide a tough armor protecting the easily injured soft body parts. Only the vertebrate skull bones, near the surface under a thin layer of flesh, skin, and hair, scales, or feathers, afford armorlike protection. But the skull's job is special, as shield for the delicate and vital brain, situated unfortunately in the most exposed and vulnerable part of the body. How often, getting a good sound clunk on the cranium, have we not been thankful for being blessed with thick heads. But being also somewhat blessed with brains, we have often contrived and worn protective coverings of our own making, from hats to helmets, from baseball catcher's chest pads to shields, cuirasses, and coats of mail.

Nature, too, has on occasion fitted the vertebrate kin with protective armor, from the heavy head shields of the primitive ostracoderm precursors of the fishes (we shall meet them shortly) to armor-plated dinosaurs, turtles, and armadillos. Unlike the arthropod exoskeleton, these armors are really hardened skin, similar in this to fish and reptile scales, the feathers of birds, and the hair of mammals, all protective in their several ways. And as we shall see, skin was also the origin of horns, claws, hoofs, nails, beaks, and even teeth.

Because protective armor does have such obvious value, why is it not more common, indeed universal? The answer, simply enough, is that armor is heavy and cumbersome, hampering activity. A heavily armored animal is necessarily a slow animal. Remember the medieval jousting scene by Mark Twain, in which the Connecticut Yankee, mounted and equipped as a cowboy, by speed and maneuverability easily defeats his armor-encumbered opponent. Coat of mail for knight and charger was all very well for jousting with fellow knights burdened the same way, and abiding by the rules of chivalrous combat. It was all very well, too, for the noble ninny who wandered aimlessly over the countryside conquering imaginary dragons and picking up the maiden in distress who thereupon rewarded him by unchaperoned sharing of his shiftless life. But it does not do at all among the animals engaged in the grim business of survival in the ever-hostile world, where there are no rules of chivalrous combat, nor even a trace of mercy. They must face the practical realities, in this matter the choice between encumbered inertia and stupidity as against agility and alertness.

A few examples can be cited, the first from the geologic history of the molluscs. During the period from five hundred to two hundred million years ago, all known molluscs carried protective shells. A hundred million years later some had discarded their shells and become active forms such as our squid and octopus, swimming by jet propulsion and surviving by speed and very formidable weapons of aggression, powerful tentacles armed with gripping suckers, feeding a voracious mouth with a sharp tearing beak.

Another historic case is that of the ostracoderms of four hundred million years ago. Some were provided with a tough spreading head shield and were slow forms grubbing in the bottom muds. Others were more slender in form, with small heads, and protected by scales only on the flanks, leading swift and agile lives of predation, and in the end surviving their armor-plated kin, probably even taking part in their extinction. And still with us is a near relative of theirs, the little lancelot, named Amphioxus (meaning "double-pointed") by the scientists. It is only a couple of inches long, transparent, thin-skinned instead of armored, and surviving by its darting swiftness and its habit of quick burying in the sea sand. It is perfectly streamlined in its long spindle shape, which helps give it swiftness, and driven by unusually powerful muscles. But mere mention of Amphioxus, for most excellent reasons, brings us face to face with our central problem of the moment, the origin of the vertebrate stock.

Amphioxus, the Basic Vertebrate

The lowly Amphioxus, though very rare, is much discussed in biology textbooks and classrooms. For it is the living embodiment of that sketchy outline of the basic vertebrate which one would draw on the blackboard, it is so simple and elementary in structure. On first acquaintance, one might well think it to be in fact the very first and original vertebrate. But the knowing specialists have their doubts, suspecting it rather of being an evolutionary backslider from some more advanced form. There is no doubt, however, that it is very near the bottom of the vertebrate family tree, and it was certainly shaped by quite the same factors as gave the first fishlike vertebrates their typical streamlined form.

At the start, those first vertebrates lived only in the water. As they floated, swam, or crawled over the bottom, gravity gave them an up-and-down orientation, the dorsoventral asymmetry already mentioned. They were also surely forward-swimmers, with a fore-and-aft asymmetry. Left and right they were the same, bilaterally symmetrical. The geologic record also indicates that the early fish forms lived in fresh water, many of them in flowing streams. To keep themselves from being swept downstream into brackish estuaries and the salt sea, they had to keep headed upstream and swimming against the current. Even to remain in familiar feeding and breeding spots, they still had to do that. And if they did drift down to the sea and managed to adapt to survive, they still had to return upstream to lay eggs for the next generation of fresh-water fishes. In any case, they had to keep right side up, front upstream, and swim more or less vigorously against the current. For that they had to develop effective swimming means, form, and method (Figure 14).

AMPHIOXUS

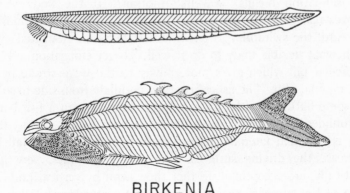

BIRKENIA

Fig. 14. Amphioxus and an Ostracoderm.

Nature has tried many experiments in swimming strokes and equipment. In Paramecium and the rotifers we found swimming by vibrating hairlike cilia, among the flagellates by whiplashing flagellae. The arthropods have developed appendages into punt poles and oars, and the lobster a tail flap for backward retreat.

Even jet propulsion has been tried, as in the scallop, squid, and octopus among the molluscs, and in the pulsing bell of the jellyfishes. But now a better method was to be worked out, sculling by undulation of the whole body.

Undulation and the Backbone

Perhaps we should instead say a "nearly new" or "improved" method, for it had already been tried by the carnivorous arrowworm. It too swims by body undulation, and even has a muscular tail extension to add undulation effectiveness. However, it does lack a stiffening notochord or backbone to give more power to its swimming stroke. So at least that much was really new, and most important, in the undulation swimming of the first fishlike vertebrate.

Undulation means "wavelike motion." If the body wave moves rearward, the swimming is forward; if the wave moves forward, the swimming is backward. It takes an elongated and somewhat flexible body to do it well. To get elongation, add a muscular tail which gives more power to the wave stroke by a strong final fillip. The fishes generally undulate from side to side, so some flattening sidewise is helpful. Even though a fish body is rounded, or flattened vertically for bottom living, at least the tail is flattened laterally, with vertical fins of body and tail to increase the driving surfaces. The skates and rays, very flat vertically, are exceptional in that they swim by vertical undulation of the lateral wing fins, coupled with lateral undulation of the tail. There is also vertical undulation in the side fins of other fishes, but with little driving power.

At any rate, undulation has proved to be the strongest and swiftest method of swimming that Nature has ever evolved. If you have watched a fish, porpoise, or seal flash through the water at high speed, you know what that can mean. Contributing greatly was the notochord or its backbone equivalent. The notochord may have first developed largely as a firm support for the new dorsal nerve cord. But also it became a general fulcrum for effective applications of muscular power in producing vigorous undulations. Now it serves in the embryos of all vertebrates as a temporary scaffolding for the vertebral column of cartilage or bone which soon replaces it.

So we can assume that undulation swimming, probably up against the currents of fresh-water streams, was a major factor in evolving the fish, in both outer shape and inner structure. The outer shape became the model for all streamlining, terminating in a flattened tail broadened by fin margins to give maximum power to the swimming stroke.

Segmentation prevailed through the inner structure: a backbone segmented into separate vertebrae; muscles correspondingly arranged into segment bands; nerves in a branching pattern to control the several segments for coordinated undulating body waves rearward or forward to give forward or rearward drive. Even the details of skeletal structure were adapted to undulation need. Thus, the vertebrae were pivoted one to the other to give the flexibility (normally lateral) for undulation. The bony processes of the vertebrae and the attached ribs serve for effective leverage when pulled by the attached muscles, giving great power. To you, trying to take a toothsome fish apart, those many bony ribs may seem but a mealtime nuisance, perhaps even hazard, but to the fish in life they meant speed for survival. For in this way, as in every way, the fish had become thoroughly organized for powerful undulation swimming. Thus, it was that the fish became the athlete of its early world, swift in both escape and aggression, pre-eminently fitted for survival and predominance.

As we proceed with our story of our over-all ancestry, we shall note one predominant fact: that the relatively simple axial skeleton of the fish is to remain as the axis on which all higher forms are constructed, the greater variations occurring in the appendages and the head end. If that basic backbone had not been there originally to build upon, those higher forms, including our human selves, would probably never have appeared here on Earth. And now it appears that the real reason for the back-bone's beginning was the presence of swift-flowing streams coursing down the slopes of ancient continents protruding above the level of the primal seas. How those continents came to be, how they were constantly being worn down by those selfsame streams, and then renewed by periodic mountain upheavals powered largely by radioactive heating was told in detail in my earlier installment of this story entitled *Our Emerging Universe*. There, too, it will appear that the Earth's possession of a relatively large Moon may have much to do with those continents and their streams, and therefore with the originating of that first backbone, and so with the final emerging of upright Man. Indeed, one might even truly say, "No Moon, no Man."

Seeking Our Backboned Ancestor

But be that as it may, it is now evident that in seeking for the first prevertebrate, we are looking for an animal which could readily become a fish. And behind that prevertebrate we are looking for a likely ancestor among the invertebrates. Stated otherwise, where among the invertebrates do we find the makings of a notochord and a dorsal nerve cord? If we find more than one such possible lineage, we must run down all the known clues, eliminate those we can, and in every way emulate the very best in detection methods to pin down the most likely suspect.

As things are, we should perhaps call this "The Case of Too Many Suspects." Our first job is, in fact, to do some sort of wholesale eliminating to narrow down our suspect list to workable proportions. This, fortunately, is now quite possible, using a test which is scientifically proper, though at first glance perhaps a bit technical.

Remember back in Chapter 7 how the lowest multicelled animals are two-layered in their embryonic development and matured structure, while the higher ones are three-layered. The added layer is in between and therefore called the mesoderm. From it developed new organs, largely of the muscular and supporting tissues. What is pertinent here is the manner in which that mesoderm originates in the embryo. There are two distinct ways. In one group the middle layer develops by a general splitting off of cells at the juncture edges of the ectoderm and endoderm. In the other there is a distinct folding and budding off of endoderm pouches. We can leave the technical details to the competent embryologist and take his word for it that the first way (teloblastic) is used by the annelid worms, molluscs, arthropods, while the other way (enterocoelic) is used by the flatworms, echinoderms, brachiopods, ostracoderms, Amphioxus, acorn worms, vertebrates, etc.

Because these two ways are basic and distinctive, we can be quite sure that the immediate ancestors of the vertebrates are not to be found among the invertebrates with teloblastic mesoderm development. Furthermore, this is supported by other basic evidence. Thus, in these two broad animal groups some have free-swimming larvae. These are of two differing types, the one limited to the first group, the second to the other group. Also, there is chemical evidence to the same effect. In both groups reserve energy, of a sort which can be drawn upon quickly by overworked muscles, is stored as phosphagens. But in the first group the phosphagen is arginine phosphate, while in the echinoderms and vertebrates it is creatine phosphate.

The upshot of all this is obviously that it rules out derivation of the vertebrates from any invertebrate of the first group. For instance, it bars the theory of the early evolutionist Étienne Geoffroy Saint-Hilaire (1818) that the vertebrate represents an insect turned upside down. Similar ideas involving turning over of some annelid or arthropod, to put the nerve stem above instead of below the digestive tube, were offered from 1876 to 1912 by C. Semper, A. Dohrn, C. S. Minot, and W. Patten. All involved such complications as moving eyes and brain upward around the inverted gullet, or opening a new mouth and gullet, to mention only a few of the serious difficulties. Patten particularly went into much detail, deriving the head-shielded ostracoderms from some head-shielded relative of the sea scorpions and the horseshoe crabs. Another theory starting with some kin of the horseshoe crab was that of W. H. Gaskell (1896 to 1910), who, however, did not turn the arthropod upside down, followed a different series of changes, and wound up with the larval form of the lamprey eel. Thus, he explained that the branches of the arthropod ventral nerve stem encircled the digestive tube, joined above it, and then merged into the single dorsal nerve cord of the vertebrates. In the scientific battle over these theories, many detailed objections were brought forth which added up to a conviction that they involved too many tricky changes, all pure assumptions anyway, without any intermediate stages to confirm them. And then there still remains the big over-all objection that arthropod and vertebrate are too remotely related, as evidenced by their basic differences in mesoderm development, supported by consistent further evidence such as has been cited already (Figure 15).

A somewhat similar objection must be raised against the theory of A. T. Masterman (1897) who derived Amphioxus from a comb jelly (related to the jellyfish). For this presumed ancestor is two-layered in its development, while Amphioxus is three-layered, a difference which separates them widely. We are much more likely to find the immediate ancestor of the vertebrates among the three-layered group, and specifically among those with the mesoderm of enterocoelic development.

In accord with this, A. A. W. Hubrecht in 1887 suggested a vertebrate origin from the nemertinean worms (questionably related to the flatworms), but this theory was superficial, took

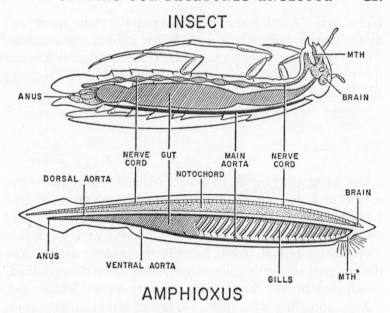

Fig. 15. Saint-Hilaire's "Notonectid" and Amphioxus.

too much for granted, with no new facts since found to support it.

But that leaves us with only two existing groups of invertebrates among which to look for the ancestor of the vertebrates, namely the brachiopods (lamp shells) and the echinoderms (starfishes, sea urchins, sea cucumbers, etc). We are of course gratified by this wholesale elimination of possibilities, but when we look over these remaining suspects, our hopes are seriously lowered. Thus, the lamp shells have two-hinged shells, look superficially like bivalve molluscs (oysters, clams, etc.), and seem utterly unlikely as vertebrate ancestors.

Nor do the echinoderms look one whit more promising, with their normal radial structure, ring nervous system, hydraulic tube feet, snapper spines, and other highly specialized features. Only the sea cucumber has even the bilateral form basic to the higher animals, but against that it shares the many specialized echinoderm features which seem to bar it from consideration. And so once more we apparently have come to a dead end in our quest for that most important ancestor capable of becoming backboned and dorsal-nerved as a prevertebrate.

The Promising Clue

But let us not give up so easily. Remember that the origin of the primeval vertebrate must have occurred perhaps half a billion years ago, that the echinoderm ancestors of that day could have been (in fact, were) very different from the highly specialized forms of today. Actually the geologic record does disclose just such early echinoderm forms, as yet unspecialized, which hint toward the common ancestry we are looking for.

Supporting this is the suggestive fact that these ancient echinoderm forms resemble somewhat the tadpolelike, free-swimming larvae of present-day echinoderms and of certain types of humble prevertebrates found today. Among these prevertebrates are Balanoglossus, the acorn worm, rather remotely related to Amphioxus, which burrows through the sea sand for its food. Perhaps even more important are the ascidians or tunicates, commonly called sea squirts, which have this same type of tadpole larvae but grow up to attach themselves and settle down as lazy inert bags covered with thick tunics of plantlike cellulose. These ascidians have been long familar in the theories of vertebrate origins for quite another reason. As early as 1866, within a few years of Darwin's *Origin of Species*, Alexander O. Kovalevsky published his discovery that the ascidian tadpole larva had a notochord, which then disappeared as the adult settled down to its sedentary life. This was promptly popularized by Ernest Haeckel, the great German battler for Darwinism, as a vital clue to the ancestry of the vertebrates. We now know that Balanoglossus also has a temporary larval notochord, confirming its proper place among the prevertebrates.

And then, in 1894, W. Garstang broached a novel and helpful idea which was revived by G. R. de Beer in 1936. That idea was to look for the ancestor of the vertebrates not among adult invertebrate forms but among their larvae. He went further to assume that this ancestral larva just did not grow up to become an adult in the usual manner. Instead, it would have retained a tadpole form, its swimming reinforced by a tail and also by development of a simple dorsal stiffening rod or notochord. Previously it would have grown up normally into an invertebrate adult, such as a primitive unspecialized echinoderm. But as time went on, it delayed its invertebrate adulthood but otherwise matured in reproductive capacity, and thus slowly differentiated into a new adulthood, the first prevertebrate. Unfortunately, if this is the true story, we have not found any specimen of that first prevertebrate, either in the geologic record or among the living animal forms.

However, that does not mean that it could not have occurred, for this sort of thing is known to happen. Thus, the well-known Axolotl of the cold mountain lakes of Mexico, a foot-long tadpolelike creature with gills and fins, when transferred to warmer waters or given a dose of thyroid, becomes a four-legged land salamander usually identified as *Ambystoma tigrinum*. Left in its native cold lakes, it does not grow into the land form but does become sexually mature and reproduces its kind. This phenomenon, through rather rare, does occur elsewhere in the animal world, and is known as neotony, meaning "youth extending." Garstang's theory is therefore quite reasonable as the mode of origin of the backboned tribe, and is generally favored by top authorities on animal evolution.

By now it is quite obvious that Amphioxus, with its adult dorsal nerve cord and notochord, belongs definitely among the prevertebrates. However, there are strong rivals for this honor in the primitive and now extinct ostracoderms which we know only from their fossils. But some of those fossils have been remarkably well preserved and, as studied by E. A. Stensiö and others, have given us an intimate knowledge of their anatomy, internal as well as external. Many authorities in fact consider them as probably the very earliest of the known vertebrates, even antedating Amphioxus, which may have descended from them by a dropping of some of their specialized features. Some of the reasons for thinking so will appear in the next chapter, where we go into the further steps in vertebrate evolution.

But in ending this chapter, it should be made clear that the authorities in this field are fully agreed in only one way on this problem of vertebrate origins: they all agree that it is still an unsettled puzzle, that all the theories are tentative and arguable, that more facts are needed and should be searched for; in short, that our scientific minds must be kept open, ready to consider any likely theory, always of course on the basis of factual evidence and its own merits.

Chapter 14

OUR OLD FISH FACE

Man's face is a made-over fish face, and the original fish face was essentially just a food trap. So when you are impolitely told to "shut your trap," that insult is at least scientifically correct. For without the slightest doubt, we have inherited the ground plan of our human face from old Grandfather Fish, and can trace the pedigree step by step with complete certainty and in virtually unbroken continuity.

That old fish face was built up of two groups of features. Up front in the middle was the food trap proper, the mouth itself and its accessories. Then about it was a set of detector organs, all in pairs for locating food to right or left or points between, two eyes, two nostrils, and two ears. Or perhaps we should not call them ears at this point. Rather, they are mixed-up sense organs, partly scattered as little spots over the surface, partly located deep inside, not yet used for true hearing but merely to detect water pressures and disturbances and to maintain balance. But more of that later.

Of course the facial profile of the fish, then and now, differs greatly from our own. Compared with us, he is literally a low-brow, and for two good reasons. First, he has but little brain within to bulge his brow. Second, necessity demands that his face taper to a point. For he lives in water, the density of which resists motion through it, so he must have perfect streamlining to make speed easily. We ourselves, in thin yielding air, do not need the tapered shape, for at ordinary speeds air offers negligible resistance. So we are free to take on any convenient shape to fit our ways of keeping alive. This the fish can do only within narrow limits. Primarily he must keep his streamlining, but can grow thin and tall to slip through narrow spaces between upright stems and rocks, or he can flatten down wide to fit himself for feeding close to the bottom. But if you look him over closely, you will find that he is always carefully organized to help his mouth feed his face. For first and foremost, he is an animated, aggressive, and highly successful food trap.

The Primitive Fish Face

The story of the evolution of that old fish face to our own is a fascinating one which we shall recount in due course. But first, naturally, we must learn how that original fish face itself took shape. Of course there have been other faces before among the invertebrates, with a food-trap mouth assisted by various accessories and detector sense organs. But this new face really did have features all its own, and these we must trace. Among these innovations, for instance, were jaws and teeth, obviously very important. Some of the sense organs were also quite new, while others were merely improved. And above all, behind that face was a new kind of brain, destined for an extraordinary future.

In the previous chapter we discussed several prevertebrates and the very first vertebrates. The latter, at least, were fish in general outward looks. We were uncertain which came really first, since there were at least two leading contenders, Amphioxus and the ostracoderms. We did find the latter tentatively preferred by modern authorities as the lowliest and earliest of the known vertebrates. Amphioxus would then be somewhat simpler, a presumably backsliding descendant. Other probable descendants, more or less direct, are the living hagfishes and lamprey eels, slender and somewhat advanced forms which share at least one important feature with Amphioxus and the ostracoderms: they lack the true fish jaws.

Jaws, as we know them in nearly all the vertebrates, were definitely not original equipment in the early vertebrate models. On the whole, those first vertebrates presumably fed by food sifting. Originally their mouths were just toothless openings, more or less round, for taking in small particles as food. Amphioxus has cilia about its mouth to sweep in food particles, and mere sucking doubtless served the same purpose in other forms. In the hagfishes and lamprey eels, toothlike horny points may edge the mouth opening, being used to saw their way into the bodies of their prey. And some ostracoderms did develop sharp bony mouth plates which could move and bite. True teeth, however, were lacking, and food sifting was the prevailing and probably original method of feeding. Water was drawn into the mouth, carried back through a tubular mouth cavity, and expelled through gill openings on the two sides at the rear of the head. The food particles in the water were strained out by a comblike structure and then swallowed. But also the oxygen in the water was extracted by absorption through thin gill membranes suffused with circulating blood, the fish means and method of breathing (Figure 16).

Originally the gills were most likely a series of separate openings in the walls of the mouth cavity. But for absorbing efficiency, they soon developed into thin and delicate membraneous structures which required rigid supports, a series of cartilaginous frameworks called the visceral or gill arches. Eventually, too, a tough outer cover flap, the operculum, developed on each side to protect the whole delicate and vulnerable gill assembly. As the openings were only rearward, they did not interfere with the streamlining for forward movement, but pulsed rhythmically as they let water out from the mouth cavity.

The earliest ostracoderms, which left us fairly complete fossil remains, reveal a broadly flattened and heavily armored head and trunk, with a roundish mouth set underneath and forward for convenient bottom feeding, the mouth cavity being a bellowslike structure edged with gill openings. These creatures were obviously only sluggish food sifters. But about the same time there were others with narrow head and body, the armor much reduced, quite streamlined for swift swimming. Among them there developed the mouth edged with movable biting skin plates, marking the active and aggressive predator attacking and feeding on larger animal victims, such as the abundant squids and other mollusc relatives which up to then had dominated

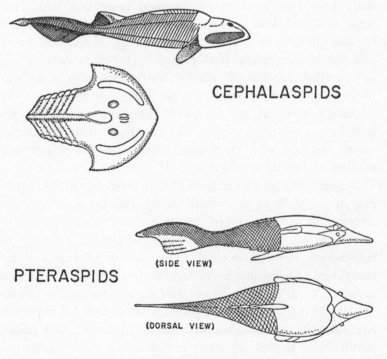

CEPHALASPIDS

PTERASPIDS

(SIDE VIEW)

(DORSAL VIEW)

Fig. 16. Early Jawless "Fishes."

the seas. Those predator ostracoderms undoubtedly represented the beginning of the end for the molluscan dominance, and perhaps, too, the eventual nemesis for the sluggard ostracoderms, which relied largely on heavy armor plate.

The improved ostracoderms certainly did flourish, multiplying their kinds by taking many strange forms. Today their most direct descendants are the hagfishes and lamprey eels, jawless still but otherwise become equipped with thorny horn teeth, making possible their lives of piracy. Those teeth, however, are not ancestral to the true teeth of modern design developed by the later fishes. But before those ultimate teeth there came jaws.

True Jaws and Teeth

The first true jaws were developed by the placoderms, another well-armored group doubtless descended from ostracoderms. The mouth was still edged with hard skin plates, but behind them were simple upper and lower skeletal supports of cartilage, attached by loose joints at the rear on each side, permitting opening and closing of the mouth by vertical movements. Those cartilages, however, were not new formations but transformed gill arches. Those gill arches had already developed joints to permit rhythmic spreading as the fish breathed in and out, were now further adapted to serve as the first jaw cartilages. Later in evolutionary progress they were to be supplemented and replaced by bone.

To serve their purpose, jaws have to be clamped together by powerful muscles. And these developed from gill muscles. Originally only strong enough for gentle rhythmic breathing, the gill muscles grew larger and stronger as jaw clamping demanded. In the end, the firmly supported jaws, jointed for wide opening and operated by powerful muscles, made possible the seizing, overcoming, and swallowing of large animal prey. Only strong sharp teeth were then needed to make the fishlike vertebrate a superior pirate.

In our sharks of today we can see just how those teeth finally originated. They are definitely made-over skin tubercles. Even before the sharks, some ostracoderms had reduced their armor plate to a scattering of horny knobs anchored in their thick hides. On the sharks that same protective knobby hide is our familiar shagreen, so tough it has been used for the shoes of lively youngsters who are really hard on the footwear budget. Examining this shagreen closely, we find that each little knob consists of a thickened horny layer of "enamel" laid down between skin and pulp cavity, finally becoming pointed and breaking out through the skin. But that is also the basic structure of full-fledged vertebrate teeth.

To see exactly what must have happened, take a close look at the edges of the mouth of a shark specimen. Outside, about the lips, the skin tubercles are just the ordinary sort found all over the body. But where the skin folds in over the lips, the tubercles grow into larger, sharper, and inward-pointing denticles, very effective for seizing, holding, and tearing living prey struggling to escape. Thus, the skin knobs become real teeth, moving in over the lips to replace older teeth that break or come loose. About all that the higher animals have since added are some reinforcing cement, firmer seating in stronger bony jaws, and adaptive modifying into special tooth shapes for cutting, grinding, etc.

The same sort of skin tubercles elsewhere on the body later developed into the flat enamellike scales of the ganoids (meaning "shining") to which sturgeons, bowfins, and gar pikes belong. From these ganoid scales later came the thin shingle-lapped horny scales of the familiar bony fishes. Incidentally, the scales found on insects and reptiles, even here and there on birds and mammals, are very different in both their structures and their origins.

Future of the Face

Anticipating a bit, we can summarize briefly the later general evolution of the old fish face, at least in its outward aspects. Beginning with the original streamlined and tapered face of the fish, we find it built up of a great many pieces of cartilage or bone to make skull, face, jaws, gills, etc. Muscles are generally inside, and the skull and face bones are covered not with mobile flesh but only thinly with skin, scales, or hard plates, presenting the general staring aspect of a mask. In the course of later evolution, many of the skull bones were discarded, and several fused to make one, thus gradually reducing their number to the comparatively few we have today.

Another broad development was that the original skull and gill units were often changed greatly in shape and size and use, gill arches becoming jaw structures or ear parts, etc. But more important for outward looks, the muscles found outside attachments and so crept gradually outward, finally clothing the old fish mask with a covering of animated flesh and expressiveness. Much of the expressiveness resides in the mobile lips, which represent the culmination in evolution of the facial muscles. Making the new mobility expressive is a large part of the business of the facial nerves, which of course accompanied the muscles they controlled to the outside, in the fortunate evolutionary migration which transformed the old hard fish face into a living face.

We are luckily able to follow all this series of changes in skull and face with convincing certainty. Here and there are gaps in the record as preserved by living and fossil forms, but they are all minor gaps. So the story can be clearly traced and told in much detail and continuity. Here, of course, we must boil down the story to essentials, but for details clearly told we can refer the reader to the remarkable book *Our Face from Fish to Man,* by Dr. William K. Gregory of The American Museum of Natural History. Some of the further essentials, however, will be introduced in the proper settings of time and circumstance as we proceed with our story.

Senses of Smell and Taste

Quite as important as the powerfully muscled jaws equipped with sharp teeth for the capturing and tearing up of food are the paired sets of sense organs for detecting and locating that food. Among the detector organs of the early vertebrates, those concerned with smell and taste were certainly of great importance. Thus, in the lamprey eel and the sharks the nose organ is much enlarged and the smell center comprises a third or more of the total brain weight. The reason, of course, is that in water, smell and taste are the most certain and immediate means for locating and recognizing food, nearly always the matter of prime interest to the animal.

Smell and taste are chemical senses, acted upon by substances dissolved in water or, in dry-land animals, dissolved in the mucus of mouth and nose. Chemical reactivity was already an old sense, guiding even the most primitive animals in finding and selecting food. Paramecium guided by bacterial acidity, the tentacles of Hydra recognizing and seizing food particles, such are early instances of chemical reactivity, destined to develop into highly sensitive and discriminating senses embodied in specialized detector organs and much enlarged brain centers. In our sharks, for example, the entire forebrain is devoted to the smell sense, and is connected by the largest pair of nerves in the body to great areas of exposed sensory surface folded compactly into two big rosette-shaped smell organs placed front and center in the snout, with paired nostril openings to bring in water tainted with the odors which tell of food nearby. The pairing of the nostrils to left and right may help in locating the prey and guiding search for it.

A primary function of smell is detection of prospective food at a distance. The stimulus is therefore normally a weak odor diluted through much water or air, requiring high sensitivity to detect. Taste, on the other hand, is a test of nearby substances, guarding against the noxious and inedible, selecting the suitable and desirable in foods. Its organs are therefore usually taste buds within the mouth itself, for sampling foods before final swallowing. But taste organs may also occur elsewhere—for example, the catfish, with taste buds distributed generally over the body and concentrated at the tips of its whiskerlike barbels. These are constantly used in the search for food, the barbel tips reaching into crannies and bottom mud, literally tasting the food particles which the catfish then instantly snaps up. In this instance the taste sense and the muscular response are so primary that more than half the catfish brain is devoted to them.

In ourselves, taste is a simpler sense than it ordinarily seems, since there are only four basic tastes: sweet, sour, salt, and bitter. The multitude of differing flavors which we readily distinguish are simply compounded out of mixtures of these four in various proportions, normally plus a blend of odors. One can easily test this by holding the nose while sampling some bits of onion and potato, then trying again with the nose open. This combining of smell with taste is made possible by the opening of the nasal passages to the rear of the mouth cavity. In the sharks, however, there is only a groove between nostril and lip, but this undoubtedly serves quite the same purpose.

This does not mean, however, that our lowly shark is an epicure, discriminating in choice and deliberately prolonging the savoring of tasteful delicacies. Instead, its rosette organ, stimulated by a faint diluted odor of prey in the vicinity, sends an instant message to the forebrain, which is relayed to lower brain centers which set going the muscles for swimming, in fast search and rushing attack. As the odor grows with nearness, taste, too, is stimulated. The taste buds are also brain-connected, but to the centers which control opening of the jaws, their clasping bite, the tearing apart of prey, and the gulping down by the eager throat, all to meet the primary physiological need for energy-giving food.

Broadly, such were the beginnings of the senses of smell and taste among the vertebrates. They developed, of course, as the animal kinds met new conditions, but on the whole the changes were minor. Such as they were, and when significant, we shall note these changes as our story goes on.

The Equilibrium Sense

We turn now to another group of senses, basically of touch, but varying widely in use and combining in ways that at first seem odd, though we shall discover that they are natural enough when we go into their development.

When you and I are standing, sitting, or lying down, we are resting on something solid and have a sense of the downward pull of gravity. Though we rarely give it conscious thought, we also have an awareness of the relative positions of our body parts. So we know which way is up, how we are oriented in relation to up and down, and how our body parts are placed, folded, or otherwise disposed. Standing up, for instance, we feel the floor pressing up against our feet, feel the erectness of the body and the balancing strains of the muscles holding us upright, and so know quite clearly our positions of the moment relative to both ourselves and our outer world. And as we move, each shift of positions is felt, consciously or semiconsciously, to guide us progressively in the making of our movements.

But the fish, floating in buoyant water, at least does not have the guiding pressure of a solid underneath to indicate up and down. He may well have a sense of body parts and their momentary disposition, but he also needs a sense of orientation and equilibrium. For in his watery world, up and down are really important, even though he cannot fall over as we can. Thus, he is usually colored differently top and bottom: dark on top to merge inconspicuously with dark bottoms when viewed from above; light underneath to merge with the light from the sky when viewed from below. Such inconspicuousness helps him hide both from enemies that may detect and attack and from prey that may take warning and escape. To stay hidden, the fish must keep constantly right side up. If he rolls over a bit, you instantly catch the flash of his white belly. Right position also helps greatly in the making of effective movements.

So from the very first the fishes needed a sense of balance and, of course, a corresponding sense organ for maintaining balance. That organ, which we have inherited almost intact, is located close to the hearing ear and consists of three semicircular tubes or canals containing fluid which splashes back and forth within them when we or the fishes turn or tip in any direction. For each is lined with nerve endings which register the pressures of fluid flowing by as we turn and tip our heads. They do this in three directions, for the plane of one tubular loop is vertical from front to back, telling us when we tip forward or backward; the second is vertical again but set sidewise to catch tipping movements in that direction; while the third is horizontal to tell of movements of turning around. This last probably gives us the dizzy feeling when we have been whirling around rapidly, perhaps because its fluid has also been set whirling and keeps on doing so after we have stopped, giving us the impression that we are now whirling in the opposite and unwinding direction.

Furthermore, those same semicircular canals register not only turning and tilting movements but also our balance position relative to up and down. But since our ancestral fish days there has evolved a supplementary organ, a pouchlike sacculus below the canals, devoted more particularly to maintaining balance. For its floor is lined with fine hairlike nerve endings, and nestled among these are little limestone bodies called *otoliths* ("oto" for "ear," "lith" for "stone"). If we are right side up, these bodies register the fact by their normal pressures on the surrounding hairs. But if the body is tipped off balance, these bodies press sidewise against adjacent hairs and so register the off-balance position.

This equilibrium sense and its organs are professionally known as the *otic* sense and organs, meaning "near the ear." For in ourselves and our vertebrate ancestors, this organ and inner hearing ear are mixed up together structurally. In the fishes, however, sense of hearing and the hearing organ are rather primitive. But they did develop in due course, though in a rather odd way. To trace that development, however, we must first consider another basic problem of fish position and movement.

The Orientation Sense

In the previous chapter, while explaining the streamlining of the fish shape, we noted that the early fishes probably originated in the flowing waters of streams and so developed both their body form and their muscularity for strong and swift swimming upstream. That same swimming capacity, once acquired in flowing water, would also serve most usefully in still water, for swift pursuit of prey and swift escape from enemies. But especially in streams, keeping headed continuously upstream against the current became a major necessity.

To do just that the fish had a special sense and a corresponding sense organ, the so-called lateral-line sense and organ. It is called this because it is exactly that, a lateral line on each side of the fish body. Varying somewhat among different kinds of fishes, the lateral line is essentially a system of fine tubes underneath the skin, branching (mostly at the head end) over each side of the body and generally associated with spot sense organs scattered over the surface. These are all connected to the same hindbrain centers as the otic or equilibrium organs, which is natural enough as they all have to do with sensing and controlling body positions and movements. For experiments have shown that the lateral-line and associated organs sense changes in water pressures and, what comes to the same thing, water vibrations. Thus, if the fish should swing broadside to the current of the stream, pressures would increase on the upstream side, decrease on the downstream side, and the fish would be warned to turn back to face upstream, when the pressures on the two sides would again be in equal balance and at a maximum at the head end. Of course this whole adjustment is made automatically and instantly, without the fish giving it even a thought, and so constantly that one does not realize that any deviation from the upstream pointing has even occurred.

To realize how important and effective this sense and control must really be, watch a salmon climbing upstream through swift rapids and even up the sheer face of a waterfall. Notice that the fish does not head for still waters, which of course settle down behind upstream obstructions, though it may sometimes leap right over such obstacles. Instead, it dashes into the swiftest-racing water, which naturally comes through channels which are open upstream. The only guide the fish really has is that rush of water, and the only way through is up into the very swiftest current, including that sheer drop of the waterfall. The marvel of it is not just the power to drive up through the swift and falling water, but the precise guiding afforded by the lateral-line sense of water pressures. In that seething turmoil, visibility is nil, so the eyes probably help not at all. So there is nothing but that mighty drive, and the automatic steering upward through the downward-rushing currents, guided by the simple pressure-sensitive organs inconspicuously marking the sides of the body. Were the course not steered true, right into the teeth of the current, the fish would be caught by side pressure, swept aside and downstream, to be buffeted by swirls and dashed helplessly against obstructing rocks.

The Sense of Hearing

The same lateral-line organs probably sense even slight vibratory disturbances in the water which may mean enemies or prey. Such disturbances may be due to surface waves, the splash of something falling into the water, or true sounds produced by the animal life of sea or lake or stream. Dr. James M. Moulton, after a season of underseas microphone listening along the Atlantic Coast from Maine to Bermuda, reported on the various characteristic sounds produced by animals: the snapping of the oversize claw of a tiny shrimp, fish rubbing teeth or hard plates together to make sounds like the "noisy eating of celery," or of a "klaxon horn," others that grunt, bark or whine, even whales that "talk together." Then there are the fishermen of Syria, Japan, and Malaya who locate good fishing spots by listening for the characteristic sounds of the fishes they seek. Experiments have shown that some fishes respond in various ways to such sounds "uttered" by their own kin, and it is a widespread practice for fisherman to thrash the water, bang their boats, and otherwise use noises to herd their fish prey into nets or shallows for easy catching. And a recent report by Donald R. Nelson and Samuel H. Gruber of the Institute of Marine Science at Miami, Florida, tells of sharks attracted by low-frequency pulsed sounds resembling those of a struggling fish, confirming a familiar observation by fishermen and skin divers that sharks frequently appear in the vicinity of wounded or struggling fish.

Yet despite such evidence, there are doubts whether the fish hears and interprets sound as we do, and it is suspected that there is no sensation except of water vibrations, some of which may be recognized as significant in the life of the fish. We do know that the fish lacks the characteristic structures of our own ears, the shell and tube of the external ear, the transmitting bones of the middle ear, and the very specialized spiral cochlea of the inner ear. But on the other hand, the amphibian descendants of the fish that climbed out of the water on to the land did in fact evolve true ears from skin organs of the lateral-line group, plus bits of reconstructed gill arches, etc. One result is that the semicircular canals, the organ of equilibrium, became thoroughly mixed up with the general structure which includes the true ear. Also, the nerves leading from the lateral-line organs persisted as hearing nerves for the ear proper, and led to the same composite center of the brain, which started as the third or hindbrain of the fish.

The Headquarters Brain

So we have accounted for the origins of at least some of the conspicuous senses and their sense organs—those of smell, taste, balance, and water pressures and vibrations (eventual hearing). Their nerves led originally to two of the three basic brain segments, those of smell and taste to the forebrain, the two others to the hindbrain. The midbrain was the center for the sense of sight, to be taken up later. Each of the three early brain divisions represented an original segment of the dorsal nerve stem, harking back perhaps to a general segmentation of the whole, as do the muscle bands of the fish and the separate vertebrae of our own backbones. To this basic brain structure were then added other lobes, among them a transitory one called the valvula, present only in fishes and somehow associated with highly developed lateral-line organs, but still a mystery as to its exact functions. More permanent were two new lobes, both paired left and right. First of these, the cerebellum, developed from the front end of the hindbrain segment, and later the cerebrum from the forebrain, the latter destined to become the seat of our highest intelligence.

So we see, behind the food-trap face of old Grandfather Fish, at least the ground plan of a brain with many remarkable future possibilities. It was the front office where pertinent facts were gathered and filed, and response activities worked out and controlled. It was departmentalized for handling diverse kinds of facts and their related response activities, yet it was also sufficiently coordinated for over-all relating of facts and for over-all courses of concerted action. It was well organized at least to take care of current and pressing needs, but fortunately was also to prove elastic and adaptable enough to meet many diverse future needs as they became pressing. In short, it had the makings of all the brains which the higher vertebrates would come to need and evolve.

As we proceed with our story of the evolving vertebrates, we shall of course find collateral changes in the sense organs which feed facts to the changing brain, and have already touched on such a change from lateral pressure organs to ears for hearing. Also, we shall note a series of changes in the physical skull and face, always of course in adaptation to changing conditions of life. But we shall defer the details to the proper times and places.

Chapter 15

WE CLIMB ASHORE

Had a space traveler from a distant solar system landed on our Earth some half a billion years ago, he would have gazed upon a barren landscape quite unlike that we know today. Where we find delight in the verdant expanses of grasses, shrubs, and forests, he would have seen only the bare earth devoid of all visible life, either plant or animal, with only exposed rock or coarse sand, but nowhere the fine surface soil derived from disintegrating plants. Every slope and plain, lacking plant roots to bind the loose material together, would be rutted and channeled by rainstorm freshets and running streams, or in drier areas billowed by shifting windblown sand dunes. Only the mountains, though even more bald than now, would seem at all the same. It would be altogether a harsh and inhospitable landscape.

But some still day, had he stood on the shore of sea or lake, he would have noted patches of floating green, or now and then splashes or lesser disturbances as animate life here and there broke the water surface. And in seashore pools left by the receding tide or the departing storm, he would have discovered some of these animate forms squirming and gasping for air, or already dead and rotting away, or dried out and half buried, but on the land proper no signs of present life, either plant or animal. Only if he had peered into the waters of streams or shore shallows would he have dimly seen the moving shapes of strange creatures, crawling over the bottom, or floating quietly, or darting swiftly in dashing pursuit or escape. For the waters were abundantly populated with life, from the most lowly plants to strange and primitive precursors of the backbone fishes. But none as yet lived ashore, except perhaps some subsurface bacteria hidden in the moistened earth.

The Unpromising Land

But climbing ashore was about to begin, though it would not near completion for another couple of hundred million years. The plants would lead the shoreward exodus, despite the fact that the animals were largely motile, which the plants seldom were. For the animals, after all, lived on plant food, either directly as plant eaters or indirectly as carnivorous eaters of plant eaters. So they had to wait until their plant food supply had established a sufficient foothold on the land, and therefore could not themselves lead the procession shoreward.

Besides, mere motility was not nearly enough for taking the serious step from water to dry land and air. Any life form, either plant or animal, adapted to living in the water could not simply move ashore without undergoing a whole series of evolutionary changes fitting it to land and air life. For land and air presented a wide array of new practical conditions and problems making necessary profound evolutionary adaptations. That took time, lengths of time that we describe by geologic ages, each literally tens of millions of years during the over-all period of landward migration we are here describing. That meant plenty of time for stepward moving ashore generation by generation, even without benefit of motility.

Compared with the water, the land was a seriously difficult habitat. There was the matter of constancy of temperatures. Sea and lake were reasonably constant in temperature. They did vary from equator to the poles, and changed slowly with the seasons, but except in shallows heated by the Sun, changed little through the day. But land and air temperatures were most inconstant, varying hourly, daily, and seasonally through extreme ranges.

Furthermore, water contained a convenient supply of the materials essential to cell growth and functioning. Air had few of these. It had plenty of nitrogen, but not in usable chemical combination. But particularly there was lack of water, the chief constituent of protoplasm and most necessary to all cell life.

The water habitat also provided flotational buoyancy absent on the land. Soft-bodied organisms were feasible, not subject to collapse under gravitational pull. To conquer the land, rigid and sturdy supporting stems, shells, and skeletons had to be evolved. For the motile animals, this meant also muscle systems powerful enough to move them. Eventually this imposed real limitations on the sizes attainable by the land animals, though less so on the plants.

The Plant Pioneers

The plants had long before already accomplished the fundamental achievement of photosynthesis, the ability to capture the energy of sunlight and store it chemically as a source of living energy. This, we have learned, gave them a basic self-sufficiency but deprived them of the need for movement and alert responsiveness. They were thereby condemned to inertness and probably a lack of conscious awareness, either of self or of the world about them. Instead, as we say, they merely vegetated.

Their needs were simple: ambient water to give them floating support, that same water bringing raw materials and carrying off wastes; and sunlight providing energy to be absorbed, converted, stored, and then tapped as needed for life processes. In streams and tidal shallows, anchorage against flowing waters necessitated attachment by filaments, but not true absorbing roots. The great need was for sufficient sunshine, best secured at or near the water surface by means of flotational airspaces, etc.

But excess sunlight might do damage, and protective devices evolved, such as filtering pigments among the algae and daily movement of some single-celled forms to float deeper to temper bright sunlight and rise toward the surface as the light waned. Some forms grew to huge sizes spreading out over much surface by lengthened filaments, by branching and flattening, any means retaining thin structures exposing the greatest amount of surface both to light and to surrounding water. By this process no cell was buried too deeply for ready access to raw materials and foodstuffs, or for rapid removal of wastes, with a minimum of internal transport of its fluids.

But subject to such limitations, mere size was not in itself either greatly advantageous or disadvantageous, and we find the algae and their plant associates ranging in size from the simple single-celled to the giant hundred-foot lengths of kelp and sargassum, and these last perhaps limited more by breaking apart by wave violence than by inherent growth factors. They grew abundantly then as now as the "grass of the seas," and even today far exceed all plant life on the land. But through all geologic history, despite many variant adaptations to their water habitat, they never developed proper roots, stems, bark, flowers, seeds, and leaves, nor the fundamental internal structure characteristic of the sturdy land plants.

The fossil record suggests that the great landward exodus of the plants may have started during the Ordovician Period, which began about 490 million years ago and lasted some seventy million years. But the migration was still feeble in the next period, the relatively short twenty million years of the Silurian, when the pioneer land scorpions and millipedes began the animal procession shoreward.

The occasion and opportunity for plant migration was probably the exposure of mud flats by tidal ebb and flow and by shrinkages of lakes in dry seasons. Plants occupying the exposed borders would have to develop adaptations for at least temporary survival in dryness and air. But this would be a step toward permanent occupancy, first in moist land areas, eventually in drier ones.

At the very outset, mere spreading out flatly over exposed surfaces might well do. But with such continued spreading came inevitable crowding, making advantageous any variations involving upward reaching toward light by stem growth, branching, and leaf exposure. This required more rigid and sturdy woody structures for support and firmer anchorage. More and more water had to be drawn from the moist earth through true absorbing roots and up through stems to the spreading green foliage. Eventually this foliage would become thin flat leaves exposing much surface, with chlorophyll, energized by sunlight, compounding energy-storing foodstuffs from that water and the carbon dioxide now absorbed from the air. So on the one hand, tougher substances, largely the carbohydrate cellulose, gave rigidity and strength, while on the other hand, the foliage retained a porous vascular structure through which a watery sap could rise from root to leaf, carrying usable nitrogen compounds and needed minerals. Much of the water would be decomposed and recompounded in the chlorophyll laboratories of the green cells, and much also lost by mere evaporation. There was therefore a great need for water, a serious handicap during times of drought or in areas with a slight water supply.

Such basic adaptation were generally accomplished early in the evolution of the land plants. But other problems, especially those of cross-fertilization and of species dispersal, also demanded important adaptations, some of them delayed until relatively recent geologic times. These, however, belong in a later chapter.

The First Land Animals

Our fossil record for the first animals to climb ashore is very scanty, the conditions on the land being altogether adverse to the fossil preservation of any but animals with hard parts. In fact, it even seems unlikely that any soft-bodied ones succeeded in gaining an early foothold on the land, though much later the land snails did manage it, aided perhaps by the hard shells by which we know them. To this day, however, they live in moist places, and they did have the luck of developing an air-breathing lung out of a convenient mantle cavity. Some of their descendants went back into the water, and these kept their lungs. But the other snails, which never gained the land, still breathe with the original gills.

But the very first animals we know to have climbed ashore were Silurian land scorpions, probably descended from sea-scorpion relatives called eurypterids. Next came the millipedes, still Silurian, followed in due course by other arthropods. A close relative of our own tough cockroach appeared early, but the whole tribe of the insects probably originated from more generalized land arthropods and soon diversified to all their wide variety to occupy every available niche in the economy of Nature, even growing wings and taking flight, the very earliest fliers being probably dragonflies during the warm Pennsylvanian or Coal Period.

In their conquest of the land and air, the arthropods were no doubt helped greatly by their impervious exterior integument which reduced water loss by evaporation, a very great advantage in the dry air. And the scorpions inherited an old apparatus for breathing in water, which was apparently readily adapted for air breathing. It consists of branching tubes called tracheae starting as surface openings in the integument and extending inward throughout the body to carry air (initially mixed with water) to all the tissues, and there removing the carbon-dioxide wastes. These tracheae were sometimes retained, in other cases evolving into leaflike structures in so-called "lung books." Thus the exchange and transport of oxygen and carbon dioxide was quite direct between air and tissue, with little transport via the bloodstream.

But the hard exterior integument also had its disadvantages. First, it imposed a general limitation on attainable over-all size, the bulk and weight increasing faster than the surface area, progressively demanding relative thickening to maintain adequate supporting strength.

Even more serious was the need for repeated molting as the individual arthropod grew, from initial small size as hatched from the egg to the full growth of maturity. During each molting the unprotected creature not only had to hide from aggressively hungry enemies, but also had to retire from exposure to excessive drying.

Another complication arose from the hereditary tendency described and perhaps overemphasized by Haeckel as the Biogenetic Law. The individual animal, in its development from egg to adult, tended to pass through a recapitulation, with many omissions and modifications of stages of its ancestral evolution. This, for many arthropods, meant laying their eggs in water, these hatching to water-living larvae, and eventual metamorphosis to a land-and-air stage. Or even for those kinds which laid their eggs in moist places on land, in protective nests, in living hosts, or on organic matter providing food for the hatched larvae the tendency toward recapitulation was often strong, resulting then in series of metamorphoses and moltings complicating growth, living, and reproduction. The chances of survival were thus greatly reduced, this being generally offset simply by prolific laying of eggs.

The Vertebrate Migration

Very probably, the vertebrates were roughly a hundred million years behind the invertebrates in their exodus from water to land. Yet they did have some definite advantages, one of which was the internal backboned skeletal support making larger sizes feasible and permitting individual growth without periodic molt-ings and awkward metamorphoses.

But on the other hand, the very absence of a protective exoskeleton meant easier drying out, and the early land verte-brates stuck closely to the water, spending not too much time in the drying air. We call them amphibians, which translated means that they led a double life, in water and on land.

This was also partly because they laid their eggs in water, these then hatching into fishlike tadpoles breathing with gills, which as they fed and grew, by a relatively simple transforma-tion, developed legs and substituted lung breathing for gill breathing. Among the few surviving modern amphibians, the transformation of the frog from egg through tadpole to adult is our most familiar example.

Obviously the problem of breathing dry air instead of air dissolved in water was the major difficulty faced by the primitive fishes whose descendants took to the land. But fortunately these early fishes had already developed one or two air bladders, which helped in flotation to reduce the efforts of climbing up-ward through the water, the buoyancy offsetting the weight of the solid parts of the fish. Such air bladders may well have be-gun as gill pouches in which air happened to get trapped. At any rate, each air bladder was connected by tube to the mouth cavity, through which air could be drawn in or expelled to main-tain flotational balance. Such bladders could then be easily evolved into air-breathing lungs.

Some of the early fishes, the dipnoans, have a few modern survivors we call lungfishes, which live in South America, Africa, and Australia and use the air bladder as a lung for sup-plementary breathing. During dry seasons, when lakes and pools dry out, they are able. to bury themselves in the mud and, through an air hole to the surface, breath in enough air for their limited needs during this period of inactivity.

But these are not among our ancestors. For their solution of the problem of drought by burial, inactivity, and limited air-bladder breathing did not lead to active land life. One reason for believing this is that the fossil record shows that they never evolved their fins into even crude leg stumps sturdy enough for crawling over the land.

Another group of early fishes, however, did evolve such leglike fins. Thomas Henry Huxley named them the crossopterygians, which merely means "tassel or fringe fins." Without disrespect, however, we may call them just crossopts for short, or more familiarly and descriptively as "lobe-fin fishes." They deserve respect, for very likely they conquered the land for the vertebrates and lie close to our line of ancestry. And until 1939 we thought them extinct for some seventy-five million years. But then a lone specimen was caught off the east coast of South Africa, and since then several more have been fished from the ocean deeps nearby. Naturally they have been dissected and studied with the utmost care. But we already knew a great deal about them from their fossil remains dating back perhaps four hundred million years to the Devonian.

Though our surviving lobe-fin fishes were found in the deep sea, it is thought that the ancient ones who made the landward step lived either in shallow shore waters or more probably in the fresh waters of lakes or swamps. At any rate, what started them landward was being caught in tidal shallows, in isolated pools when lakes or streams dried up, or in muddy swamp waters lacking oxygen. The only escape to deeper and better-aerated bodies of water would then be overland from pool to pool, possible only for those crossopts with the bladder lungs for emergency breathing and the sturdy lobe fins for creeping through mud, sand, and grass to new havens of water comfort (Figure 17).

From Fins to Feet

But the waters of sea, streams, or lakes, though havens of comfort, were not havens of safety. For they were already teem-

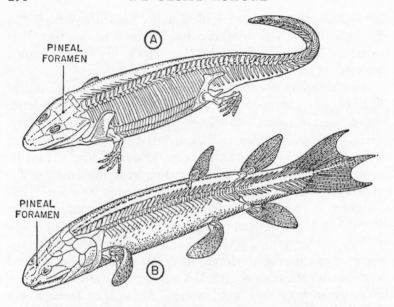

PINEAL
FORAMEN

PINEAL
FORAMEN

Fig. 17. Amphibian and Lobe-Fin Fishes.

ing with a mixed population of swift and dangerous predators, dominated by most aggressive pirate fishes. And one way of escape was to the land. So the land, which was initially only an emergency route to a new water haven, became in time a haven itself, affording a new habitat for survival. But it became so only because the descendants of the lobe-fin fish evolved new adaptations to land life.

Exteriorly the conspicuous change was that from fins to feet and legs. The lobe fins of the crossopts were still fins, essentially paddles, and the front ones at least placed as in other fishes on the sides of the body. There were other fins along the median line, top and bottom, but they were destined merely to disappear as useless on the land. But the two pairs which first served as makeshift legs went through a progressive evolution making them more efficient for land locomotion. Thus they moved downward on the sides of the body to make better contacts with the ground, and in due time would even shift underneath. They were already lobelike because they had a sturdy support of bones and muscles. The bones were a complex derived, no doubt, from the spreading fin rays giving fish fins their flat and thin shapes for paddle efficiency. As lobe fins, they retained a basic ray arrangement, but compressed rather than spread out, with perhaps some freedom for lobe bending. But later, on the land, in the amphibian lobes becomes legs, the bones interlocked more rigidly, with joints at definite points for leg and foot bending. The muscles, of course, evolved correspondingly to move these limb levers.

There were also collateral changes in the general skeleton, chiefly a strengthening of body support by a heavier rib structure, but quite as important, sturdier shoulder and pelvic bony girdles as connectors between limbs and backbone. The backbone itself was already substantially built and jointed in the fishes for purposes of vigorous undulation swimming, and so needed less change. Important also was a general release from the need for fishlike streamlining. For swift swimming in dense and resistant water, it was an over-all factor limiting body shape. But in the thin and nonresistant air this factor simply disappeared. To the extent that the amphibians spent their time in water, it of course remained, as we see in the frog tadpole. But on the land it simply did not matter, at least not at first when locomotion was by slow crawl with poorly developed limbs. Later, among the swift-flying birds, air-resistance was to become a factor, necessitating some streamlining.

But among the primitive four-footed amphibian descendants of the lobe-fin fishes, there were other serious problems of effective locomotion. The paired legs, fore and aft, of the basic tetrapod, at this stage an unknown pretetrapod, were already jointed to bend, and correspondingly muscled for movement. For greater efficiency, certain joints (those we know as wrists and ankles) were also built to rotate. But the legs were short and spread out sideways in a sprawl, without real lift of the body clear of the ground. Locomotion was therefore a dragging, assisted by body undulation, and propulsion with only a minor lift. Among the later reptiles this mode of slow land locomotion was to be sometimes retained—for example, by the crocodiles.

To realize just what mechanical problems were involved, try it yourself. Face downward on the floor, spread out arms and legs, and try moving forward. Then bending the elbows and knees to shorten leverages, and lifting the body slightly, you find moving forward becomes a bit easier. But it is not really effective and easy until you get arms and legs directly under you, with the body lifted clear of the floor. Whatever awkwardness then remains is due of course to your having evolved beyond the four-legged locomotion of even your advanced tetrapod ancestors.

The trick was of course to get the four legs directly underneath the body lifted clear of the ground, and this was gradually attained among the amphibians and particularly the reptiles. But this meant that finally the weight rested wholly on the feet terminating the legs. And especially among the amphibians, living never far from the water, those feet usually stood in mud or on ground soft with moisture, requiring wider spreading feet for firmer support. So quite from the start, the amphibian foot, probably by reduction of crossopt fin-rays, evolved as a spread-out structure on a framework of bones arranged into separate digits, with a more or less complete pad of muscles and skin in between.

Quite by chance, the amphibian foot settled down to five digits. At least we know of no reason why it could not have been four or six, or any other small number. And from then on, the normal foot of the land vertebrates had five toes, though some of them, from time to time, dropped some of the five—for example, the horse, with one toe per foot. In the end this was unfortunate, for Man, with those same five toes per foot and five fingers per hand (evolved from the tetrapod front foot) and the natural and convenient habit of counting on his ten fingers, developed the decimal system of numbers. If only our amphibian progenitors had possessed the foresight and good sense to settle on six toes per foot, we should today be counting by dozens and using the far more convenient duodecimal system of twelve number figures.

But our first amphibian pioneer of course gave no thought to such remote future concerns, being much too preoccupied with more immediate problems of survival in a difficult world. As a matter of fact, we do not actually know just what he looked like, for all the fossil record we have found at this stage is a single footprint left in the Devonian mud, and it already showed five toes. And for a good part of a hundred million years we find no more than that, merely footprints in the mud flats, but nothing of the four-footed walkers themselves. Not until we reach the strata of the Pennsylvanian or Coal Period, dated about three hundred million years ago, do we find the bones of the actual amphibians, then numerous, some up to fifteen feet long, with a stride of two and a half feet. But within another hundred million years, during the hardships of the Permian Period, these early type of amphibians would become extinct, only the more specialized modern types surviving.

Full Conquest of the Land

While the early amphibian types were becoming extinct in the Permian, the early reptiles appeared. So distinctive and important was the change in life at that time that the geologists made it the end of the Paleozoic or Ancient Life Era (by then 370 million years long), and the beginning of the Mesozoic or Middle Life Era, which began about 230 million years ago and lasted some 165 million years, leaving only sixty-five million years for the Cenozoic or Recent Life Era. The Mesozoic is divided by great mountain uplifts interrupting deposition of fossil-bearing strata, with resulting drastic erosions marked by major unconformities, into three geologic periods, the Triassic,

Jurassic, and Cretaceous, respectively forty-five, forty-five, and seventy-five million years long.

The Mesozoic Era, because it was dominated by the reptiles, is more popularly known as the Age of Reptiles. Even in the Triassic, there were early dinosaurs on the land, streamlined ichthyosaurs in the sea, flying pterosaurs in the air. And potentially important, small reptilelike mammals lurked inconspicuously in the background. In the Jurassic, the reptiles expanded their domain and gave rise to the first primitive birds. But in the Cretaceous, though the dinosaurs diversified into new and strange forms, they were on the whole on the way out. And by the end of the period (and of the Mesozoic Era), for reasons quite unknown, all but the modern types of reptiles died out. The next era belonged to the mammals and the birds.

But meanwhile the reptiles were most important because, for the vertebrates, they first accomplished the full conquest of the land and the air, and from them were to evolve both birds and mammals. The amphibians, because they always began their lives in water where their eggs were laid, could never go far from bodies of water to occupy drier habitats. Otherwise, too, the amphibians were not yet physically fit to migrate and live anywhere and everywhere. That required certain anatomical and physiological improvements which the amphibians only began but which the reptiles, birds, and mammals progressively perfected.

Chapter 16

PERFECTING THE LAND ANIMAL

With more time spent upon the land and increased competitive activity, the amphibians' primary need was that of improved lungs for more effective breathing. Moving about on land, without benefit of water flotation, demanded much more effort and energy, and therefore more oxygen consumption and carbon-dioxide removal. For the lobe-fin fishes, lung breathing was only for emergency portages overland from pool to pool, for which simple bladder lungs proved sufficient. But for the greater part-time land life of the amphibians, a lung with more exchange surfaces was needed, and was secured by infoldings and branchings into myriad pockets called alveoli.

This need was aggravated as the amphibians and other land animals multiplied into larger populations which crowded and actively competed, the increased activity demanding better breathing. One improvement, well begun by the amphibians, was forced breathing in and out. The lungs themselves did not become muscular, but they occupied a chest cavity lined with ribs and muscles. By the muscular expansion and contraction of this cavity, air was alternately drawn in and expelled from the lungs, which thereby became effective bellows for vigorous pumping in and out of the air supply.

The oxygen of that air was then passed through the thin walls of the lung surfaces into the fine capillaries of the blood-circulation system, and carried by the bloodstream to body tissues where it combined chemically with the carbon and hydrogen of stored carbohydrates to release energy (by a process somewhat akin to combustion), forming carbon dioxide and water. The carbon dioxide, however, was actually a waste product which would poison the organism if not properly eliminated. It was therefore transported by the bloodstream to the lungs, and there exhaled with the breath. At this point, of course, the blood would take on a fresh supply of oxygen. This attached itself loosely to the hemoglobin of the red blood corpuscles, turning them a brighter red. They of course returned from the tissues, minus the oxygen, and darker again.

Improving the Heart

Obviously the whole process of oxygen intake and carbon-dioxide elimination depended not only on effective lung action but also on a rapid transport between lungs and body tissues by means of a vigorous blood circulation. But that depended upon the vigor and efficiency of the heart, which pumped the blood through the circulatory system. Improvements here could become great assets, and over the ages of vertebrate evolution, several were made and developed to permit more energetic and active life.

In the fish, breathing with gills, the heart had but two chambers, an auricle to receive and accumulate a quantity of blood, which then passed to a relaxed ventricle chamber. Then by strong muscular contraction, the blood was forced out into the tubes of the circulation system. There were of course mechanical valves, as in any pump, suitably placed to prevent the fluid from going the wrong way. With this two-chambered heart, the blood got but one pumping push in each circuit of the blood vessels, moving from the heart to the gills to absorb oxygen and discard carbon dioxide, then going directly on through the tissues before it returned to the heart. We can abbreviate the circuit thus: heart—gills—tissues—heart, etc.

But with the development of lungs in the amphibian, a second circuit was established. The blood which had passed through the lungs came back to the heart for a second pumping push before going on to the tissues. Abbreviated, the full circuit became: heart—lungs—heart—tissues—heart—lungs, etc. This meant more vigorous double pumping action, a definite improvement.

But there was one hitch. The blood returning from the lungs came by a new vein which opened up to become a new auricle, a third heart chamber. But then, unfortunately, it poured its freshly oxygenated blood back into the same old ventricle, so it mixed with the impure blood returned from the tissues. There were two pumping pushes per full circuit, but still a bad mixing of pure and impure blood in the one ventricle.

The correction of this defect began in the reptiles, which started development of a septum or wall dividing the single ventricle into two. But there remained an opening between, through which the pure and impure bloods could still mix. Eventually, in the birds and mammals, this opening was closed, so the heart became really four-chambered, with a double pumping action in the full circuit, but meanwhile no mixing of pure and impure bloods. This was certainly part of the secret of bird and mammal activity and success in survival (Figure 18).

Stabilizing Temperature

But another important part of that secret was undoubtedly a second group of adaptations which enabled the birds and mammals to go places and do things impossible for the amphibians and reptiles. These were the adaptations permitting control of

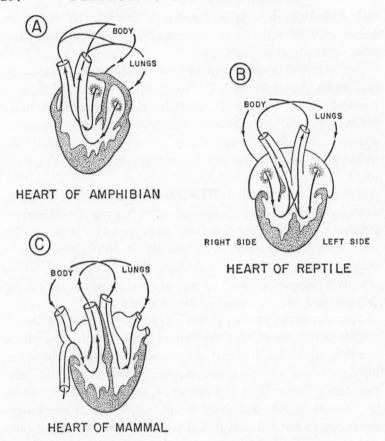

Fig. 18. Evolution of Vertebrate Hearts.

body temperatures and consequently the maintenance of constant higher temperatures. Lacking these improvements, the amphibians and reptiles could not carry on actively under extremes of heat and cold. On cold days the reptiles bask in the heat of the sun, and on hot days, retire to the cool of underground burrows. The amphibians, in heat or cold, can submerge in the more temperate water. Or over the long hard winter, they and even some mammals will hibernate in some protective retreat and live through at a lowered temperature and activity, sustained by a reserve of stored body food tissues.

Fundamental to bird and mammal maintenance of constant temperature was a virtual thermostatic control through suitable nerve centers. But these actuated physical means for controlling intake and outflow of heat, largely at the exposed skin surfaces. These included dilation and constriction of capillaries under the skin to vary heat radiation, and sweat glands for cooling by water evaporation. Important, too, was the amount of physical activity, such as exercise, to stir up breathing, circulation, and heat production. This was generally voluntary on the part of the individual animal, but there was also an automatic substitute when the muscles became cold and tense: the shivering which stirs up circulation and thus warms the body.

An important improvement, too, was the covering of the body with an insulation of fur or feathers, effective both in retaining body heat and in cutting down heat intake from the outside. Among the amphibians an opposite development had often occurred. For when they first took to the land, it was with relatively inefficient lungs, and some supplemented their lungs by breathing through the thin moist skin. Our frogs do that to this day, and the adult hellbender relies on skin-breathing altogether, having discarded whatever lungs his ancestors may have developed. But to acquire such a thin skin, the impervious scales of the fishes must have been discarded.

On the other hand, the reptiles, having left the water for good, again needed the protection of scales and necessarily depended on lungs alone for breathing. And when the time came that a group of primitive reptiles evolved into birds, these were the scales which became modified into insulating feathers, some of which being adapted for flying wings. And even earlier, another primitive reptile group evolved into the early mammals, but the origin of their fur remains uncertain.

Eggs for the Land

It is obvious that while the vertebrate conquerors of the land and air were thus evolving to survive better as adults, there was also that other necessary business of reproducing their kind under the new difficulties of transition and land life. At the outset that resolved itself into the problem of what to do about their eggs.

Because the eggs of fishes and amphibians were expelled into water, their coverings could be rather thin membranes. First, because of water buoyancy and balanced pressures, the egg held together without a strong covering. Second, a thin membrane permitted passage of foodstuffs and oxygen inward and of wastes outward. Of course, a thin covering gave no real physical protection, so that many eggs were inevitably destroyed, but this was overcome by supplying enormous numbers.

This was all changed when the reptiles abandoned the water. For the eggs were now laid on land, and tougher membranes or shells were needed, partly to hold them together, but also to protect them otherwise. For several reasons the eggs had to be larger and necessarily fewer, and therefore not wasted. The tougher coating helped prevent drying out, but there was also developed an internal membranous sack, the amnion, containing fluid in which the developing embryo floated. They served the multiple purpose of reducing drying out, of buoying up the embryo, and of minimizing mechanical shocks.

But in the air and out of the water, and with such double prevention of passage of fluids in and out, no foodstuffs could be derived from outside the egg. For nourishment and growth of the embryo, the egg had to be wholly self-contained and provided with an ample food supply in the form of a yolk, the chief reason for the larger—and fewer—eggs.

On the other hand, as gases, oxygen can be brought in from

the outer air and carbon dioxide expelled into it. This is facilitated by development of a special respiration sack, the allantois, connecting the deeply seated embryo with the inner surface of the egg covering. Nongaseous wastes, either solid or dissolved in water, must be handled differently, of which more in a moment.

Such were the essentials of the fully evolved land eggs of the reptiles. They were at first merely laid on the ground, perhaps buried slightly in the sand. But the reptiles, themselves without means for self-temperature control, had to depend upon the heat of the Sun to provide the warmth which speeds the chemical reactions of embryonic development. But as this lack also prevented them from living in cold climates, there was normally enough such heat for the hatching of their eggs.

The birds, however, did better. For they did have the self-regulating thermostatic controls and the insulating feathers for maintaining high and constant body temperature. As a result, they could and often did live in colder climates and seasons and could warm their eggs with their own body heat. But that required hard-shelled eggs which would not break and collapse when sat upon. As fliers, they could nest in trees and on cliffs, harder for predatory enemies to get to. But that meant the danger of eggs falling to destruction. Round eggs would of course roll and drop off too readily, so quite generally, but especially among the cliff nesters, the eggs became (as we say) "egg-shaped," which means ovoid, larger at one end, this general taper causing them to roll in circles and come to rest without falling off even a flat sloping surface.

On the other hand, the mammals, descended from another branch of primitive reptiles, very soon abandoned egg laying altogether. Instead, the female retained the fertilized egg within herself, and there it developed to sufficient completion to be born as a miniature adult, needing only to grow to become of mature size and proportions. Indeed, through a period of infancy, short or long, it was more or less helpless, needing parental protection, feeding, and other care. But all of this and the very important collateral consequences—mental, emotional, and social—belong later in our story.

The Disposal of Wastes

The exodus of life to the land gave new importance to an old and broad problem which has existed from the very beginnings of life. It was really an interlocking twofold problem—on the one hand, that of maintaining a suitable water balance within the body, and on the other, that of disposal of certain wastes. It could have been taken up at several stages of our story but can probably be discussed more coherently at this point. Besides, the shift to the land aggravated the problem most seriously.

Water is overwhelmingly the chief constituent of living organisms and occurs both as its physical self and in chemical combinations in living matter. In proper proportions it is therefore essential for health and even survival. And maintaining water balance within suitable limits is a primary problem facing all living things. Even in the primitively simple Amoeba, we noted the pulsating vacuole pumping out the excess water always accumulating by being absorbed through the cell surface.

Until the exodus of life to land and air, all life lived in the water where there was normally no problem of too little water, as each organism evolved adaptive means for controlling intake and avoiding excess. But on land the problem was often the finding of enough water. Among amphibians this might be solved by frequent immersion, with water absorption through the skin. This applied also to the primitive land plants, which kept to wet or moist spots, and even higher plants which by long roots penetrated deeply to water levels in the ground. The strictly land animals resorted to periodic drinking and therefore lived not too far from streams, water holes, or larger bodies of water. Some, however, got part or all of their water supply from eating juicy plants or from the body fluids of animal prey.

Also, where water is scarce, means are developed for storing and conserving it. Thus, desert plants such as cacti have bulky stems serving as water reservoirs, meanwhile exposing the green chlorophyll surfaces to sunlight only on the stems and reducing the leaves to mere thorns, which discourage eating by hungry —and thirsty—desert animals.

Among animals, water conservation can be secured by impenetrable skins and scales, or by insulating surfaces of feathers or fur, perhaps made water-resistant by extrusion of body oils, and by habits of retirement to moist burrows or forest shade during hot days.

Correlated to water supply, absorption, and elimination is a general problem of maintaining a suitable salt content. All the body fluids contain salts, chiefly sodium chloride, our ordinary table salt. The sea waters also contained such salts, though perhaps somewhat less in Paleozoic times, as the land streams have since been adding continuously to the ocean supply. At any rate, the waters of streams and lakes are ordinarily fresh, comparatively salt-free, while the sea and undrained lakes are full of accumulated salts.

But salts lower the diffusion pressure of the water in which they are dissolved, and therefore reduce the tendency of the fluids to pass through membranes. In consequence, when organisms adapted to salt water then move into fresh water, they suffer an influx of excess water, with body bloating and dilution of the normal body salinity. Or by moving to salt water, the fresh-water organism will shrink from loss of water and increase the salinity of the body fluids. Among the water-living invertebrates, this sort of thing often happens without being necessarily fatal, the body fluids merely assuming the salinity of the ambient water. But among the vertebrates the result is usually death. However, some fishes, such as salmon, spawn in fresh water, then take to the sea without becoming dehydrated, being able to control gill permeability to keep out excess water and to maintain the normal salinity of the body fluids. On the other hand, certain frogs of Thailand and European toads can go to sea but are tolerant to the resulting higher salinity of the body fluids, while the kidneys increase water elimination to prevent death by body bloating.

Kidneys, and their primitive and various equivalents, are really filtering devices for removing certain products, without too much loss of body fluids. Other devices take care of other types of wastes. Thus, gaseous carbon dioxide and some water pass out in the exhaled breath. And the indigestible components of our foods pass on through the intestines as semisolids eliminated at the anal opening terminating our digestive tract.

But some waste or excess substances, such as salts, are in fluid solution and pass out through the kidneys. Particularly proteins break down in organic processes to produce waste nitrogen compounds which, being toxic in varying degrees, must be excreted quite immediately and continuously. One of these is ammonia, most toxic but readily dissolved in water and thus removed. Another is urea, less toxic, but also less soluble and therefore less easily removed. A third is uric acid, almost insoluble but fortunately even less toxic. And even the useful amino acids are sometimes wastefully excreted.

The kidneys, as finally fully developed among land vertebrates, consist of myriads of minute filtering units called nephrons. Each is actually a double-acting filtering device. First, high-pressured blood fluid is forced from thin-walled capillaries into a collecting unit. This fluid contains all the dissolved ingredients of the blood, except the heavy protein molecules, including even the useful food materials such as glucose. But as it passes through the tubular nephron, nearly all the fluid and its useful contents are filtered back into the returning and lower-pressured bloodstream, while the nitrogen wastes are left and highly concentrated in the remaining fluid, becoming the urine which then drains into the urinary bladder, to be passed out of the body from time to time. The net result is that the wastes are eliminated while the body fluids and their usable contents are effectively conserved. Thereby, too, not only the water but the proper salt and other chemical balances are suitably maintained throughout the organism.

The forms of the nitrogen wastes generally depend upon the availability of water. Among protozoans, sponges, molluscs, and crayfish, for example, the waste is largely ammonia dilutely dissolved in the abundant water. Among those with a lesser and conserved supply of water, urea becomes the principle nitrogen waste. But where water conservation becomes more critical, as in insects, reptiles, and birds, the less toxic uric acid is favored. And in the eggs of reptiles and birds, covered with an impervious membrane or shell, the nitrogen wastes cannot be eliminated at all and are merely isolated and stored as solid uric acid crystals to render them harmless.

New Opportunities

At any rate, it is evident that any migration of life from one habitat or medium to another, as from fresh to salt water, or the reverse, or from water to land and air, demands adaptive changes, often profound enough to involve slow evolution of structure and function. Especially was this true of the exodus to the land.

But mixed with the new problems were new opportunities. The land was a far more difficult world, but also it was a wider and more diversified one. And in adapting to it and taking advantage of its possibilities, a multitude of new forms developed, living generally more actively, with more alert senses and increasing intelligence.

All the senses were profoundly affected. Even smell, despite its occasional high development among water forms, as in the sharks and other predaceous fishes, probably became more effective in the air. In the water it depended largely on slow diffusion of dissolved odors and gave poor indication of the direction of the source. But land breezes carried odors swiftly downwind, giving prompt information of food or danger, always upwind. Or the grubbing animal was directed in his digging by the very local position of odor, intensifying as he came closer to his buried prey. On the other hand, those animals that lived in the trees had little use for smell as it served neither as guide to buried food (except in bark) nor as warning of imminent enemies. And we can often see the resulting differences in the smell organs in the snout and the smell lobes of the brain. Thus, the ground shrew, grubbing for its food, has large organs and brain lobes for smell, while its close kin, the tree shrew, has relatively small ones.

The conditions and sense of hearing changed even more drastically. It is true that sounds travels faster in water than in air, but the rate is always swift and the differences are merely fractions of seconds for nearer dangers. Besides, it is even doubtful that the fish actually hears the vibrations of sound as we do. At least our own elaborate organs of proper hearing are quite absent in the fish. There is probably a sensing of water disturbances by the lateral-line organs, including warning of dangerous movements in the watery environs. And these may even be discriminating enough for recognition of characteristic sounds given off by fish kin or struggling prey.

The sense of orientation relative to water pressures and currents was closely involved with that of equilibrium, the organ for which had been evolved by the fishes. These senses were related in the function of maintaining body positions, and fed through one pair of what we now call acoustical nerves to a common center in the brain. And throughout the further evolution of the organs of hearing, they remained together.

The fully developed ear, say of the mammals, consists of three parts—the outer, middle, and inner ears. The outer ear became the conspicuous visible structure, generally protruding, and roughly shaped into a cup for gathering and directing sound through a short channel ending in a membrane stretched like a drumhead to vibrate under the impacts of the air vibrations of sound. In the frog we see that membrane as an area of mere skin stretched over an opening in the amphibian skull.

That membrane transmits its vibrations to a chain of three bones comprising the middle ear and thereby to a plate in the wall of the inner or true hearing ear, which is filled with fluid. Those bones, despite their drastic changes in shape and function, can be very clearly traced without a break to their origins in the fishes. Thus the innermost bone, the stapes or stirrup, is a transformed gill arch of the fish, while the middle bone, the incus or anvil, and the outermost, the malleus or hammer, originated from lower jaw bones abandoned when the complex fish jaw progressively simplified into the one-piece jaw of the mammallike reptiles. Together, these middle ear bones transmit and magnify the vibrations received and sensed by the inner ear.

Meanwhile that inner ear began in the reptiles as a simple fluid-filled pouch, which in the mammals became long and coiled up like a snail shell as the cochlea. Its base membrane tapers in width and its hairlike nerve endings decrease in length toward the tip, and vibrate and bend respectively in resonant response to sound vibrations of various frequencies, enabling us to distinguish tones of various pitches.

Meanwhile, too, the sense of equilibrium through the semicircular canals has been retained and somewhat developed. A fish can accidentally roll over much more easily than a firmly planted four-footed animal, but with increasing activity of the mammals, the flying and bipedal postures of birds, and the bipedal erect standing of Man, the sense of equilibrium remained important. It has been increasingly supplemented, however, by the senses of pressures under the feet and of tensing muscles used in steady standing or moving (Figure 19).

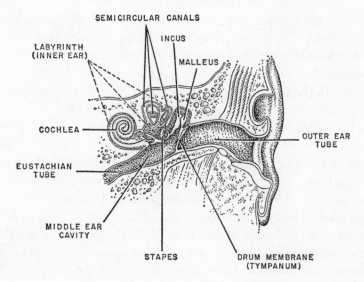

Fig. 19. Inner Structure of Human Ear.

Making Eyes

Because we ourselves find vision so important, we are likely to assume its primary importance among all lower forms of animal life. And sometimes it is really important, as among the birds. But quite often it is less vital than other senses, such as smell and hearing. Certainly among the sharks, smell came first; among the catfishes, taste. Undoubtedly one reason is that seeing is not too good in water. Sunlight comes from the world of air above and rapidly diminishes with increasing depth. The same water density which prevents deep penetration of light also limits the distance we can see through it. Water, too, is usually disturbed by surface waves, stream currents, agitating movements. Disturbances often stir up suspended matter and cause murkiness. So altogether the range and clarity of vision in water are quite limited, and eyes have much less use than we think.

Fisheyes are therefore generally shortsighted, useful largely for detecting movements (even though ill defined) which may mean enemies or prey. Yet the first vertebrates, though living in water, did introduce eyes of rather superior basic design, capable of development to our own and other very serviceable organs of sight.

Several times in our story we have already come across eyes, but without stopping to describe their states of development. Some were actually highly developed, like those of the octopus. Some were very different, like those of the insects. Others were primitive, but important to us because they suggest origins and the course of evolutionary development.

Sensitivity of the whole body to light seems fairly common among the one-celled protozoans, less so among the multicelled animals. The earthworm is eyeless but has light-sensitive skin cells scattered generally over the body. He may come out of his burrow at night but retires with the coming of the morning light, undoubtedly for the very practical reason that the late worm is caught by the early bird. Amphioxus, despite its advanced prevertebrate status, has no proper eyes but relies on the sensitivity of small optic cups embedded within its notochord and exposed to light because the whole body is almost transparent.

A first advance on such general sensitivity to light was the development of special organs so shaped as to indicate direction of the light source. A very simple form is found in the tiny eyespot of the single-celled flagellate *Euglena viridis*. Its name *Euglena* means "pretty eye," and the *viridis* means "green." For it has the green chlorophyll of a plant, using it as the plant does for building up foodstuffs by trapping sunlight. The eye is a tiny red spot near its front end, and within it are six little buttons which probably indicate direction of the light. For *Euglena viridis* whiplashes itself through the water with such directed determination that we realize the little rascal must really be "seeking the light," a quest we should all emulate.

In the multicelled there is more opportunity for elaboration of eye structures. In the flatworm, the paired eyes are pigmented capsules placed just under the thin skin. Nerve fibers with brush-like ends extend into each capsule through an open side. The capsule eyes are placed up front to left and right, so that light from straight ahead falls upon them equally, while light from either side falls more on the near capsule, less on the distant one, thus indicating the direction of the light source. Of course eyes thus constructed can form no optical image to see objects as we do, but they do warn of objects nearby and indicate their directions and movements. For image making an eye lens is needed, and that did evolve from just such beginning eyes as those of the worm.

We can illustrate some steps in that evolution by the eyes of various invertebrates. Thus, some jellyfish eyes are mere patches of pigmented skin cells alternating with smaller light cells, placed at the base of the tentacles. In other jellyfish eyes the skin patch is sunken to form a goblet eye. Here certainly we have an effective device for locating illuminated objects, as light coming from one side will fall within the goblet on the farther side while leaving the near side in shadow. Even a single unpaired eye can do this trick. But again, such a goblet eye, having no lens, can form no proper visual image. However, the goblets are sometimes filled with a transparent jelly, perhaps originally for protection but capable of eventual conversion into a lens for image forming.

Incidentally, in these examples of stages of eye development prior to true image formation, lay the solution of the difficulty felt by Darwin and his contemporaries (cited in Chapter 5): How could the complex image-forming eye have evolved gradu-ally, for what use would there be for a partially developed eye, to bring about its step-by-step selection and evolution? For at each stage, as we have just seen, these primitive eyes did have their uses, limited perhaps but positive enough to have selective value to make inevitable the eventual adaptive formation of an eye lens and image formation. At any rate, such perfecting of the eye occurred apparently more than once and quite independently.

The Camera Eye

Thus, in the squid and octopus there is such an eye lens, as well as a transparent cornea formed from the skin. In essentials these eyes, just as in vertebrates, are cameras. There is a front aperture with a lens which gathers and focuses light from outside objects to form images on the light-sensitive rear surface, the retina. The retina consists of a multitude of nerve endings which receive and transmit suitable messages to the visual center of the brain, which thereupon interprets the nerve messages as a mental picture of the objects seen. These molluscan eyes are probably very efficient, and certainly the octopus pair do look malevolently intelligent. And superficially the eye structure does look much like that of the fish and its vertebrate descendants.

But in structural detail and embryonic development there are great and fundamental differences, another reason for concluding that the vertebrate eye was not inherited from the molluscs. But how it did actually evolve is something of a mystery. The successive stages of original development are not represented in either living or fossil forms, so when in 1918 F. K. Studnicka undertook to trace its history, he did so on the basis of the embryology of the lamprey eel, a suggestive but admittedly uncertain procedure. The details, however, are very involved and technical and boil down only to a still-unsolved mystery rather than a meaningful story. We really only know that the lowliest of the living vertebrates already have well-developed camera-type eyes, destined to be improved only in minor ways among the higher animal forms. In the early fishes the eyes are connected to the midbrain, itself not too well developed, being quite obviously subordinated to the more primary sense of smell. As we go on, we shall discover when and how all that was later changed.

But before we go on with the subject of vertebrate eye development, we must digress for a moment to note a very different solution of the problem of vision which the arthropods evolved. Spiders and some insects do have pairs of simple eyes much like those of the worms, shortsighted at best, perhaps not even image-forming. But the crustaceans and insects also have compound eyes of much longer focus, and apparently were effective, if we judge by the difficulty in swatting a fly. The bulging corneal surface is broken up into lenslike facets (from seven to twenty-seven thousand in number), each lens sending its portion of light down its own long tube ending with a nerve receptor. It is generally assumed that an image is formed, if only a mosaic built up of separate facet impressions. These paired compound eyes are set on the two sides of the head and fixed in position on a head not readily turned, but as the facets point in virtually all directions, the warning vision is effective in practically all directions, which of course explains why the fly so often gets away from the swatter.

Eyes on Land

Inevitably, the vertebrate migration to the land involved serious problems of adaptation in vision. Already in the fish the front of the eye was protected adequately by a tough but transparent cornea. But when the amphibians came ashore, added protection was provided by a movable eyelid, and eventually by tear glands providing the fluid for lubricating the eyeball in the drier air and for washing dirt from the eye. Partly as a matter of streamlining, the front of the fish eyeball was flattened, a feature kept even by the reptiles and birds but not the higher mammals.

But always the central cornea and lens through which the light passed were curved enough to focus the light as an image upon the retina at the rear.

Optically, the change from the conditions of water to those of air demanded drastic adaptations. We have noted that even in clear, unmuddied water the distances to which light could penetrate were much shorter than those in air. And with increase of distance, objects appeared not only dimmer but more blurred by agitations in the water. Long vision was therefore rather useless to the fishes, and we described them as short-sighted. However, the difference between the optical densities of water and air are such that the fisheye actually focuses farther off than it would in air. Yet when the amphibians took to the land, there was a double adjustment needed. First, an adjustment still had to be made to more distant focusing even for nearer objects. And second, as objects could be seen to much greater distances through the clearer air, an adjustment had to be evolved for a greater range of focusing, near and far.

This latter adjustment varied considerably among different animals. In the fisheye it had been done by moving the lens forward for distant objects, rearward for near objects. In the mammals, encircling muscles pull the eye lens out flatter for distant seeing, relax to let it get rounder and thicker for near seeing. In the birds, however, the cornea curvature changes from a flattened shape for distant objects to a bulging curvature for near objects. Thus, a hawk swooping down from a great soaring heighth right down to clawing contact with its prey on the ground keeps its vision continuously sharp by increase in convexity of its cornea. Incidentally, that hawk has a visual acuity some eight times that of Man, enabling it from a great heighth to detect and distinguish the movements and shapes which it identifies as living prey. This, however, is not so much due to any optical superiority as to the fact that its retinal nerve endings are smaller and far more numerous than those of Man (Figure 20).

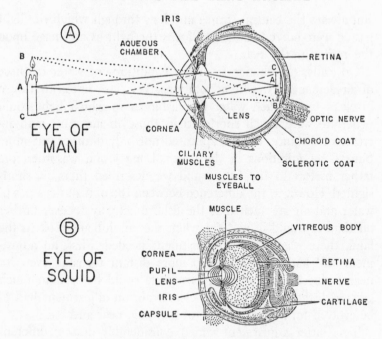

Fig. 20. Evolution of the Eyes.

Migration out of the water to the land and dry air brought other needs for evolutionary change, some so important that we must devote the whole next chapter to them. But those we have so far considered add up to a general increase in alertness and swiftness, greater mobility of body and effectiveness in survival activities, and particularly in perceptive powers and capacity to think intelligently in the solution of practical problems. In overall effectiveness, the culmination was to be Man himself, but of that more later.

Chapter 17

SEX REARS ITS HEAD

When James Thurber and E. B. White, some decades ago, gave us their delightful book *Is Sex Necessary?*, it was with tongue in cheek, to laugh at the absurd attitudes we ordinarily hold so seriously on this central interest of our human lives. Theirs was obviously a rhetorical question to which they gaily avoided any serious answer.

Yet the same question should be asked and answered seriously in such a book as this on the evolution of life as we find it. Indeed, in the light of our modern technical knowledge of the processes of heredity, variation, and selective evolution, the answer proves vitally significant. For while some life forms do reproduce even usually without sex, they must nevertheless resort to sex reproduction occasionally. There seems today to be but one possible exception, the lowly blue-green algae, and even that may merely represent a lack in our present knowledge of facts. Yet knowing what we do today of the advantages of sexual reproduction, we can hardly conceive of the over-all evolution of actual life without it.

Yet these advantages are far from obvious to the unscientific observer. On the contrary, when one watches an amoeba dividing into two again and again by mere fission, or a Hydra or a yeast cell budding off numerous replicas of itself, or a strawberry plant spreading its kind by sending out runners which take root, or a potato or onion bulb sprouting new plants, all these instances of asexual reproduction seem so simple, direct, effective, and economical that one wonders why sex was ever resorted to at all. And when, on further detail study, we learn what complexities of structures and processes are actually involved and evolved in sexual reproduction, the wonder only increases. Why should asexual simplicity have been so largely supplemented, when not wholly supplanted, by sexual complexity?

Sexual versus Asexual Reproduction

In discussing bacteria, Amoeba, and Paramecium back in Chapter 10, we described their reproduction by simple fission. At least the process of fission did seem simple, though complications began to appear in the division of the rather complex visible structures of Paramecium. And we have of course become aware that in the division of merely a nucleus, there are separations of chromosomes and the splitting and replicating of the gene DNA chains, etc. And even in the bacteria and blue-green algae which seem to lack cell nuclei, that is merely because their chromosomes are not concentrated into nuclei but scattered through the cell substance. Even cell fission is therefore not so simple as it looks, though of course it still remains simpler than sexual joining.

Nevertheless there is an obvious straightforwardness about fission. The cell just grows to a limit of size, then divides to double in number. If this occurs at short intervals, the multiplication in numbers is very rapid. This is even more true in that variant on fission, the budding off of more numerous smaller units, as in the yeasts. And it remains generally true in all types of asexual reproduction; greater numbers of offspring can be produced more directly. When rapid reproduction is the prime requirement, asexual reproduction is often present, if only to supplement sexual reproduction. But on the whole, as life has evolved, sexual has supplanted asexual reproduction, which certainly implies that sexual reproduction must possess important advantages.

Observation and experiment indicate strongly that the mixing of genetic materials which occurs in sexual reproduction does somehow invigorate the stock. Thus, in Paramecium there is an occasional conjugation of two individuals, followed by a renewed series of fissions. But if such conjugation be prevented, the Paramecium stock eventually degenerates and dies out, a fact long ago discovered by Maupas, a French librarian of Algiers. And while, in plants and animals generally, the invigorating effect of genetic crossing has been amply confirmed by the practical experience of breeders and farmers, the basic reasons have not been too well worked out. Thus it is an undoubted fact that hybird corn yields a crop from 30 to 50 per cent higher than self-fertilized corn, but we do not actually know why. It remains merely an observed advantage of sexual reproduction, which in the course of evolution has had an undoubted selective value.

More understandably, the constant reassortment of genes arising in sexual reproduction provides a very direct advantage in the adaptive evolution of life forms. It is obvious that all the individuals of a series of Paramecium generations, reproduced by fission only, must necessarily have identical gene patterns, subject only to very rare mutations. And when a favorable mutation does occur, it will be inherited by only the direct fission descendants, and by no others. In such a Paramecium strain, thus asexually reproduced and thus rarely mutated, there is little likelihood of genetic variation between individuals upon which natural selection can seize to cause adaptive evolution.

But conjugation of Paramecium pairs of differing strains do occur from time to time, and this means reshufflings of gene combinations by which various advantageous mutations can be exchanged, combined, and spread widely through the Paramecium community. As the combinations then vary greatly, the variety of Paramecium individuals multiplies, and natural selection has actually something to choose between. Even recessive traits, though appearing less often, can be spread widely, and if advantageous, eventually selectively preserved. And not merely single traits but combinations of traits become subject to selection as advantageous. And in diverse environments there are more likely to be traits and combinations of traits adapted to differing conditions and possibilities, thus permitting even more adaptive differentiations. By sexual conjugation all manner of adaptations become possible and likely. Obviously all of this can be done only by gene reshufflings through sexual pairing. The over-all result of sexual reproduction is inevitably an acceleration and diversification of adaptive evolution.

The Essentials of Sex

In Paramecium pairing, the two individuals which conjugate may appear quite alike, though there are now thought to be differences distinguishing them as male and female. And recent experiments with amoebalike ciliates, and with a common bacterium which lives in the human lower intestine, and with the bacteriophage virus which uses that bacterium as host, indicate that without actual conjugation there are nevertheless some exchanges of genes, perhaps by free genes traveling or being carried by viruses from cell to cell or from one virus unit to another. The evidence for this is that new gene combinations do occur, as shown by changes in form or function which are then inherited in accord with Mendelian rules.

Should such pairing of like individuals by fusion, or exchanges of genes without actual pairing, be described as sexual? Or must there be a difference of male and female between pairing individuals, or at least female egg cells (usually larger and inert), each of which develops to a new individual when fertilized by entry of a male sperm cell (usually smaller and motile)? Or should we call sexual any exchange of genes between life units by mating of pairs?

Here we will ignore any contrary tradition and define sexual pairing as any exchange of genes between individual life units. For this includes all cases of departure from strictly asexual reproduction and emphasizes the basic distinction between the two types of reproduction.

But it should be pointed out that such sexual pairing normally involves two essential steps, not just one. For there must be more than a mere joining of chromosomes (or genes). There must also be a reduction (halving) of the number of chromosomes (and genes) by a process which earlier we called meiosis. For unless such a halving does occur with each sexual fusion, the number of chromosomes (and genes) per cell will double, redouble, etc., to produce life units which are somehow different. For example, when by accident a chromosome doubling does occur without a compensating reduction by halving, we get the sort of misleading pseudo-mutations observed in the evening primrose by Hugo De Vries.

Each sexual reproduction cycle is therefore divided into two alternating stages: one of doubled chromosome numbers following fertilization by fusion; the other of reduced chromosome numbers following meiosis by fission. These we can abbreviate as the double stage from fusion to fission, and the reduced stage from fission to fusion. Biologists call the first diploid, the second haploid.

Either one, or both, may be a mature stage in the life cycle of the organism. For example, in some single-celled protists, in the green alga Spirogyra, and in the mosses the doubled stage may be brief and secondary, most of the mature life being spent in the reduced stage. Or the opposite may be true, as in the brown algae Laminaria and Fucus and in the flowering plants. Or, as in the brown alga Ectocarpus and in the ferns, both stages may be more or less mature. In some instances further complications occur, like alternating generations of polyps and medusae in the doubled stage of jellyfishes or females in the doubled stage (from fertilized eggs) and males in the reduced stage (from unfertilized eggs), as in the bees and ants.

Another frequent complication is the interruption of either stage by a series of asexual reproductions. Thus, in the green alga Spirogyra this occurs in the reduced stage; in the brown alga Ectocarpus, in the doubled stage. When it occurs among the flowering plants, it is always in the dominating and mature doubled stage. Among the multicellular animals (except among bees and ants) any asexual reproduction is in the doubled stage, male, female, or both.

Male, Female, and Variations

At any rate, it is now obvious that sex is no recent innovation but occurs throughout the world of life and with many variations. But it was not long restricted to mere conjugation of like individual cells as in Paramecium. With the evolution of multicellular organisms (see Chapter 10), special cells are set apart for reproduction and soon differentiate as male and female. Thus in Volvox, in addition to certain larger cells which reproduce asexually, there are also some which enlarge into inactive eggs, while others become small flagellated free-swimming sperm cells. When one of these reaches an egg cell, its nucleus enters and fuses with the egg nucleus, thus fertilizing it for further development. The Volvox egg then secretes a tough wall enabling it to survive through adverse conditions of cold or dryness. Then when warmth and wetness return, it resumes development into a new Volvox individual. Such interruption of development under adverse conditions is common among plants, especially in the seed stage. Otherwise, development of the egg proceeds without interruption following fertilization.

In all higher life forms, both plant and animal, sexual reproduction involves this basic differentiation between female eggs and male sperms. The female egg is larger and relatively inactive; the male sperm, smaller and provided with means for swimming or otherwise reaching an egg to fertilize it. The egg either remains attached to the parent organism as source of its food during development or is provided with a reserve food yolk within an egg covering, or the egg is laid in some other source of food supply, the egg of the threadworm Gordius, referred to in Chapter 1, being thus deposited and hatched in the body of some insect host.

Almost universally the eggs and sperm are produced by cell differentiation in special organs, the gonads; female ovaries for the eggs, male testes for the sperm. As a rule they occur in separate individuals, female and male. But in many lowly forms both kinds occur in the same individual, which is then called hermaphroditic. For example, the sexual phase of Hydra and some of its relatives, some flatworms, our common earthworm, and oysters are hermaphrodites. In Hydra the testes are near the anchoring base, the ovaries midway on the stalk, but when the sperm are discharged into the surrounding water, it is wholly a matter of chance whether they will swim their way to and fertilize the eggs of the same or some other individual. In the flatworms the testes develop first, the ovaries later, reducing the likelihood of inbreeding by self-fertilization. In the earthworms the ovaries and testes develop simultaneously, but elaborate means are provided for preventing self-fertilizing. As earthworms never travel far, it is an advantage for any two individuals which meet to be able to mate. This they do by extending in opposite directions and bringing their posterior ventral surfaces together. The sperm of each one pass into a sperm receptacle of the other. Then a band of mucous forms around each worm and moves forward, first picking up the worm's own eggs, then the other worm's sperm deposited in the receptacle so that fertilizing occurs, and finally slips off over the head, and then closes to form a cocoon preventing drying out of the developing eggs. In the oyster the gonads are first testes producing sperm, and later change into ovaries producing eggs which are then fertilized by later sperm from younger individuals. All these devices preventing self-fertilizing emphasize the importance of the cross-fertilizing which assures sexual reshuffling of gene combinations. When self-fertilizing does occur, it is because conditions preclude meeting of the opposite sexes, as among parasitic worms attached within a host body, or otherwise as a last resort to ensure reproduction at any cost.

Sex differentiation, as we know, also manifests itself in the outward and inward aspects of male and female bodies, in size, forms, coloration, and the sexual organs, usually partly visible externally. Thus, already in the lowly rotifers the adult male may be only a fraction the size of the female. But these aspects of sex are so various, yet so generally familiar, that we need not undertake to enumerate and sort them out here.

Getting the Sexes Together

It is already obvious that the primary and persisting problem of sexual reproduction is getting the male and female sex cells together. Where this can be done without bringing male and female individuals together, the problem is generally less serious. Thus, for plants and animals living in the water the provision of numerous male sperm, suitably equipped for swimming at random in search of eggs to fertilize, usually solves the problem. But that method is uncertain and wasteful. As very few sperm can be expected to reach their goals by what amounts to aimless wandering, they must be produced in enormous numbers to ensure the fertilizing of enough eggs.

Yet among the water plants, and the water animals anchored in fixed positions, there is hardly any other solution of the problem. But among the motile animals more economical and efficient methods become available. The sperm can be carried to or near the eggs. Thus with many fishes the female ejects her eggs into the water, or even into a nest of materials assembled and shaped for the purpose, whereupon the male immediately ejects his sperm at the same spot. Or the male frog clasps the female and both then eject sperm and eggs simultaneously into the water where these sex cells, close together, can find each other more readily and surely. Or even better, the male places the sperm directly within the female. Some rotifers do this, the male inserting his sperm duct into a suitable female opening, or depositing the sperm on the female's body wall, through which it penetrates to the egg. Among squids and octopuses much the same is done by means of a modified male tentacle, the so-called hectocotylus organ, which deposits the sperm deep within the female mantle cavity, close to the store of waiting eggs.

With the migration of plant and animal life to the land and air, the problem of getting the sex cells together becomes much more difficult. This perhaps accounts for the long period during which the animals did not get beyond the amphibian stage. As adults, they lived more or less on land but returned to the water to lay their eggs, then fertilized by sperm swimming to reach them. Among the plants there was an equivalent amphibious stage, exemplified by the land-living mosses, which have flagellated sperm which swim through a film of water on the plant's surface to reach the eggs. The egg-producing organ exudes a sugar into the water film, and the sperm is guided toward higher sugar concentrations to reach the egg, probably by no sense of taste but by chemical reactivity.

In the ferns the sperm still swims to the egg, but both are produced in male and female organs on a heart-shaped leaflike plant (the reduced stage), very small and inconspicuous, anchored in some damp spot. The sperm develops first and swims to an egg of an older plant, assuring cross-fertilizing. The fertilized egg develops into a different plant (the diploid stage), at first parasitic on the heart-shaped one. But soon it takes root in the ground and grows to the large and familiar frond-leafed fern.

The higher plants, which evolved from the ferns in comparatively recent geologic times, are characterized by the production of seeds. In these the young plant embryo, developed from the fertilized egg, is halted in growth at a resting stage, during which it is enclosed, with a food reserve, within a protective coat. This is an adaptation for life on drier ground and away from open surface water. It made possible a much wider distribution, greater diversity, and a great multiplication of numbers of the land plants. But it also meant an end to free-swimming sperm. Other ways of reaching the egg had to be evolved.

So the sperm, which once took to the water, among the seed plants, at first took to the air. It became the pollen grain, small and light, which the wind could pick up and carry to an egg of some near or distant plant of that same kind. The chances of arriving were of course very slight, a difficulty offset only by prodigal production of enormous quantities of the pollen sperm. And since, even then, cross-fertilizing must often fail, many of the wind-pollinated plants are hermaphroditic so that, as a last resort, they can still self-fertilize their eggs and reproduce their kind.

But even this left too much to chance, and of course involved too much harmful inbreeding. One way to prevent the inbreeding was for the sperm and eggs of a given plant to ripen at different times so that self-fertilizing could not occur. But this still did not overcome the enormous wastage and uncertainty of wind pollination.

The Bees and the Flowers

This need led to the evolution of plants depending upon animals to carry their pollen. Usually the carriers are flying insects, less often birds, and only rarely other animals. These carriers are nearly always involuntary ones, but their messenger services are generally well paid for in good foods, the sugars of nectars and the proteins of pollens. To lure their respective pollen carriers, the flowers flaunt bright colors and enticing odors. And in all of this one fact stands out: each kind of flower is definitely adapted to lure and utilize the kinds of carriers best serving its needs.

Flower shapes may have some identification value for aiding recognition by the various pollen carriers. But generally the shapes are primarily adapted in structure to particular carriers. Thus, deep-throated funnels go with birds with long beaks, such as hummingbirds, or with insects having long sucker tubes such as butterflies and moths. When Darwin, who pioneered in the study of flower adaptations, received a report of a Madagascar orchid with a nectar spur eleven inches deep, he confidently predicted the existence of an insect with a proboscis of this unlikely length; and within a few years a hawk moth was in fact discovered with a coiled eleven-inch sucker tube.

The orchids, with their wide variety of complex flower structures, are outstanding examples of detailed adaptations to particular pollen carriers. Among the simplest is our common lady slipper. The closed entrance to the pouchlike flower has enough spring to shut out crawling ants and smaller flies, and is too small for larger insects, but yields to the weight and the push of a bee seeking the nectar within. But the entrance is also a one-way valve, so the bee can only crawl out, first under the sticky stigma (female) which picks off pollen grains brought from another flower, then under an anther (male) which dusts on a fresh supply of pollen to be carried to the next flower visited.

Further examples could be given indefinitely, but only two need be added to suggest the wide variety of flower adaptations. There are flowers with the noxious odor of rotting meat to attract pollen-carrying flies which feed on carrion. The flies are of course cheated of their reward, but never seem to learn, and constantly make the rounds from flower to flower. Then there is the common jack-in-the-pulpit, which, like the other spring flowers, sprouts early from a food reserve in a fleshy root bulb to hurry through its cycle of leafing and flowering before the sunlight is shut off overhead by the later leafing of the forest trees. Its flower is the tube and overhanging hood of its pulpit, which gives protection and warmth to tiny gnats which, during the cooler hours, swarm about inside, and carry pollen from jack to jack (the anthers and stigmas) when they venture out during warmer hours.

The undoubted reason for such specialized adapting of flowers to particular carriers is that pollination is made more certain when the carrier visits only the flowers of the one species. The visits that count are more frequent, the trips between flowers more direct, and the wastage of pollen on other species very much reduced.

But on the other hand, such specialization reduces the number of potential carriers, and there is always a danger that a shortage of the exclusive carrier will cut down pollination and reproduction of the plant species. And, of course, any shortage of the given flower would be disastrous for the carrier species dependent upon the one flower for food. This is perhaps the reason for the greater success and numbers of the bees and of the wide variety of flowers they can feed on and pollinate.

The Busy Bee's Business

Yet among the honeybees there is a well observed tendency for individual bees to visit flowers only of one kind, at least on each foraging trip. This "flower constancy" has often been considered an inherited instinct, though how it could have been evolved remains very much a mystery. But careful observational and experimental studies, notably by Karl von Frisch, offers a much more probable explanation. In that marvelous social organization, the beehive colony of tens of thousands of individuals, there is a considerable division of labors, in which individual bees, though helped by basic instincts, do learn by practice to do particular tasks better. Thus, a bee which has begun its foraging career (perhaps quite by chance) in a field of lady slippers has learned just how to enter and leave the flower pouch, learned also to recognize this familiar source of nectar by color and odor, perhaps even by shape, and thereafter sticks to that flower by habits both of recognition and its own practiced proficiency in exploiting it. Among bumble-bees, however, which live in very small colonies, such specialized division of labors is not possible, and the individual bee must remain a jack-of-all-trades. So where a honeybee comes back from a foraging trip dusted with but one color of pollen, the bumblebee returns streaked with an assortment of white, lemon-yellow, orange, and red grains from the variety of flowers it has visited on its tour of nectar and pollen gathering.

The detailed studies by von Frisch (fully reported in his *The Dancing Bees*) entirely confirm this explanation. By a simple code of color and position spots, he marked hundreds of bees in a colony for individual identification and then followed their activities both afield and at home in a specially designed "observation hive." The bee scout that discovered an abundant source of nectar, such as a field of freshly blooming flowers, first took a sample of nectar, identifiable by its flower fragrance, and then, carefully taking her bearings, headed for home. There she imparted the news of her discovery, giving information as to its abundance, the direction and distance of the find, and, by the fragrance of the nectar, the kind of flower. Only the bees which habitually foraged that flower and knew that scent now took an interest and joined in the ensuing bee dance. The leader moved in a double loop, up the middle axis, around the loop to the right, up the middle axis, around the loop to the left, alternating right and left, again and again. By her excitement she indicated the abundance of her find. By the direction of the axis of her dance she indicated its direction. Out on the landing board of the hive, this would be the actual direction. But inside, on the vertical face of a honeycomb, the perpendicular would be the direction of the Sun, with the axis of the dance inclined to it to show the direction for flight. And as she danced up the axis, her body would waggle from side to side, with rapid waggles for short distances, slower waggles for increasing distances. All of this would be understood and acted upon, with the right bees setting out in needed numbers in the right direction and to the right distance to harvest the discovered crop.

In the scouting and searching for the flowers at a distance, color is the undoubted guide for daylight carriers—the bees, butterflies, and hummingbirds. For nocturnal carriers, such as the moths, strong odor is the guide, with the flowers usually inconspicuous in color. But the color senses differ. Butterflies and birds see much the same range of colors as we do, from violet to red, and flowers pollinated by their visits are often bright reds. Bees, however, cannot see pure reds but can readily distinguish ultraviolet (invisible to us), blue, blue-green, and yellow; and flowers for them are therefore colored accordingly, including whites. Some whites may lack the ultraviolet and then probably appear blue-green to the bee. And some flowers may have a reddish hue but are visible to the bee because they are mixed with other suitable colors. Our poppies are an important example: they appear red to us but ultraviolet to the bees.

Flower shape, however, probably means little to the bee at a distance. For the eye of the bee, as noted in the previous chapter, has poor resolving power. But close up, shape may take on meaning, but here the really sensitive smell takes over to distinguish characteristic fragrances. To this we should add taste for nectar sweetness, but with a useful lower limit of sensitivity among the bees. Unless the sugar content of the nectar is high enough to make honey which can be stored, the bee will reject it, and may even not be able to taste it. But among the birds, butterflies, and moths, which do not store honey but consume the nectar at once, far more dilute nectar is usable and can be tasted.

This evolution of reciprocal adaptations between the flowering plants and their animal pollen-carriers may have begun some two hundred million years ago during the Triassic Period, but probably first among upland plants now no longer preserved in the fossil record. For fifty million years later, in the Jurassic, the fossil record shows this evolution already well along. By the Cretaceous, a hundred million years ago, the flowering plants and the pollen-bearing insects had definitely attained a marvelous and widespread collaboration through mutually specialized adaptations which benefited them both. Since then this evolution has continued, but only to multiply the instances and to increase the perfections of the reciprocal adaptations. The result was of course a general enhancing of the beauty of outdoor nature, but the occasion for that was always practical need and not at all a provision for our own human pleasure. That need was the avoidance of self-fertilizing among the plants, with the bees, birds, butterflies, and moths only opportunistic beneficiaries.

From Under the Shadows

Among the plants there is another problem, parallel to that of pollen transfer, which was aggravated by migration to the land. It was stated by Maurice Maeterlinck as that of getting the offspring out from under the stifling shadow of the parent plant. It was also part of the general problem of each generation of life to find space for living—among the plants, mainly the finding of open space for amply exposing green leafage to the sunlight. Also, if every favorable spot can be planted and occupied, the obvious advantage must be that the chances of survival are greatly increased, as local extinction need not mean race extinction. Among water organisms, both plant and animal, the problem is solved readily by floating spores or seeds, and free-swimming larvae and offspring. A few land plants, growing on the banks of streams or along the shores of ponds, lakes, and seas, can readily drop their seeds into water for transportation near or far. But on the dry land, well removed from water transport, the plants must again depend upon the wind and animal carriers. Minute spores, light as dust, are readily and widely air-borne to great distances. But seeds, with their loads of reserve foodstuffs, require accessory means for wind transport. They may grow wings on their seeds, like the maple, basswood, and Ailanthus. Many smaller plants grow plumes and tails and tufts for seed parachutes, like Clematis, fireweed, milkweed, bulrush, and dandelion. In our prairie West another effective method of wind dispersal is used by the Russian thistles or "tumbleweeds." After growing into large balls of twigs full of ripe seed pods, they break loose and roll off before the wind, shaking out their seeds along the way. Often they pile against fences or other obstructions until the wind shifts and sends them tumbling over the prairie again.

Several kinds of plants contrive to throw their seeds to some distance without depending on outside aid. The fruit of the wild cucumber fills with water until it bursts, squirting a stream and its seeds several feet. The pods of the violet and the witch hazel are pinched and the seeds shot out with considerable force. The pods of the wild bean, "touch-me-not," and a domesticated "artillery plant" develop twisting tensions which cause them to throw their seeds away violently when they dry out and split. Tropical travelers often hear the detonations of the exploding seed vessels of *Hura crepitans*, the "monkey dinner bell." Ordinarily the trunks of palms stand straight up, the firmest posture for resisting gravitation, but the trunks of coconut palms often lean over at a big angle, though not from weakness. The prevailing winds may determine the direction of leaning, but the better reason for leaning at all is that the heavy coconut seed may drop several yards away from the parent plant to avoid crowding it, while still spreading the grove as a whole. And because the tree often grows near the seashore, the leaning permits dropping coconuts into the water, to float away before the prevailing winds to distance islands, thus becoming one of the most widely distributed tropical plants on Earth.

Animals also carry plant seeds, usually inadvertently. But as seeds are usually much heavier than pollen grains, the carriers are normally the larger and warmblooded animals active in the cool autumn when the larger seeds ripen. If you take a walk through the fall woods and fields, you come back all stuck up with seed burrs of Spanish needle, beggar ticks, cocklebur, and burdock. All their seeds have grappling hooks to catch the furry coats of wandering mammals and thus literally hook free rides to distant spots for widespread planting. And seeds of any sort buried in mud will often get stuck to the feet of migrating birds and carried to great distances. Darwin, ever the curious and imaginative observer, detached pellets of mud from birds' feet to check on the many included seeds, and on one occasion from a teacup of mud, kept covered for six months, pulled 537 plants which germinated from the seeds and spores it contained.

Another method, more pleasing to the animals, is employed by the plants which enclose their seeds in pulpy and tasty fruits which ripen in conspicuous and attractive colors, so tempting to be eaten that the seeds are swallowed and carried away. As the seeds are hard and indigestible, they are presently dropped unharmed and thus planted far from the parent plant. And with these should be included the hard-shelled nuts carried off, perhaps stored, by birds, squirrels, etc. Though normally eaten, enough are dropped, lost, or left over to make this method of dispersal worthwhile. Ordinarily such fruits and nuts are only large and palatable enough to tempt their animal carriers, but Man, using deliberate artificial selection, has improved many of them greatly in both size and flavor.

And should you have any doubts as to the effectiveness of all such means of seed dispersal, you can convince yourself next spring and summer when you get down on your knees to weed the garden. You will then learn that the job has been well done indeed.

Direct Sex Contact

Among the motile animals, even on the land, the whole problem of sexual fertilizing can be readily met by the simple method of direct contact between male and female. Though such contact is of course possible among the water animals, it is resorted to only occasionally, the commoner method being the older one by which free-swimming sperm search out eggs already extruded from the female. However, even among the lowly rotifers the end of the tapered male body, or sometimes a protruding male organ, inserts sperm material into a suitable female opening. And we have already mentioned the modified male tentacle of the squid or octopus, which reaches into the mantle cavity of the female to deposit the sperm near the waiting unfertilized eggs. And among the sharks and rays the pelvic fins have lobes inserted into the female to place the sperm.

Among the animals of the dry land, however, the only practical method is clearly that of direct sex contact by which the sperm of the male are deposited within the female. We have noted the rather elaborate process by which the hermaphroditic earthworms copulate merely by pressing their ventral surfaces together. But nearly always special organs are developed, such as a protruding and often erectile male penis to be inserted into a complementary female opening. But there are many variations. Thus among the insects the female organ is a capacious receptacle in which an enormous number of sperm from a single copulation are then stored for fertilizing eggs throughout the remainder of the female's life, as in the queen bee up to seventeen years. But among the vertebrates the sperm are not thus stored, and either find eggs to fertilize soon or shortly die, necessitating fresh sperm for subsequent fertilizings of eggs of later broods of offspring. This of course requires repeated copulations between male and female throughout the spans of their reproductive lives.

Yet in the evolution of the land vertebrates the amphibians improved but little upon the reproductive methods of their ancestral fishes. There was pairing (without actual copulation), the male clasping or staying close to the female, under which stimulus the eggs and sperm were extruded into the water simultaneously and close together. But among the early reptiles the important step of full copulation was at last taken, securing fertilization within the female, and at least the early development of the embryo within the mother.

The Evolution of Motherhood

At this stage of what may properly be called motherhood the developing embryo became enclosed more or less immediately in a protective membrane or shell, which was then laid as a land egg. Within it was enclosed not only the growing embryo but what amounted to a fluid environment, together with a yolk food supply and means for breathing in and out, all as described in Chapter 16. This stage is still retained by the reptiles and their descendants, the birds, and among a few primitive mammalian descendants of the reptiles.

That early stage in the evolution of the mammals is now represented by the monotremes, which lay eggs yet nurse their offspring with milk after hatching. There are but two present examples—the duckbill platypus and the spiny anteater echidna, both of the Australian area.

From there on, however, the mammalian egg was not covered by membrane or shell for external development but was retained within the uterus, a new and special organ evolved in the mammalian mother, through the wall of which food and oxygen were supplied to the developing offspring, and carbon dioxide and other wastes were removed. The egg then simply developed through the ill-defined stages of embryo and foetus to be finally born to independent living in the outside world.

But this was accomplished by stages. Among the marsupials, descended from the ancient monotremes, the young are born at a very immature stage of development and must complete their nursing and infant growth in an external abdominal brood pouch of the mother. And aside from the American opossum, the existing marsupials (kangaroos, wombats, and several others) are all native to the Australian area. Elsewhere they are supplanted by the true mammals, in which a temporary organ of the mother, the placenta, facilitates exchanges of food, oxygen, and wastes between the independent bloodstreams of the mother and the offspring. This permits a much more advanced development of the young before birth, so they are then born as smaller replicas of the parents, at least nearly enough so to be independent organisms more or less capable of carrying on by themselves.

But whether hatched from a reptilelike monotreme egg, or protected in a marsupial brood pouch, or born to offspring independence from a placental mammalian mother, the young of all the mammals are fed for a while by milk sucked from the mother's breast nipples or licked from diffuse glands through the fur of a monotreme mother. This, in fact, is what defines the class of mammals from the other members of the vertebrate family: they feed their young on the milk secreted by the glands of some form of udder. But this is also the beginning of that superior parental care which outstandingly marks the mammals, and which makes possible the development of a new and higher intelligence in this top class of animal life.

The Urges of Sex

Baron Cuvier, a century and a half ago, discovered that the several structures of an animal are consistently correlated to its way of life. To this we must now add that its behavioral nature, its complex of physiological and instinctive urges and reactions, must be included with the correlations of structure and way of life. Or put otherwise, the adaptations developed by evolution include not only organic structures, physical and chemical, but the inherent nervous patterns of feelings, urges, and reactions which fit the organism for survival under the conditions of its existence.

That means, among other things, that its sex urges, both direct and secondary, are adapted to its methods of reproduction and care of young, and these, in their turn, are conditioned by the circumstances under which it is fitted to survive.

Illustrative of this are the adaptations involving timing of reproductive activities. Thus, to assure matings between males and females, the palolo or clamworms of each area in the South Seas come to the surface all together to breed on some one November night when the local moon phase and tide are right, an occasion for holiday gathering and feasting by the native islanders. Along the southern California coast, a fish, the grunion, from February to August, swarms ashore at high night tides, the females to burrow tail down to lay eggs in the wet sand, while the males squirm about ejecting sperm which travel down the wet female flanks to reach the eggs. Among birds, such as the English sparrow, living in tropical regions, the breeding continues throughout the year, while those that live in temperate climates, north or south, breed only during the respective springs and summers. Among hibernating mammals, such as bears, the urges of the rutting season are so timed that the young are born and nursed during hibernation, and the mother comes out in the spring lean and hungry, but the babies well fed and roly-poly. But among those mammals, including Mankind, living where seasons do not much matter, there may be a shorter cycle of periodic egg readying and female sex urgings, while the males remain continuously ready and eager whenever opportunity presents.

The instinctive habits of sexual mating, monogamous or polygamous, the associated ratios of males to females, and the consequent makeup of the family units also depend upon factors fitting for survival under conditions prevailing. It is an obvious sexual economy if one male can impregnate several or many females, as a rooster in a flock of hens, or a bull in a herd of bisons, walruses, etc. This male then usually assumes leadership, is distinguished by greater size and aggressiveness, or grows special weapons, such as spurs, tusks, or antlers, both to defend the group and to fight for possession of the females.

But such a polygamy is practical only where the food supply is adequate, the care of the young at a minimum, and defense is found in group numbers. It would hardly be feasible among tree-nesting birds, where the work of nest building, foraging for family food, setting on eggs, and extended caring for helpless young requires constant cooperation and activity of the parental pair. Even among human beings the practicing and moral sanctioning and enforcing of polygamy or monogamy depend largely on equivalent factors of livelihood, defense, child care, and other group needs. In the background are of course the basic urges of sex, but the practices of sex are subjected to directions and restraints reflecting local and current material and social needs. While conformity generally prevails, the results are often sinful breaches of codes, or internal conflicts which affect emotional health and stability. At the best, however, the sex urges are well exercised, intertwined with personal and parental affections, and otherwise joined into a satisfying fulfillment of at least this group of life's needs.

On the whole, the conditions of land life have favored

development of closer family units with fewer offspring given better care over longer childhoods. One effect has been greater selectivity in choosing mates. Darwin pointed out the consequent sexual selection and evolution of secondary sex characteristics, the fine feathers, the admired colorations of coat, feminine beauties and graces, the manly looks, all those qualities of form and behavior, displayed especially in courtships, which have enhanced the sexes in each others' eyes. Sex has thereby become more personal and intimate, and altogether better for it.

So in the evolutionary sense, sex has indeed been rearing its head. Not an ugly head, anything but that, except we make it so ourselves. Certainly among the birds and beasts, sex is never indecent and shameful. Only among men and women, and the generations of offspring they indoctrinate, have we converted necessary and rationally adaptive social restraints into shames and indecencies by corrupting and petrifying them into unhealthy puritanic obscenities. As sensible human beings, we would do better by learning, and then teaching our children, to view sex as natural and fulfilling, making its control rational as a matter of responsible regard for its necessary consequences. The only effective basis for that is obviously the wholesome instruction of children in the essential facts of sex.

Chapter 18

THE OVER-ALL ADVANCE

In modern scientific opinion life as we know it probably began on the Earth, much less likely elsewhere, but in any case through the workings of causes we call natural. By that we mean in the normal ways of Nature, constant and universal, and at work in the past as we observe them to be today. This view, which was only a sensible suspicion a few centuries ago, has been consistently enforced and confirmed by all we have since learned. Not that we have yet learned all that must be pertinent. Nor are our detail conclusions always certain, nor in consistent agreement, nor unchanging, yet always, thus far, they have fallen within the area of the natural.

Today, a century after Darwin, one conclusion rather stands out: that an evolution of life forms is inevitable. Two well-confirmed facts serve as causal background: (1) the characteristics of life forms do change by genetic mutations, evidently accidental and random; and (2) the genetic means of replication then transmit the characteristics of the organism, thus changed, to succeeding generations. Then in the struggle for existence, changes aiding survival tend to be preserved, as against those which hamper survival. By such natural selection, organisms must, over the generations, inevitably evolve.

But that evolution is primarily adaptive toward current fitness and not at all purposely directed toward any ultimate goal. Man himself, clearly the present culmination of the historic course of evolution, is therefore not a foreseen, nor intended, nor planned culmination. He is merely the fortunate end resultant of the natural selection of a series of quite accidental mutations which quite constantly happened to be more fit. We shall shortly return to Man, and what made him thus most fit.

The Broad Incidental Advance

Fitness for immediate survival is always the test in natural selection, and may lead in any direction advantageous at the moment. But that direction may be upward or downward, into broad avenues of continuable improvements or into dead-end pockets of specialization leading nowhere. Thus, adoption of parasitism may be advantageous at the moment, but involves degeneration and loss of parts or functions which are then gone forever. Or the useful adaptation of birds' forelimbs into wings for flight then proved irreversible, thereby preventing among them any subsequent evolution of more versatile and useful hands.

Yet while adaptive advantage is always the test directing immediate change, there nevertheless does result an over-all advance in the general course of organic evolution. For from time to time there do occur broad innovations which prove of general and persisting advantage, and which can be varied and adapted so as to permit further evolutions without serious restraints. Any such broadly useful innovation then means an uplift to a higher plateau of life, usually described as a superior group of plants or animals. And each broad superiority has equally broad survival values leading to its being retained by natural selection as a permanent advance. Thus broadly, evolution does tend upward.

So far in this book we have concerned ourselves largely with reasons why, and have paid but little attention to historic sequences and datings. But to leave a clearer impression of the evolutionary past, an orderly calendar of that past, together with a proper family tree alongside, should prove useful. The dates of the calendar are those derived from the geological record and, thanks to radioactivity determinations, are now surprisingly accurate. An adequate account of the geological periods has, however, already been given in my former book, *Our Emerging Universe*, and need not be fully repeated here. That history can be summed up as a series of physical events, such as risings and sinkings of the earth crust, with consequent alternations of mountain-buildings and encroachments by shallow seas, but tied in with the principal events in the evolution of life forms as disclosed by fossil remains embedded in the muds and sands since compacted into our present rock strata.

This fossil record of evolving life has proved most revealing and fortunately is fairly adequate, with but few serious gaps. As might be expected, the initial record for the origin of life is quite missing, and hopelessly so because the time is so distant and the first life was so minute, soft, and probably unidentifiable in its utter simplicity. The fossil record is also rather lacking for the important origin of the vertebrate backbone and dorsal nerve stem, but not hopelessly so, as fossils or other clues may yet be found to fill that gap. Fortunately, the controversial onetime "missing link" between ape and man is now being filled in promisingly. So in general it is now possible to reconstruct the family tree of earthly life with fair accuracy as to dates and geneological relationships, as shown in the chart on p. 307.

On Seizing Opportunities

We speak normally of the family tree of evolution because it does in fact branch out like a tree from an apparently single original main stem along many diverging lines of development. Such branching, both general and detailed, is the result of random mutations selected as adaptive to various conditions and opportunities. There is always the tendency toward such "adaptive radiation" whenever any group successfully occupies an environment of varied opportunities.

A classic example was discovered by Darwin in 1832 on the

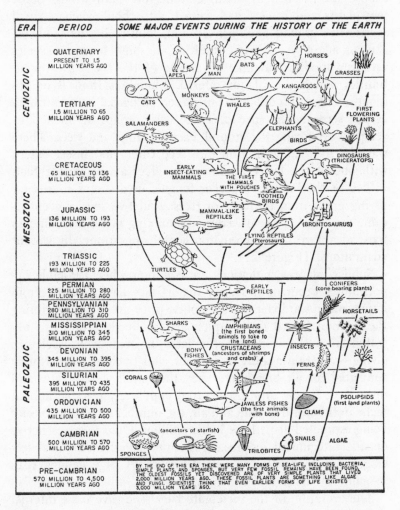

Fig. 21. The Family Tree of Life.

Galápagos Islands. This compact group of equatorial volcanic islands had never been connected physically with the mainland of South America some six hundred miles to the east. So all plant and animal life must have been transplanted to them by chance means such as ocean currents or storm winds. Some few plants and insects had gained a foothold when a small sparrowlike ground finch arrived and, multiplying its kind, began an adaptive radiation resulting in some fourteen species variously modified to take advantage of the few basic opportunities which the islands offered. Migration from island to island was not too difficult, but presented partial barriers which helped separate the species. Three basic groups of finches developed, occupying the ground, cactus plants, and trees. There was also a broad separation into seed eaters and insect eaters, with one of the latter becoming in effect a woodpecker that, in lieu of the long woodpecker tongue, used cactus thorns for prying grubs from the bark of trees. And two species even became warblers. As there were no competing birds, these finches took advantage of every environmental opportunity by variant adaptations. (Figure 22).

Similar adaptive radiations are common when favorable opportunities occur, and several major ones have resulted from important upward steps in the course of evolution. Thus during the Silurian Period the scorpion and millipede arthropods migrated from the waters to the land, favored by exoskeletons giving protection against drying out, and tracheal tubes readily converted for air breathing. They then multiplied greatly and diversified, largely into insects, to occupy every possible habitat niche in the world of land and air, the number of present species being estimated at perhaps half a million. Only their restrictive outside integument, essential for support and mechanical leverages, has apparently prevented growth to large enough sizes to gain real mastery of their new world.

The evolution of the vertebrate backbone gave basic internal skeletal support and leverages without restricting growth to dominating sizes, while making possible high-speed undulation swimming, which made the fishes the pirate masters of the waters. In consequence, they, too, diversified and multiplied within all the opportunities of that watery realm to which they were superbly fitted.

During the Devonian and Carboniferous Periods, some of the fish kind developed lobe-fins and in due course proper legs for walking on the land, and bladder lungs for breathing dry air. The full migration to the land, however, was very slow, delayed because the amphibians laid their eggs in water and so could not travel far inland. Only when the reptiles had evolved the land egg were they free to radiate to every type of land habitat. For 165 million years, through the entire Mesozoic Era, the reptiles dominated the land, notably as Dinosaurs, reinvaded the seas as ichthyosaurs, and even took to the air as soaring pterosaurs.

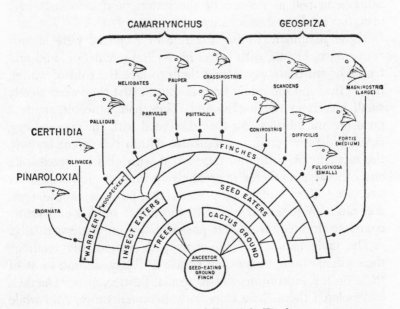

Fig. 22. Radiation of Darwin's Finches.

The Warm Bloods Take Over

But despite this overwhelmingly successful adaptive radiation, the reptiles lacked organic means for keeping warm, and could therefore not invade areas of cold, nor actively face all the seasons. But they gave rise to two groups of descendants not thus handicapped, the birds and the mammals. Because the birds took to the air as active fliers, they required high energy production and heat conservation, which they secured by warm blood, an improved heart and circulation system, and an insulating coat of feathers. But their highly specialized forelimb wings deprived them of any future opportunity to develop arms and hands. And while the birds did spread to land and water in addition to the air, they found severe competition. The fishes remained as masters of the waters, and mammals took over the land most efficiently.

Those mammals, during the Age of Reptiles, were already active warm bloods, with better hearts and circulation, and protected by fur coats, permitting them to face the cold of winter, the arctics, and mountain heights. But at first they were merely small lurkers in the background. They had, however, made a great organic advance, for they dispensed with the exposed egg, developed their young to infant size within the parent body to the moment of birth, and then fed it with gland-secreted milk and otherwise mothered it protectively while it grew to mature size. And they undoubtedly loved the taste of reptile eggs, and probably took active part in the rather sudden and nearly complete decimation of that powerful but unprogressive tribe.

The early mammals were marsupials temporarily retaining their infant young in suckling pouches. Today we find most of these on the subcontinent of Australia. Barriers of sea channels had isolated them there since early mammal times. And while these Australian marsupials took no part in the further evolving

of higher mammals elsewhere, they did diversify adaptively to
fit into all manner of environmental niches, becoming herbivores
and carnivores, and taking on forms and life habits paralleling
many found elsewhere among higher mammals. Having the
whole remainder of the world to occupy and fit, those higher
mammals also radiated adaptively, chiefly on the land, but a
few also took to the air as bats, and more successfully into the
seas as seals, mantees, porpoises, and whales, the last attaining
huge sizes with the flotational help of the ocean water.

The Emergence of Man

But the main habitat of the mammals was the land itself.
And there they diversified in their turn, multiplied in over-all
numbers, grew in sizes, lived more actively, thus in all ways gaining dominance. Most fed on plants, a fewer number on fellow
animals. Predator and victim, both had to become alert and
swift and cunning, in pursuit and in escape. Altogether, competition intensified and, through severer natural selection, ac-
celerated evolutionary change.

The general need for alertness, swiftness, and intelligence was
met by a marked development of the brain in both size and
structural detail. Indeed, a new brain area, the neopallium, developed as the seat of increased learning and thinking, opening
up a whole new way of fast adapting to changing and urgent
needs. This new way was, in fact, soon to lift Man to a new
level apart from all his animal kin.

Most of the mammals remained four-footed for firm stance
and swift travel. But a change came when some kin of the
lowly ground shrew took to the trees, probably merely to dig
grubs from the bark. But soon the descendants of the tree
shrew, namely the tarsiers, lemurs, and monkeys, began swinging by their arms from branch to branch, developing flexible
and gripping hands to seize and hang by. Meanwhile they be-

gan to sit on their haunches and handle things with those hands, the big toes of which became thumbs opposable to the other toes, which became slender bending fingers. Then, perhaps because they had grown too heavy for constant tree life, maybe because the forest was thinning out into open stretches of plain, they descended as apes to the ground, walked as bipeds on their hind legs and feet with semierect posture, and thereby finally freed their arms and hands for handling things instead of for locomotion.

But also, while they were still in the trees, a valuable improvement in sight had occurred. Swinging or leaping from branch to branch, with the hard ground far below, was a risky business, a miss being as bad as a mile. So judging their swings and leaps accurately became important, a capacity their immediate ground-dwelling ancestors did not possess. The two eyes moved forward on the face to allow viewing the same things together, and new nerve pathways to the seeing center in the brain permitted a blending of visual images into one, while convergence of the eye directions instantly triangulated the all-important distances. This capacity also proved most useful in the precise handling of things and in giving three-dimensional objects the solid look. Seeing and feeling more accurately and clearly, handling more deftly, the eyes and hands fed better facts to the brain, and performed more precisely the practical acts which the more intelligent mind set them to do. In all of this, we realize, Man was emerging.

What We Owe the Babies

But there was another vital factor contributing decisively to the making of that unique and culminating creature, Man. This was the mammal practice of parental care of their young. The birds shared this practice, too, but between their annual egg layings and migrations, they could not carry on the practice far enough to make it a major factor in developing intelligence.

What made parental care so important was that it permitted the babies to begin helpless and remain so over a long period of infancy which could then be devoted not only to growing physically but to gaining skills and learning facts for guiding judgments in the solving of current problems peculiar to their world and time.

A long period of helpless infancy sounds like a severe handicap. Is not a chick better off since he can scratch a living quite from the start after hatching? Indeed, someone has said that the chick, one and a half days old, is the smartest thing alive— for its age. But note that when it grows up, it is only a stupid hen, which can still do little more than scratch for a living. On the other hand, compared with the chick, the human baby can do literally nothing for itself for many months, and takes years to grow up. But it can learn, which the chick cannot, and in the end hopelessly outdistances the chick in skills and adaptive intelligence.

The chick's trouble is that it is all encumbered with inherited instincts, urges which enable it to respond and go into action with little delay. But those instincts, being inborn, clutter up the chicken brain with pre-emptive urges which cannot be altered to meet unfamiliar emergencies. Only by slow evolution do they change, over many generations. The human baby's brain is not thus overly encumbered with ancient and set instincts, but is freer to learn the facts of its life here and now, freer to think out fresh answers to fresh problems, without waiting for genetic mutations and natural selection to evolve better inborn answers and responses. So if there are parents about to protect and feed and give care, the long period of helpless babyhood represents not a handicap but a new freedom and high capacity to learn facts, skills, and judgments, those features of intelligence which have lifted Man to his practical mastery over his world.

There were also collateral evolutions arising out of parental care and babyhood, largely because they were essential to their success. Such were the developments of the fundamental emotions of responsibility, trust, and mutual attachments, the beginnings of the wider social feelings which make easier and more effective all our human living together.

From babyhood to maturity, individual knowledge is gained from experience, imitation, and communication. Speech, distinctively an evolved capacity of Man, became the effective means of communication by which the knowledge of others could be made the possession of each. And with the human invention of symbols for writing, all the knowledge from the past could be passed on to the future and thus accumulated to serve Mankind for guidance and use. These were then the means by which human progress could begin.

But unfortunately, not all that is spoken or written is necessarily true, early Man not having yet learned the important modern art of objective testing for truth. So much that we have communicated and learned has eventually had to be unlearned, and human progress has thereby been seriously retarded. Though the new human capacity to shortcut adaptation by learning and contriving is well developed physiologically, Mankind has badly fumbled in its effective use. For the vast majority of us, over thousands of years, have persistently indoctrinated our young with the ancient prejudices which we ourselves blindly cherish, while instead we should be encouraging their highly educatable and adaptive minds to search and test for truth realistically. Only thus can they use effectively this unique human capacity to face and to meet, with open and clear and informed minds, the novel and urgent problems of our world of today and of their tomorrows.

Thus Life Began

So there is the history of life, from what we know and what we can guess. First, eons of preparation through dateless time;

a waste of chaotic raw materials and aimless primal forces; a compacting into hot glowing suns and cooler attendant worlds, among them at least one world not too small nor too large, not too hot nor too cold, and in consequence blessed with a surface firm enough, bathed in oceans of water and air, all auspiciously ready.

Came an instant, perhaps a long period of brewing, when matter and energy, not by touch of magic nor vitalism, but by natural physicochemical causes, took on minute yet self-contained forms and continuity of reaction with other matter and energy. Life had emerged.

More ages, but now roughly dated, while accidental changes were guided into order and meanings by the picking of successes and the rejection of failures, thus evolving the forms and activities of life, generally upward, and with an awakening of awareness of itself and of the world.

And only recently arose one form, the fortunate resultant of Nature's selections of the fit, who above all others was given longer carefree infancy, and so time for gaining personal skills and for individual learning of facts and the orders and meanings of facts. By applying those meanings, his bettered brain could at last contrive immediate answers to the novel, diverse, and urgent problems without having to wait for slow evolution to work them out by trial and error and success over the generations. Thereby, we know, Man emerged, and we are brought at last to the human revolution in the midst of which we now live.

But obviously that is not the theme of this book on beginnings. And so we find that our history of life's origins is done.

INDEX